AMERICAN CELEBRATION

ISSUED AS NUMBER 100
in a Series of Rare Book Catalogues

AMERICAN CELEBRATION

*The Creation and Evolution of the United States
as Reflected in the Printed and Written Word
1776–1976*

BY JOHN H. JENKINS

Austin **THE JENKINS COMPANY** 1976

Catalogue One Hundred

THE JENKINS COMPANY

Postal Box 2085 • Austin, Texas 78768
(512) 444-6616

INTRODUCTION

In the summer of 1966 I was in counterintelligence school in Ft. Holabird, Maryland, where John Dean and Charles Colson later did their time. It was during the Vietnam war, and almost all of us in our unit were straight from college or graduate school. Between sessions, two young lawyers from Chicago and I, all P.F.C.'s, were assigned to the gardener. He had us us digging a one-foot ditch across a long field about two blocks long, although for what purpose I never found out. The only thing worse than that was K.P., which I loathed. One day at formation I was called out in front of the troop and told to do thirty push-ups. Of course, I wasn't allowed to ask why, so I hit the dirt. Then that big fat son-of-a-bitch of a sergeant leaned down and said, "Some ass down in your home town is on top of the university tower shooting people. It just came in on the radio." He was referring to the maniac, Charles Whitman, who shot 45 people from the University of Texas Tower on August 1, 1966.

"Is that what you four-eyes college guys from Texas like to do for kicks?" the sergeant yelled, as I puffed away on the ground.

"Only to sergeants," I said, realizing immediately that I shouldn't have.

"All right, Texas," he said, "take K.P. for the rest of the week, morning shift, in addition to garden duty. Heaven help us, this country will be two hundred years old in ten years and the best we've got to offer is you weak-sister college boys. The country will never make it to celebrate."

His last remark stuck with me all week while pulling kitchen and garden duty, and I couldn't get it out of my mind. First of all, it astonished me that he was able to subtract 1966 from 1976 and come up with 10. But, also, I was already in the book business in a small way, and for some reason it clicked in my mind that I ought to start saving items back for what was sure to be a big celebration.

Several weeks later I managed through totally nefarious means to obtain a leave to attend the annual meeting of the Manuscript Society in Boston. There I saw for the first time Lexington, Concord, Old Ironsides, and some history of what we Texans tend to call "that other Revolution," since the Revolution, of course, took place in 1836. Right then, from Ken Rendell and Goodspeed's, I bought the first items for the catalogue that follows.

I have been setting them aside ever since, as I have also been doing for a special catalogue in 1984. I've become so attached to the collection that I hate to see it split apart, because I really don't believe such a collection could readily be built again.

Some of the later materials came from experiences of my own. I liked Harry Truman in junior high school because he used curse words, and can state with pride that I wrote my first, of many, anti-Nixon letters in 1952 when he attacked Truman. I collected presidential material from about that time on, including Mr. N. One group of books in my private collection that I prize is a complete set of books by every U.S. President since Roosevelt, inscribed to me. I had some from President Hoover, too, but someone stole them and I surely do wish he would send them back.

I also did some civil rights marching, and set aside a lot of material on those pre-Vietnam days when the integration cause was so clear and its heroes so shining. Another group of heroes were the astronauts — I still collect anything relating to the space program, and hereby insert my pitch to anyone who has any to be aware I am a sucker for such.

One night in 1960, a friend and I were out drinking beer; how many can be deduced from the fact that we sent a telegram to Fidel Castro, who had just taken over Cuba and hadn't yet espoused Communism: "Two American law school students wish to study structure of revolutionary government. Request financial aid." Two weeks later, after we had entirely forgotten about it, we received a pair of airline tickets in the mail and a letter saying to come to the Havana Hilton, recently renamed the Havana Libre, where Castro would receive us.

After checking with the State Department and suffering an interview by some CIA lovelies, we went. For a week we had a free run of Cuba with special passes from Castro. Unfortunately, at the end of the week Castro decided to tear up the friendship treaty with the United States, and I have some home movies of him doing so. We cleared out that afternoon —on the last airline flight from Havana to Miami. I brought with me a stack of revolutionary propaganda, some of which is in this catalogue. We published an article entitled "The Reverse Monroe Doctrine," pointing out what we had heard, that Castro was putting out the anti-American hoopla because he had made a deal for Russian support. We have Kennedy to thank that it failed.

My wife and I were invited to attend some of the functions when Kennedy came to Texas in 1963. We saw more of what happened than we wanted; my only recurring nightmare is of that day. I was 23 and loved Jack Kennedy and have never gotten over November 22 — yet I admit that after the tears and after watching Air Force I carry Lyndon back to Washington, the bibliophile in me induced me to stop by the newspaper building and pick up some of the Dallas extras of that day. That a book person will do things like that is a well-known psychological malady, and I can offer no excuse for it.

In 1970 I was able to acquire a big chunk of the Lowdermilk Book Store stock. Lowdermilk's was the oldest bookstore in Washington, founded in 1872. The cellar, which was verboten for decades contained some unbelievable treasures, not so much in monetary as in historic value. There were over 300,000 items in that cellar, and we are still sorting them out — and still finding eye-openers — although I haven't found a Dunlap Declaration of Independence. If there was one in Leary's, there's just got to be one in Lowdermilks, damn it, but I just can't find it — yet.

One unopened dust-covered box contained 1899 postal markings and a free-frank from President McKinley. I thought, lordy, it's his handwritten autobiography, or a thousand holograph letters, and I let it sit for two days enjoying its potential. Alas, it contained a dozen copies of the *Yearbook of Agriculture* and nothing else. But another box had a long run of general orders from the Civil War and Indian campaign era, and what a find that was!

Another hoard of materials came from the Eberstadt Collection, but since I've sounded off about that purchase enough already, I'll just state that about twenty percent of this catalogue is from that fabulous stock.

If I were Croesus I would not be a bookseller; I would just collect. But since that is only possible in a relatively small way, the next best thing is to share some of my treasures with others who suffer my bibliophilic disease.

Here they are.

John H. Jenkins
July 4, 1976

AMERICAN CELEBRATION

The First Hundred Years

1776 [Declaration of Independence]

IN CONGRESS, JULY 4, 1776, A DECLARATION BY THE REPRESENTATIVES OF THE UNITED STATES OF AMERICA, IN GENERAL CONGRESS ASSEMBLED.

Boston: The New England Chronicle, Printed by Powars and Willis, July 18, 1776. 4pp. Large folio. In handsome full morocco slipcase. The first Boston printing of the Declaration, along with that printed in another Boston paper the same day, and possibly the first printing in New England, it having been read publicly in Boston for the first time the evening before in Faneuil Hall. Oswald, p.65. Brigham, pp.321-22, locating only six other known copies, all in institutions, making this the only known copy in private hands. Evans 15161 cites a broadside version, probably printed subsequently, locating only one known copy; however, a copy sold at auction in 1970 for fourteen thousand dollars.   (1) 6500.00

On July 4, 1776, a group of men who called themselves ''Representatives of the United States of America in General Congress assembled,'' voted to approve a resolution adopted on July 2, declaring ''that these United Colonies are, and of Right ought to be, Free and Independent States . . . and that all political Connection between them and the State of Great Britain is . . . totally dissolved. . . .''

Late into that evening and into the early morning of July 5, a committee of five, including Thomas Jefferson, Benjamin Franklin and John Adams, worked with Philadelphia printer John Dunlap to produce an official printed version of the document that created the United States of America. No one signed the original manuscript on July 4, or probably even in the month of July, although Adams and Jefferson often swore that they did—later evidence has shown that most members signed it on August 2, and some even later than that. In fact, the names of the Signers were deliberately held secret until January 18, 1777, when the Continental Congress released an authenticated copy.

From Philadelphia, copies of Dunlap's broadside were dispatched throughout the Colonies, now for the first time States, appearing in Baltimore on July 9, New York on July 10, and Portsmouth, N.H., on July 20. The Declaration was read in Faneuil Hall in Boston on July 17, and printed by Powars and Willis in their paper on the next day. Samuel Hall had moved from Cambridge to Boston in 1775, printing the *New-England Chronicle* there beginning April 25; on June 13, 1776, he sold the press to Edward E. Powars and Nathaniel Willis, who published it until Sept. 19, 1776, when they changed the name to the *Independent Chronicle* and issued it thusly for forty-four years thereafter.

Only six other copies of the issue with the Declaration of Independence are recorded: at the Library of Congress, Penn. Hist. Society, Univ. of Mich., and three in Massachusetts institutions. The issue contains other vital data on the first days of the United States, including an account of the reception of the Declaration in Pennsylvania and New York, as well as the following: ''A tory has been taken into custody for making plans of our works for the enemy. These rascals will be continual plagues to us, unless some effectual measures are taken with them.''

10

All of the men who signed the Declaration knew they would have a price on their heads. Of the men who signed, Richard Stockton was captured and thrown in a dungeon, Francis Lewis had his estate destroyed and his wife imprisoned, Thomas Jefferson and Elbridge Gerry escaped capture by a matter of minutes, and six others were chased and narrowly escaped. One can easily understand that from the adoption of this document onwards for seven years, each of them strived mightily for that day in 1783 that would make them no longer war criminals and traitors to the Crown, but Founding Fathers instead.

1777 [Revolutionary Broadsides]

Hancock, John.

IN CONGRESS, APRIL 14, 1777, RESOLVED . . . RULES AND ARTICLES FOR THE BETTER GOVERNMENT OF TROOPS . . .

Philadelphia: Printed by John Dunlap, 1777. Broadside, 1 page, folio, signed in type by Hancock as President of the Continental Congress of the United States. Evans 15662, locating only the Library of Congress copy, but Shipton & Mooney locate a copy in a Boston institution. Church Cat. 1143. A rare and near-unique broadside of an important set of four articles for governing troops in the American Army. (2) 1250.00

IN COUNCIL OF SAFETY . . . [PROCLAMATION ORDERING THE CONFISCATION OF TORY PROPERTY]

Lancaster, Pa.: Francis Bailey, October 21, 1777. Broadside, 1 page, long folio, signed in type "By order of the Council of Safety, Thomas Wharton, jun., President." Superb text, appointing Charles Wilson Peale and others as commissioners to confiscate the property of tories who have "joined the army of the king of Great-Britain . . . or that shall [aid the British forces with] provisions or intelligence, or other aid. . . ." The Council of Safety states that the commissioners are "fully authorised and impowered, to search for and seize the said goods and effects of such offenders . . . to use force, and to break open doors, in all cases where the goods may be secreted and concealed" and "all officers and others, civil and military . . . are hereby required and commanded to aid and assist them accordingly." Evans 15529, locating no known copy. Shipton & Mooney locate only the Library of Congress copy, making this one of two known copies, and the only one in private hands. (3) 1250.00

In the winter of 1776-1777, Washington crossed the Delaware twice, winning victories at Trenton and Princeton. This unnerved the British, who were appalled at the idea of fighting battles in the winter. In March, the Continental Congress reconvened, and under President John Hancock issued basic orders and regulations for revolutionary activities.

One important act was the passage on April 14, 1777, of four special "Rules and Regulations for the Better Government of Troops," in which Congress asserted its rights to appoint and review Courts Martial, to pardon convicted offenders, and to regulate the lives of authority in the Continental Army.

During the summer, the British managed to drive the Continental Congress out of Philadelphia. On October 7, Washington moved the American army to Valley Forge, where the horror of the war was most keenly felt. It has been estimated that of the 10,000 Americans there, some 2,500 died during the winter of starvation, exposure, and disease.

In nearby Lancaster, a Council of Safety was established to aid the revolution and succor Washington and the troops. One of the most interesting and important of these was that issued on October 21, authorizing Charles Wilson Peale and other commissioners to confiscate tory property on behalf of the American cause.

12

In Congress,

April 14, 1777.

RESOLVED,

THAT from and after the publication hereof, the second article of the 8th section, the first article of the 11th section, the 8th article of the 14th section, and the 2d article of the 18th section, of the Rules and Articles for the better Government of the Troops, raised or to be raised, and kept in pay by, and at the expence of the United States of America, passed in Congress, the 20th day of September, One Thousand, Seven Hundred, and Seventy-Six, shall be, and they are hereby repealed, and that the four following articles be substituted in the place and stead thereof.

ART. I. All Officers and Soldiers shall have full liberty to bring into any of the Forts or Garrisons of the United American States, any quantity of eatable provisions, except where any contracts are, or shall be entered into by Congress, or by their Order, for furnishing such provisions, and with respect only to the species of provisions so contracted for.

ART. II. If any Officer shall think himself to be wronged by his Colonel or the Commanding Officer of the regiment, and shall, upon due application made to him be refused to be redressed, he may complain to the Continental General, commanding in the State where such regiment shall be stationed, in order to obtain justice, who is hereby required to examine into the said complaint, and take proper measures for redressing the wrong complained of, and transmit as soon as possible to Congress, a true state of such complaint, with the proceeding had thereon.

ART. III. No sentence of a General Court-Martial shall be put in execution, till after a report shall be made of the whole proceedings to Congress, the Commander in Chief, or the Continental General commanding in the State where such a General Court-Martial shall be held, and their, or his orders, be issued for carrying such sentence into execution.

ART. IV. The Continental General commanding in either of the American States for the time being, shall have full power of appointing General Courts Martial to be held, and of pardoning or mitigating any of the punishments ordered to be inflicted for any of the offences mentioned in the aforementioned Rules and Articles for the better government of the Troops, except the punishment of offenders under sentence of death by a General Court-Martial, which he may order to be suspended, until the pleasure of Congress can be known, which suspension, with the proceedings of the Court-Martial, the said General shall immediately transmit to Congress for their determination. And every offender convicted by any Regimental Court-Martial may be pardoned or have his punishment mitigated by the Colonel or Officer commanding the Regiment.

By ORDER of CONGRESS,

JOHN HANCOCK, PRESIDENT.

PHILADELPHIA: PRINTED BY JOHN DUNLAP.

In COUNCIL of SAFETY.

Lancaster, 21st October, 1777.

WHEREAS divers of the inhabitants of this common-wealth, not regarding their duty to the state, but renouncing their allegiance thereto, and disclaiming the protection thereof, have wickedly joined themselves to our unnatural enemies, giving to them aid and assistance, by furnishing them with provisions, and otherwise; thereby contributing, as far as in them lies, to increase the distresses of their injured country. AND WHEREAS it is highly unjust, and repugnant to the practice of all nations, to protect and preserve the property of their avowed enemies; Therefore,

Be it ordained, resolved and declared, and by virtue of the powers and authorities to us committed, by the legislature of this state, it is by the council of safety, of the commonwealth of Pennsylvania hereby ordained, resolved and declared, That all and every the personal estate and effects whatsoever, of such of the inhabitants, of this common-wealth, as have, or hereafter shall abandon their families, or habitations, and joined the army of the king of Great-Britain, and of all such as shall resort to any city, town or place, within this common-wealth, in possession of the troops or armies of the said King of Great-Britain, carrying to them provisions; or that shall otherwise afford to them, such provisions or intelligence, or other aid, shall be seized upon, and safely kept by the commissioners herein after appointed, for the use and purpose herein after declared; and all sales and alienations thereof, and of all or any of the real estates of such offenders, in the mean time, made by them, or any of them, their or either of their agents, factors or attornies, are hereby declared to be null and void, to all intents and purposes whatsoever.

And be it further resolved, ordained and declared, by the authority aforesaid, That the commissioners for the respective counties, herein after appointed, or any or either of them, shall and may with all convenient speed, after the publication of this ordinance, seize upon, and take into his or their custody, and make a true and perfect inventory of all the personal estate and effects of every such offender, and dispose of all the perishable part thereof, and at his or their discretion, convey away, and remove to places of safety, sell, or otherwise dispose of, where it may be necessary, all such goods and effects of the said offenders, as they shall apprehend to be in danger of falling into the hands of the enemy; and the said monies and goods so by them taken or received, the said commissioners are required to retain and keep safely, subject to the future disposition of the legislature of this commonwealth, keeping true accounts of their proceedings, and receiving for their trouble, over and above their costs and charges, at the rate of five *per centum.* And the said commissioners are hereby also further directed and enjoined, with all convenient speed, after the making such inventory and sale, or sales as aforesaid, to deliver on oath to the treasurer, a true copy of such inventory, or account of sales.

And be it further resolved, ordained and declared, by the authority aforesaid, That the several persons herein after named (or in their, or either of their stead and place, in case they, or either of them, shall refuse or be disabled, to perform the duties upon them enjoined, in and by this ordinance, such other person or persons, as this council shall from time to time appoint) shall be, and they are hereby appointed commissioners for the purposes aforesaid, to wit :

For the city of Philadelphia, William Will, Sharp Delany, Jacob Shriner, Charles Wilson Peale, Robert Smith, (Hatter) Samuel Massey.

For the county of Philadelphia, William Antis, Robert Lollar, James Stroud, Daniel Hiester, Archibald Thompson.

For the county of Chester : William Evans, William Gibbons, Thomas Cheney, Isaac Taylor, Thomas Taylor and Patterson Bell.

For the county of Bucks: Richard Gibbs, Joseph M'Ilvaine, John Lacey, Samuel Smith, John Crawford, Nicholas Patterson.

For the county of Lancaster : William Bauseman, Caspar Shaffner, Robert Patten, George Stewart, Francis Armstrong, James Cunningham.

For the county of York : William White, Robert Stephenson, James Nailor, Matthew Dill, William Chesney, John Ewing.

For the county of Cumberland : George Stevenson, John Bogs and Samuel Brady.

For the county of Berks: Thomas Parry, David Morgan, George Nagle, Henry Haller, Daniel Utree, Henry Speiker, Daniel Heister.

For the county of Northampton : Conrad Krider, Peter Keichline, Paul Balliott, Robert Levers, Daniel Dupuy.

For the counnty of Bedford : Robert Galbreath, Thomas Urie, John Piper.

For the county of Northumberland : John Kelly, Thomas Hewitt.

For the county of Westmoreland : John Proctor, Thomas Galbreath.

And be it lastly resolved, ordained and declared, by the authority aforesaid, That the said commissioners, or any, or either of them, shall be fully authorised and impowered, to search for and seize the said goods and effects of such offenders, and for this end to send for, call before them, and examine persons and papers; to use force, and to break open doors, in all cases where the same goods may be secreted and concealed; to commit such as shall obstinately resist their authority; and to call to their aid all officers and others, civil and military, who are hereby required and commanded, to aid and assist them accordingly.

By order of the Council of Safety,

THOMAS WHARTON, jun. PRESIDENT.

❖–❖

LANCASTER, Printed by FRANCIS BAILEY.

Wesley, John
SOME ACCOUNT OF THE LATE WORK OF GOD IN AMERICA.
London: Printed by R. Hawes, and sold . . . at the Rev. Mr. Wesley's Preaching-Houses, 1778. 23pp. Full mottled calf, gilt. Sabin 102691. *Rare first edition.*   (4) 250.00

The great Methodist minister, John Wesley, had spent some time in Georgia in the 1730's, and was interested in affairs in America throughout his career. Thus his views on the American Revolution, in the pulpit and in the press, received considerable attention. Horace Walpole called him ''as evidently an actor as Garrick'' and Walter Scott said his sermons, though ''vastly too colloquial,'' were full of ''many excellent stories.'' One of his biographers states that ''in controversy he was a consummate master of apt and telling statement of a case; as he never wrote without conviction, he convinced others.''

All the above may be applied to this sermon-essay against the American Revolution. Wesley draws on his own personal experiences there to trace what he sees as ''a hankering after Independency'' in America ''as early as the year 1737. In that year, my Brother being detained there some time, was greatly surprized to hear almost in every company . . . 'We must be Independent; we will be Independent: We will bear the English yoke no longer.' '' Wesley attributes this spirit to Satan, of course, and to crass commercialism: ''The immense *Trade* of *America,* greater in proportion than even that of the Mother Country, brought in an immense flow of *Wealth* . . . and money without end. Riches poured in upon them as a flood, and treasures were heaped up as the sand of the sea. . . . One general consequence was *Pride.*'' And pride goweth before a fall.

Thus the Americans were due to be taught the error of their ways. Once they decide to ''all work together, for the destruction of Satan's kingdom'' then ''God and his righteousness will send . . . all the Necessaries and Conveniences of Life, not *Independency,* (which would be no Blessing, but an heavy curse, both to them and their Children) . . . they will again enjoy true *British* Liberty, such as they enjoyed before these commotions.''

1779 [Franklin's Genius Displayed]

Franklin, Benjamin

POLITICAL, MISCELLANEOUS, AND PHILOSOPHICAL PIECES . . . GENERAL POLITICS; AMERICAN POLITICS BEFORE THE TROUBLES; AMERICAN POLITICS DURING THE TROUBLES; PROVINCIAL OR COLONY POLITICS; AND MISCELLANEOUS . . . BY BENJ. FRANKLIN, LL.D. . . . MINISTER PLENIPOTENTIARY AT THE COURT OF PARIS FOR THE UNITED STATES OF AMERICA.

London: Printed for J. Johnson, 1779. xi,565pp. plus 8pp. of errata. Engraved frontis. portrait. Three tables, one folding. Half calf. *First edition, one of the rare copies on laid paper.* Howes F330. Ford 342: "The work is ably performed, many pieces being for the first time printed as Franklin's; and contains valuable notes but what gives a special value to this collection is that it is the only edition of Franklin's writings (other than his scientific), which was printed during his lifetime, and was done with Franklin's knowledge and consent . . ."

(5) 450.00

Thomas Jefferson called Franklin the greatest man and ornament of our age and country in which he lived." As author, inventor, scientist, statesman, philosopher, journalist, educator, and philanthropist, Franklin ranks as a genius of the highest degree. In no other work of his is this better shown than in the above, which includes the first book appearance of so many of his lifetime studies and reflections.

It includes chapters on the lightning rod and electricity, conjectures on Aurora Borealis, on "a reformed mode of Spelling," on population and immigration, on determining the heights of clouds, on economics and industry, on the laws of inertia and motion, on the

16

American Revolution, and on philosophy. That such a book could be published in England in the midst of the American Revolution is extraordinary. It includes even his famous and hilarious "Rules for Reducing a Great Empire to a Small One," which has stood the test of time as one of the greatest of political satires ever written.

Most cherished of all, perhaps, is that it includes his Epitaph on Himself: "The Body of Benjamin Franklin, Printer, (Like the cover of an old book, Its contents torn out, And stript of its lettering and gilding) Lies here, food for worms; Yet the work itself shall not be lost, For it will (as he believed) appear once more, In a new And more beautiful edition, Corrected and amended By the Author."

1780 [Invasion from Canada]

Burgoyne, Gen. John
A STATE OF THE EXPEDITION FROM CANADA, AS LAID BEFORE THE HOUSE OF COMMONS . . . AND VERIFIED BY EVIDENCE, WITH A COLLEC- TION OF AUTHENTIC DOCUMENTS . . . WRITTEN BY HIMSELF, AND DEDICATED TO THE OFFICERS OF THE ARMY HE COMMANDED.
London: Printed for J. Almon, 1780. ix,[2],191,cixpp. Color folding maps. The second, preferred edition, with more maps and extended text. Contemporary calf, rebacked. Howes B968. Sabin 9255: "General Burgoyne writes well. His very interesting story is told in a masterly manner, and the materials of which it is composed will be held in great estimation by historians." (6) 550.00

In the summer of 1777, Burgoyne invaded New York from Canada with about 7500 men. Sir William Howe was ordered to join him by moving up the Hudson, but did not receive the order. Howe did learn of Burgoyne's movements, however, although he felt the Americans were so thoroughly crushed that the rebellion was all but over — so he belatedly sent only a small force under Clinton to Burgoyne's aid.

Burgoyne took Fort Ticonderoga in early July after Gen. St. Clair wisely withdrew, and slowly moved into New York. Gen. Gates and Gen. Benedict Arnold set out to intercept him. Meanwhile, St. Clair slowly fell back, chopping trees across the roadways, burning crops, and sniping at every opportunity. By October, Burgoyne's effective force had dwindled to under 4000, his supplies were almost used up, and he was surrounded by a superior American force. Burgoyne tried to withdraw, but was forced to surrender his army to Gates on October 17. The victory helped bring American alliance with France and greatly increased morale.

Burgoyne was paroled and returned to England to write his now famous defence. Mark Boatner states: "In his *State of the Expedition from Canada,* Burgoyne . . . tried to shift the blame for his failure onto Howe and Clinton. These arguments have convinced many historians that Burgoyne's failure was not his own fault."

1781   [Exploring Westward]

Carver, Jonathan
TRAVELS THROUGH THE INTERIOR PARTS OF NORTH AMERICA.
London, 1781. 544,[20]pp. Fine hand-colored maps and plates. The third and best edition, with added material. Field 251. Pilling p.68. Vail 670. The first book to name Oregon. Howes C215: "Carver penetrated farther into the West than any other English explorer before the Revolution. . . . His book stimulated curiosity concerning the routes to the Pacific, later satisfied by Mackenzie and Lewis and Clark." Ayer Supplement 29: "Contains account of Capt. Carver's capture and escape at the Massacre of Ft. William Henry."   (7) 850.00

THREE YEARS TRAVELS THROUGH THE INTERIOR PARTS OF NORTH-AMERICA . . . TO THE WESTWARD OF THE GREAT RIVER MISSISSIPPI.
Philadelphia: Joseph Crukshank, 1789. xvi,282pp. Half morocco. Second American edition. Evans 21728.   (8) 185.00

Jonathan Carver was born in Massachusetts in 1710, reared in Connecticut where he received "as good an education as the colony afforded," and was wounded at the siege of Fort William Henry in 1757. He set out on his famous travels in 1766, going west via the Great Lakes, where he "crossed to the Mississippi by the Green Bay-Fox-Wisconsin route, ascended the great river and entered the St. Peter's (now the Minnesota). He reached Lake Superior by the Chippewa and St. Croix rivers, and finally returned in the autumn of 1767 to Mackinac, whence in the next spring he made his way back to Boston."

He failed to get his memoirs of the tour printed there and sailed for England. In 1774 he married, in spite of the fact that he had a wife living in America. His narrative was published in 1778, and became very popular, especially in the expanded 1781 edition, of which L. P. Kellogg writes: "The 1781 edition of his travels contained a biography, portrait, and account of Carver's Indian grant, which he never claimed in his lifetime. On the strength of this grant, supposed to have been made in a cave near St. Paul, a number of speculators attempted to claim lands in Wisconsin and Minnesota."

Wayne Andrews writes: "Recent research points to the conclusion that while Carver actually made the tour he describes, he suppressed the fact that he performed it as a hired agent of Maj. Robert Rogers, who was intent on finding the Northwest Passage to the Pacific Ocean, rather than on his own responsibility." Carver died in penury, leaving children by each of his wives.

1782 [Captured by the Indians]

Hanson, Elizabeth
AN ACCOUNT OF THE CAPTIVITY OF ELIZABETH HANSON, LATE OF KACHECKY IN NEW-ENGLAND, WHO, WITH FOUR OF HER CHILDREN . . . WAS TAKEN CAPTIVE BY THE INDIANS, AND CARRIED INTO CANADA . . .
London: James Phillips, 1782. 26,[2]pp. Full morocco, all edges gilt. Gold-tooled spine. Howes H171. Ayer #28. Sabin 30265. Vail 677.   (9) 165.00

Perhaps the greatest terror for the pioneer American woman lay in the possibility of being captured by Indians. The rather large number of published accounts of those who survived testify to the horrors of such an experience. None is more vivid or concise than that of Mrs. Elizabeth Hanson, who was captured and lived to tell of it.

One day while her husband was away, eleven Indians attacked her homestead, "murdered one of my children upon the spot," and a short time later took another and "knocked out its brains before my face," whereupon they scalped them in front of her. Then she and four of her other children, one only fourteen days old, were forced to march for some two hundred miles into Canada with the Indians; they were allowed nothing to eat but pieces of an old beaver skin coat and bark from trees, although once they were given the intestines of a beaver. For over a year they suffered miserably, but finally all but one daughter were sold to the French, who in turn sold them back to her husband. The husband went out to try to find the other daughter and died of exposure during the attempt.

R. W. G. Vail notes that the versions of this book printed in England differ from those printed in America, and recounts the controversy over whether or not it was written by Mrs. Hanson herself. He states: "The English text seems the simpler and more natural while the American seems to be the same text worked over and 'improved.' An attempt was made to give it a more polished style. . . . The English text is so simply told in homely language of the period that it would almost seem that the captive had written it herself, which is borne out" by both internal and external evidence, although the Quaker preacher Samuel Bownas and Samuel Hopwood are claimed to have helped her write it.

1783   [Treaty of Peace]

*TRATADO DEFINITIVO DE PAZ, CONCLUIDO ENTRE EL REY NUESTRO
SENOR Y EL REY DE LA GRAN BRETANA, FIRMADO EN VERSAILLES . . .
CON SUS ARTICULOS PRELIMINARES.*
Madrid: De Orden del Rey, en la Imprenta Real, [1783]. [4],94pp. With woodcut vignette of
Spanish arms on title. Full-page map, engraved by Tomas de Lopez. Quarto. Half morocco.
First edition of the Spanish text. In impeccable condition. Sabin 96558. Palau
339315.   (10) 950.00

CONSTITUTIONS DES TREIZE ETATS-UNIS DE L'AMERIQUE
Paris, 1783. [6], 540pp. Full contemporary calf. On the title page the Seal of the United States
appears for the first time. Howes C716: ''Made by the Duc de la Rochefoucault, at Franklin's
suggestion, with over fifty footnotes by Franklin.'' Only 600 copies were printed. Includes the
Constitutions of each state, the Declaration of Independence, the Articles of Confederation, and
various American treaties.   (11) 1250.00

The Treaty of Paris marked the final consummation of American independence. The
treaties signed there involved not only the United States and Britain but also each of the other
belligerents, Spain and France. Negotiation of the treaties marked the end of exceedingly complicated negotiations begun in March of 1782. America and Britain formed conditional articles
of peace on November 30, 1782, not to be effective until the final treaty of September 3, 1783,
in Paris. The Spanish and French preliminaries had been signed on January 2, 1783.

The treaty, in addition to ending the American Revolution, restructured the balance of
power in Europe and had enormous import for the whole western world. The Comte de Ver-
gennes, Benjamin Franklin, John Jay, John Adams, Lord Shelburne, and other negotiators
carved up all of America and made important agreements concerning European areas. Spain got
Florida, France got Louisiana, and Britain got Canada.

But most important was the recognition by Britain, Spain, and France of the independence and sovereignty of the United States of America, and the evacuation ''with all convenient speed'' of all British troops from the United States. From this point on until the adoption of the Constitution, the Articles of Confederation (which had been drafted in 1777 and
adopted in 1781) became the acknowledged law for the United States.

Franklin, James

THE PHILOSOPHICAL & POLITICAL HISTORY OF THE THIRTEEN UNITED STATES OF AMERICA . . . AND OF EAST AND WEST FLORIDA . . . AND OF THE ORIGINAL INHABITANTS OF AMERICA.

London: Printed for J. Hinton and W. Adams, 1784. 156pp. Contemporary full mottled calf. *First edition of the first history of the United States.* Howes F334. Sabin 25620.   (12) 650.00

This is the first history of the United States of America, published at a time when the insufficiency of the Articles of Confederation was most clearly evident. Congress was rarely able even to assemble a quorum, and was forced out of Philadelphia by its own unpaid army. The population of the whole nation was about two million, less than that of many cities of today.

In this atmosphere, Franklin wrote in his introduction: ''It is not easy to say, how long they [the States] may agree among themselves, or how long so vast a continent as North America may submit to the dictates of a congress. Jealous as the colonies have ever been of each other, tenacious as they are of their liberties, and so ready to catch fire at the least spark of impression, the settlement of a regular government among them will perhaps be a difficult task. . . . While they are shaking off the shackles of the mother country, they may be imperceptibly forging chains of a more durable nature. . . .''

Franklin also warns immigrants to be careful, as ''they may leave a bad country for a worse . . . in crossing the Atlantic, they may perhaps be forced to take an active part in the scenes of war, desolation, and slaughter.'' These were realistic appraisals in 1784, and reflect what might have happened — had it not been for that 1787 convention in Philadelphia.

THE DAILY ADVERTISER: POLITICAL, HISTORICAL, AND COMMERCIAL.

New York: Printed by Francis Childs . . . Mid-Way between the Coffee-House and Fly-Market. Two issues: December 6, 1785 (vol. I, No. 241) and December 12, 1785 (vol. I, No. 246). John Jay's copies, docketed in ink, each containing material on Jay. These two issues, each in the first year of publication, are apparently the only existing copies except for the file held by the Library of Congress. No copy of either is cited by Brigham in the holdings of the other twenty institutional collections that have files of the paper. Brigham I-620. Evans 19137: "The first daily newspaper published in New York, and second in the United States."   (13) 275.00 each

The New York *Daily Advertiser*, the first New York daily newspaper and the second in the United States, was printed by Francis Childs, a 22-year-old orphan from Philadelphia. John C. Oswald writes: "He had the good fortune, however, to secure the interest of John Jay, the great American patriot and statesman, who provided for the boy's education." In 1784 Childs wrote to Benjamin Franklin asking help and proposing a partnership, to which Franklin replied "that he had made inquiries of John Jay respecting Childs and was receptive to the latter's suggestion."

Publication meanwhile had begun on March 1, 1785. A week earlier, another paper was issued calling itself a daily, but apparently did not actually become one until some weeks later. Franklin and Childs did not become partners, but Franklin sold him his type fonts from his private press in France at a giveaway price to help him out. Childs later became official printer to the U.S. Congress and a wealthy man.

1786   [A Frenchman's View of America]

Chastellux, Marquis Francois de
VOYAGE DANS L'AMERIQUE SEPTENTRIONALE DANS LES ANNEES 1780-82.

Paris: Chez Prault, 1786. 2 volumes. Two folding maps. Three folding plates. Contemporary half calf. Fine set. *First complete edition,* with the half-titles and errata. Howes C324: "Constitutes the first trustworthy record of life in the United States." Monaghan 405.   (14) 275.00

The Chevalier de Chastellux was career officer in the French army, joining at the age of 13. In addition, however, he became an accomplished linguist and writer, distinguished alike for his military, technical, literary, and dramatic writings.

In 1780 he was sent to America as a major general, third in the hierarchy of rank, and came to be known as "the diplomat of Rochambeau's army." Howard Rice writes: "He was equally at ease in staff conferences, in the drawing rooms of Philadelphia or Boston, and in roadside taverns." His celebrated account of his years in revolutionary America are now considered the best outsider's view of life in those eventful times, presenting what an early review called "a heterogeneous and multifarious account of everything that caught the lively traveller's eager eye and minute attention; and, as nothing escaped his active investigation, his work abounds not only with observations which are of importance, but with details of even the most trifling incidents that bad roads, inconvenient inns, and distracted times usually afford."

The Pennsylvania Packet, *and Daily Advertiser.*

[Price Four-Pence.]   WEDNESDAY, September 19, 1787.   [No. 2690.]

WE, the People of the United States, in order to form a more perfect Union, establish Justice, insure domestic Tranquility, provide for the common Defence, promote the General Welfare, and secure the Blessings of Liberty to Ourselves and our Posterity, do ordain and establish this Constitution for the United States of America.

ARTICLE I.

Sect. 1. ALL legislative powers herein granted shall be vested in a Congress of the United States, which shall consist of a Senate and House of Representatives.

Sect. 2. The House of Representatives shall be composed of members chosen every second year by the people of the several states, and the electors in each state shall have the qualifications requisite for electors of the most numerous branch of the state legislature.

No person shall be a representative who shall not have attained to the age of twenty-five years, and been seven years a citizen of the United States, and who shall not, when elected, be an inhabitant of that state in which he shall be chosen.

Representatives and direct taxes shall be apportioned among the several states which may be included within this Union, according to their respective numbers, which shall be determined by adding to the whole number of free persons, including those bound to service for a term of years, and excluding Indians not taxed, three-fifths of all other persons. The actual enumeration shall be made within three years after the first meeting of the Congress of the United States, and within every subsequent term of ten years, in such manner as they shall by law direct. The number of representatives shall not exceed one for every thirty thousand, but each state shall have at least one representative; and until such enumeration shall be made, the state of New-Hampshire shall be entitled to chuse three, Massachusetts eight, Rhode-Island and Providence Plantations one, Connecticut five, New-York six, New-Jersey four, Pennsylvania eight, Delaware one, Maryland six, Virginia ten, North-Carolina five, South-Carolina five, and Georgia three.

When vacancies happen in the representation from any state, the Executive authority thereof shall issue writs of election to fill such vacancies.

The House of Representatives shall chuse their Speaker and other officers; and shall have the sole power of impeachment.

Sect. 3. The Senate of the United States shall be composed of two senators from each state, chosen by the legislature thereof, for six years; and each senator shall have one vote.

Immediately after they shall be assembled in consequence of the first election, they shall be divided as equally as may be into three classes. The seats of the senators of the first class shall be vacated at the expiration of the second year, of the second class at the expiration of the fourth year, and of the third class at the expiration of the sixth year, so that one-third may be chosen every second year; and if vacancies happen by resignation, or otherwise, during the recess of the Legislature of any state, the Executive thereof may make temporary appointments until the next meeting of the Legislature, which shall then fill such vacancies.

No person shall be a senator who shall not have attained to the age of thirty years, and been nine years a citizen of the United States, and who shall not, when elected, be an inhabitant of that state for which he shall be chosen.

The Vice-President of the United States shall be President of the senate, but shall have no vote, unless they be equally divided.

The Senate shall chuse their other officers, and also a President pro tempore, in the absence of the Vice-President, or when he shall exercise the office of President of the United States.

The Senate shall have the sole power to try all impeachments. When sitting for that purpose, they shall be on oath or affirmation. When the President of the United States is tried, the Chief Justice shall preside: And no person shall be convicted without the concurrence of two-thirds of the members present.

Judgment in cases of impeachment shall not extend further than to removal from office, and disqualification to hold and enjoy any office of honor, trust or profit under the United States; but the party convicted shall nevertheless be liable and subject to indictment, trial, judgment and punishment, according to law.

Sect. 4. The times, places and manner of holding elections for senators and representatives, shall be prescribed in each state by the legislature thereof; but the Congress may at any time by law make or alter such regulations, except as to the places of chusing Senators.

The Congress shall assemble at least once in every year, and such meeting shall be on the first Monday in December, unless they shall by law appoint a different day.

Sect. 5. Each house shall be the judge of the elections, returns and qualifications of its own members, and a majority of each shall constitute a quorum to do business; but a smaller number may adjourn from day to day, and may be authorised to compel the attendance of absent members, in such manner, and under such penalties as each house may provide.

Each house may determine the rules of its proceedings, punish its members for disorderly behaviour, and, with the concurrence of two-thirds, expel a member.

Each house shall keep a journal of its proceedings, and from time to time publish the same, excepting such parts as may in their judgment require secrecy; and the yeas and nays of the members of either house on any question shall, at the desire of one-fifth of those present, be entered on the journal.

Neither house, during the session of Congress, shall, without the consent of the other, adjourn for more than three days, nor to any other place than that in which the two houses shall be sitting.

Sect. 6. The senators and representatives shall receive a compensation for their services, to be ascertained by law, and paid out of the treasury of the United States. They shall in all cases, except treason, felony and breach of the peace, be privileged from arrest during their attendance at the session of their respective houses, and in going to and returning from the same; and for any speech or debate in either house, they shall not be questioned in any other place.

No senator or representative shall, during the time for which he was elected, be appointed to any civil office under the authority of the United States, which shall have been created, or the emoluments whereof shall have been encreased during such time; and no person holding any office under the United States, shall be a member of either house during his continuance in office.

Sect. 7. All bills for raising revenue shall originate in the house of representatives; but the senate may propose or concur with amendments as on other bills.

Every bill which shall have passed the house of representatives and the senate, shall, before it become a law, be presented to the president of the United States; if he approve he shall sign it, but if not he shall return it, with his objections to that house in which it shall have originated, who shall enter the objections at large on their journal, and proceed to reconsider it. If after such reconsideration two-thirds of that house shall agree to pass the bill, it shall be sent, together with the objections, to the other house, by which it shall likewise be reconsidered, and if approved by two-thirds of that house, it shall become a law. But in all such cases the votes of both houses shall

WE, THE PEOPLE OF THE UNITED STATES . . .

Philadelphia: The Pennsylvania Packet, Dunlap & Claypoole, 1787. 4pp. Large folio. Contemporary inscription reading: "This paper to be preserved for the Sake of Antiquity. So says Mary P. Serrill." Evans 20819. Bennett, p.29. Howes C713. Brigham, 942-43. Pennsylvania Hist. Soc. Exhibit #90: "This is the first printing of the Constitution for the public." The Constitutional Convention met secretly, adopting the final version of the document on September 17, at which time Dunlap and Claypoole were employed to set up and print an official, secret version for transmission to Congress. Dunlap and Claypoole did this on the 17th or 18th, and kept the type set so as to be able to issue, on the 19th, the first printing for public perusal. Only a handful of these two issues exist today, and except for a remarkable proof copy this is the only copy known in private hands.   (15) 85,000.00

PROCEEDINGS OF THE FEDERAL CONVENTION. WE, THE PEOPLE . . .

Worcester, Mass.: Printed by Isaiah Thomas, The Worcester Magazine, for the Fourth Week in September, 1787. Contains a Supplement with the proposed Constitution. *The first magazine printing of the Constitution,* printed in the late third week of September, 1787. In half morocco slipcase. Mott, 92-93. Evans 20896.   (16) 450.00

[WE, THE PEOPLE OF THE UNITED STATES . . .]

Middletown, Conn.: Middlesex Gazette, October 1, 1787. 4pp. Folio. Contains the entire text of the Constitution. Brigham, p.35, locating five known copies. Evans 20524.   (17) 1250.00

WE, THE PEOPLE OF THE UNITED STATES . . .

Hartford, January 9, 1788. 8pp. Folio. Sewn. In half morocco slipcase. *First Connecticut printing,* with the ratification notice of the Connecticut Legislature. The Middlendorf Collection copy. Bates 269. Evans 21523.   (18) 1650.00

JOURNAL, ACTS AND PROCEEDINGS OF THE CONVENTION . . . WHICH FORMED THE CONSTITUTION OF THE UNITED STATES.

Boston: Thomas B. Wait, 1819. 510pp. Original full calf. *First printing of the proceedings of the Convention,* which had until this time remained secret. Edited by John Quincy Adams, with the assistance of Pres. James Madison. Shaw and Shoemaker 49802.   (19) 350.00

During the summer of 1787 one of the most remarkable gatherings in history met in Philadelphia. The Constitutional Convention began its debates on May 25, debates such as had never before been held in history. What they produced was a short compact of some five thousand words that is, quite simply, the greatest document ever produced by the mind of man.

At four o'clock on the afternoon of Monday, September 17, 1787, presiding officer George Washington gavelled the Constitutional Convention to a close, and James McHenry recorded that "members [are] to be provided with printed copies," whereupon the Gentlemen of the Convention departed and "dined together at the City Tavern."

Two blocks away from the City Tavern, the printers John Dunlap and David C. Claypoole stayed up late that night and on September 18, making the final corrections and printing secret copies to be taken to the members of Congress, which was meeting in New York, and where it was read on September 20.

Meanwhile, Benjamin Franklin read it aloud to the Pennsylvania General Assembly in the late afternoon and evening of September 18, and to a "large crowd of citizens" in the gallery. George Washington left at the same time for Mount Vernon. Dunlap and Claypoole were at their shop busily printing the first public copies of the "Constitution for the United States of America."

Using the type already set up for some weeks through all the debates and alterations, they ran off the entire single-column text under the heading of their *Pennsylvania Packet*. On the morning of September 19, "We, the People of the United States" had the first copies of our Constitution.

Other Philadelphia printers quickly reprinted it, followed shortly by those in other sections of the country. Not until 1819 were the secret proceedings of the Constitutional Convention allowed to be published, when John Quincy Adams enlisted the aid of President James Madison to issue the text, printed by Thomas B. Wait in Boston.

In the Supreme Court Chamber, State House, Madison, Wis.

The Signing of the Constitution. From a Painting by Albert Herter

THEY PRINTED *the* DECLARATION *and the* CONSTITUTION

Dunlap and Claypoole
Printers Extraordinary

— *By* —
WILBUR T. ROBERTS

EVERY printer that sets in type the Constitution of the United States is imbued with an exalted sense of having done something eminently worth while. What, then, must have been the emotions of the two early Philadelphia printers John Dunlap and David Claypoole whose hands were the first to spell out the words of the great charter of law and principles. And how must the same pair have felt after setting up the Declaration of Independence (at the risk of their necks) the very day after its adoption and before the document had been publicly read.

Dunlap and Claypoole conducted a small printing establishment on what was then High Street, but now Market Street, in Philadelphia. The older of the two, Dunlap, was a native of Ireland, the other, Claypoole, the descendant of a man that might have been a

John Dunlap, soldier, editor and printer of one of the earliest newspapers in the country

king, had he chosen—Oliver Cromwell. Those acquainted with English history will remember that the decline in health and passing of Cromwell was attributed to grief over the death of his favorite daughter, Elizabeth, wife of a Lord Claypoole.

The *Pennsylvania Packet*, which eventually became America's first daily newspaper, was founded in 1771 by Dunlap. Claypoole served his apprenticeship on the publication.

Always ardent and active patriots, the two young printers, master and apprentice, attracted the attention of Revolutionary leaders by issuing broadsides after the battles of Bunker Hill, Lexington, Ticonderoga and Quebec. The red-letter day in their careers occurred on July 5, 1776, when three of the nation's fathers walked unexpectedly in upon them at their shop. The callers were Thomas Jefferson,

Benjamin Franklin and John Adams, a committee from Congress bearing rush orders for the printing of the Declaration of Independence.

It is easy to imagine the flurry of excitement that swept the little printing establishment that summer day.

While Dunlap and his apprentice set to type the message that was to "ring round the world," the committee of three restlessly paced the floor. Proofs drawn from the press were carefully scanned for typographical errors by Franklin, who had been brought up on the smell of printers' ink. Jefferson, who had penned the document, was chiefly concerned with grammatical correctness. Not until a sheet entirely satisfactory to both had been produced was word given to proceed with the final printing. The next morning, when the sun was high in the sky, two tired printers lay down on improvised cots for a well-deserved rest.

That first printing of the Declaration was in the strictest sense a "hurry-up job." The ink was barely dry when fast riders were carrying broadsides to the far-flung legislators, armies and people of the colonies.

The first publication of the new Constitution was on September 19, 1787, in a regular

THE Philadelphia mansion of John Dunlap, as it appeared in 1800, at the corner of Twelfth and Market Streets, Philadelphia

issue of Dunlap and Claypoole's *Pennsylvania Packet, and Daily Advertiser.* It was the official printing and a matter of news; all four pages of the periodical were given over to the document.

Just recently a memorial tablet was placed in Philadelphia where the historic printing shop stood. The inscription reads: "On this site were first printed the Declaration of Independence, July 5, 1776; the Constitution of the United States, September 19, 1787; Washington's Farewell Address, September 19, 1796; and the First Daily Newspaper in America, September 21, 1784, in the Print Shop of Dunlap and Claypoole, Soldiers of the Revolution."

Claypoole did not become a partner in the concern until the British troops evacuated Philadelphia in June, 1778. During the occupancy, which began in September, 1777, Dunlap conducted his business at Lancaster, Pennsylvania. He had fled the home town about the time the old state house bell and the seat of government were removed to safer quarters.

That the partners prospered in their calling is evidenced by the large country place owned by Dunlap in Virginia and his sumptuous town residence at Twelfth and Market Streets. The stable of the latter served as an emergency hospital during a fever epidemic in 1797.

But above pecuniary gain the enterprising pair had pride in the confidence and trust shown them by the Republic's founders. When talk was at its height of drafting Washington for a third term as the nation's chief executive the first President sent for Claypoole and delivered to him personally, for publication, the memo-

WHERE the precious original copies of the Declaration of Independence and the Constitution of the United States are enshrined in the Library of Congress, Washington

The Pennsylvania Packet, *and Daily Advertiser.*

[Price Four-Pence.]   WEDNESDAY, SEPTEMBER 19, 1787.   [No. 2690.]

WE, the People of the United States, in order to form a more perfect Union, establish Justice, insure domestic Tranquility, provide for the common Defence, promote the General Welfare, and secure the Blessings of Liberty to Ourselves and our Posterity, do ordain and establish this Constitution for the United States of America.

ARTICLE I.

Sect. 1. ALL legislative powers herein granted shall be vested in a Congress of the United States, which shall consist of a Senate and House of Representatives.

Sect. 2. The House of Representatives shall be composed of members chosen every second year by the people of the several states, and the electors in each state shall have the qualifications requisite for electors of the most numerous branch of the state legislature.

No person shall be a representative who shall not have attained to the age of twenty-five years, and been seven years a citizen of the United States, and who shall not, when elected, be an inhabitant of that state in which he shall be chosen.

Representatives and direct taxes shall be apportioned among the several states which may be included within this Union, according to their respective numbers, which shall be determined by adding to the whole number of free persons, including those bound to service for a term of years, and excluding Indians not taxed, three-fifths of all other persons. The actual enumeration shall be made within three years after the first meeting of the Congress of the United States, and within every subsequent term of ten years, in such manner as they shall by law direct. The number of representatives shall not exceed one for every thirty thousand, but each state shall have at least one representative; and until such enumeration shall be made, the state of New-Hampshire shall be entitled to chuse three, Massachusetts eight, Rhode-Island and Providence Plantations one, Connecticut five, New-York six, New-Jersey four, Pennsylvania eight, Delaware one, Maryland six, Virginia ten, North-Carolina five, South-Carolina five, and Georgia three.

When vacancies happen in the representation from any state, the Executive authority thereof shall issue writs of election to fill such vacancies.

The House of Representatives shall chuse their Speaker and other officers; and shall have the sole power of impeachment.

Sect. 3. The Senate of the United States shall be composed of two senators from each state, chosen by the legislature thereof, for six years; and each senator shall have one vote.

Immediately after they shall be assembled in consequence of the first election, they shall be divided as equally as may be into three classes. The seats of the senators of the first class shall be vacated at the expiration of the second year, of the second class at the expiration of the fourth year, and of the third class at the expiration of the sixth year, so that one-third may be chosen every second year; and if vacancies happen by resignation, or otherwise, during the recess of the Legislature of any state, the Executive thereof may make temporary appointments until the next meeting of the Legislature, which shall then fill such vacancies.

From an original copy in the collection of the New York Public Library

THE FIRST PRINTING OF THE CONSTITUTION OF THE UNITED STATES

PUBLICATION of the document by the firm of Dunlap and Claypoole, Philadelphia printers, consumed all four pages of their weekly newspaper, "The Pennsylvania Packet, and Daily Advertiser." Eleven years before, the Declaration of Independence had been set up in the same shop

rable "Farewell Address" to the people. Claypoole wrote of the visit for the Pennsylvania Historical Society in 1826:

"A few days before the appearance of this document in print, I received a message from the President, by his private secretary, signifying his desire to see me. I awaited upon him at the appointed time and found him sitting alone in his drawing-room. He received me kindly and after I paid my respects to him desired me to take a seat near him. Then, addressing himself to me, he said that he had for some time past contemplated retiring from public life and had at length concluded to do so at the end of the then present term; that he had some thoughts and reflections upon the occasion which he deemed proper to communicate to the people of the United States in the form of an address, and which he wished to appear in *The Daily Advertiser*, of which I was the editor.

"He paused and I took the opportunity of thanking him for having preferred that paper as the channel of his communication with the people—especially as I viewed this selection as indicating his approbation of the principles and manner in which the work was conducted. He silently assented and asked when publication could be made. I answered that the time should be made perfectly convenient to himself, and the following Monday was fixed upon. The President made but few alterations from the original, except in the matter of punctuation, in which he was very minute."

Washington presented Claypoole with the original manuscript of the address and it is now at the New York Public Library.

THE FEDERALIST, NO. I
THE FEDERALIST, NO. III.

New York: The Independent Journal, October 27 and November 3, 1787. Two original complete issues, containing the first printing of the first and third Federalist Papers. *John Jay's own copies, from his private papers, docketed in his hand.* The first was written by Hamilton, the third by Jay. (20) 4500.00

Hamilton, Alexander, John Jay, and James Madison.
THE FEDERALIST: A COLLECTION OF ESSAYS, WRITTEN IN FAVOUR OF THE NEW CONSTITUTION.

N.Y.: J. and A. M'Lean, 1788. 2 volumes. Contemporary calf. *First edition in book form.* Grolier American Hundred #19. Ford 17. Howes H114: "Most famous and influential American political work." Downs Famous Books #44. Printing and the Mind of Man 234. Evans 21127. Sabin 23979. (21) 2500.00

Same, revised edition. City of Washington: Jacob Gideon, 1818. 671pp. Full contemporary calf. "A New Edition, the Numbers Written by Mr. Madison Corrected by Himself." Ford 24. Shaw and Shoemaker 44017. (22) 150.00

The newly proposed Constitution was a bundle of unique compromises, and opposition quickly arose from reactionaries and from special interest elements. Within four weeks of completion of the Constitution, three of the greatest minds in America joined forces to convince the public that the Constitution should be adopted: John Jay, Alexander Hamilton, and James Madison.

A series of essays, each written by one of the three, appeared in the *Independent Journal* of New York, where opposition was heaviest, and their logic and genius did much to achieve adoption of the great charter.

Charles A. Beard wrote of *The Federalist:* "In my opinion it is the most instructive work on political science ever written in the United States; and, owing to its practical character, it ranks first in the world's literature of political science." Alexis de Tocqueville said that it "ought to be familiar to the statesmen of every nation," and Chancellor Kent said "no constitution of government ever received a more masterly and successful vindication." Harry S Truman put it most concisely: "The papers written by these three men created the greatest republic in history."

1789   [The Bill of Rights]

JOURNAL OF THE FIRST SESSION OF THE SENATE OF THE UNITED STATES OF AMERICA, BEGUN AND HELD AT THE CITY OF NEW-YORK, MARCH 4TH, 1789.

New York: Printed by Thomas Greenleaf, 1789. 172pp. Folio. Large paper copy. Full contemporary calf. Fine copy, bound with: *JOURNAL OF THE SECOND SESSION OF THE SENATE OF THE UNITED STATES* (N.Y.: John Fenno, 1790) and *JOURNAL OF THE THIRD SESSION OF THE SENATE OF THE UNITED STATES* (Phila.: John Fenno, 1791). Further details upon request.

The designers of the Constitution worked from the assumption that individual human rights exist inborn and inalienable, and that the Constitution was an added contract to rights already possessed by the people. The very first criticisms of the Constitution, however, centered around there being no concrete statement of just what those inalienable human rights were.

The first ten amendments, now known as the Bill of Rights, spelled them out plainly. The First Congress, meeting in New York, passed them after some debate on September 25, 1789, and by December 15, 1791, they had all been ratified by the required number of states.

Three works vie for the title of first printing of these cherished amendments: *Acts Passed at a Congress of the United States* (N.Y., 1789); *Journal of the First Session of the Senate of the United States* (N.Y., 1789); and *Journal of the House of Representatives of the United States* (N.Y., 1789). Each contains the Bill of Rights, yet it is undetermined which appeared first; likely as not, they were issued concurrently. The Senate Journals, in any case, are the more desirable, as they are rarer than the other two and as they contain the debates and votes in the Senate before final approval.

1790   [American Geography]

Workman, Benjamin
ELEMENTS OF GEOGRAPHY, DESIGNED FOR YOUNG STUDENTS OF THAT SCIENCE.

Philadelphia: John M'Culloch, 1790. 124pp. Original calf. 3 maps, 1 folding. Evans 23091, locating no copies. Phillips p.869. This volume was first issued eight months earlier without any maps; this is the first to include maps. *Includes one of the earliest maps of America printed in America:* "A Map of the United States N. America," showing the U.S. to the "Head of the Oregon which runs W. to the Pacific Ocean."   (24) 650.00

With almost a whole new continent beckoning the pioneer, interest in geography was naturally great. Benjamin Workman issued his little geography in 1789, without any maps; he says in the preface to our edition, the first to include maps: "The first edition of the Elements of Geography (though scarce published eight months), being all sold off, it became necessary to print a second, which is . . . more properly a new work than a second edition. . . . The alterations, additions, and improvements [are] so numerous and important, that their introduction quite new-modelled the work, and obliged the Author to write the whole over again. . . . Philadelphia, March 9th, 1790.''

The folding map of the United States is of particular interest. It was issued in 1784 and copies are inserted in a 1784 Almanac by F. Bailey and also in this Workman volume. Another 1784 map of the United States was issued in Jedidiah Morse's *Geography Made Easy*. Which of the two takes precedence is unknown. In any case, excepting newspapers and magazines, it is either the first or second map of the United States printed in America and issued in a book.

1791 [Franklin's Autobiography]

Franklin, Benjamin
MEMOIRES DE LA VIE PRIVEE DE BENJAMIN FRANKLIN.
Paris: Chez Buisson, 1791. Two parts in one volume, as issued. Contemporary marbled boards and morocco spine, gilt. Fine copy. *First edition of Franklin's autobiography.* The work did not appear in English until 1793. Howes F323. Downs, Famous Books #49. Grolier American Hundred #21. Ford 383.   (25) 1250.00

JUGENDJAHRE VON IHM SELBST FUR SEINEN SOHN BESCHREIBEN ...
Berlin: Bey Heinrich August Rottman, 1792. 214pp. Original wrappers, paper label. Very good copy. *First German edition.* Ford 384.   (26) 250.00

ENSKILDTA LEFWERNE, UPSTATT OF HONOM SJELF OCH STALDT TIL HANS SON ...
Stockholm, 1792. [2], 218, [4]pp. Engraved portrait of Franklin. Contemporary half calf. Fine copy. *First Swedish edition.* Ford 385.   (27) 250.00

As stated in the Grolier Exhibit, this work is ''the most widely read of all American autobiographies . . . it holds the essence of the American way of life.'' It established clearly the great American tradition of the self-made man. Like Lord Chesterfield, Franklin gives sage and practical advice on how best to get along in the world, with an open and frank account of how he himself did so.

Franklin's Autobiography is full of those homely aphorisms that so endeared Poor Richard to millions of readers. ''He that has done you a kindness will be more ready to do you another, than he whom you yourself have obliged.'' Franklin pours out all the worldly wisdom gained during his remarkable career, and enriches both our lives and our literature in the process.

Paine, Thomas

RIGHTS OF MAN, BEING AN ANSWER TO MR. BURKE'S ATTACK...

London: H. D. Symonds, 1792. Two parts in one volume. iv, 78, [2]; viii, 10-90, [6]pp. Half calf. Howes P31 and P32. Printing and the Mind of Man 241.   (28) 150.00

Paine, Thomas

LETTER ADDRESSED TO THE ADDRESSERS, ON THE LATE PROCLAMA-TION.

London: H. D. Symonds, 1792. 40pp. Sewn. Howes P28: "This attack on the evils of English government is practically a third part of his Rights of Man."   (29) 85.00

Paine, Thomas

RIGHTS OF MAN: BEING AN ANSWER TO MR. BURKE'S ATTACK ON THE FRENCH REVOLUTION.

Boston: I. Thomas and E. T. Andrews, 1791. 79pp. Sewn. Evans 23662.   (30) 150.00

Same, first New York edition. C. R. and G. Webster, [1791]. 124pp. Evans 24658.   (31) 150.00

DROITS DE L'HOMME, OU REPONSE A L'SOUVRAGE DE M. BURKE

Hambourg: Freres Herold, 1791. 136pp. Original boards, untrimmed. Not in Howes. *Rare, unrecorded edition.*   (32) 250.00

Thomas Paine, who had done so much to help create public support of the American Revolution with his *Common Sense* and *The American Crisis* papers, was aroused by Edmund Burke's attacks on the American and French revolutionary movements, particularly on the French Revolution. As Carter and Muir point out, Paine's own deep and bitter knowledge of revolutionary politics (Benjamin Franklin had brought him to America in 1774, so he had experienced the entire course of the War of Independence) enabled him to see where Burke's vision had been clouded.... It was an immediate success."

It also caused alarm and Paine was forced to flee from England to avoid arrest." The government tried to suppress it, but it circulated the more briskly. Those who bought it as the work of an inflamed revolutionary were surprised by its dignity and moderation.... Considered apart from the turmoil which attended its first publication, however, *Rights of Man* can be seen for what it is: the textbook of radical thought and the clearest of all expositions of the basic principles of democracy."

Imlay, Gilbert

A TOPOGRAPHICAL DESCRIPTION OF THE WESTERN TERRITORY OF NORTH AMERICA ... TO WHICH ARE ADDED, THE DISCOVERY, SETTLEMENT, AND PRESENT STATE OF KENTUCKY BY JOHN FILSON, TO WHICH IS ADDED, THE ADVENTURES OF COL. DANIEL BOON ...

London: J. Debrett, 1793. 433, [22]pp. Three folding maps: Western Territory of North America, Kentucky, and the Rapids of Ohio. Later cloth, morocco label. Second edition, greatly enlarged. Howes I12: "This work gave the most complete information on the trans-Alleghany region available at the end of the 18th century." Church Cat. 1261n. Vail 941. Clark II-41. Sabin 34355: "A most valuable mass of materials."   (33) 450.00

This work is the most important topographical account of the American frontier in the late 18th century. It contains the adventures of Daniel Boone, adding to our folklore many of his legendary feats; and, more importantly, it contains Filson's work, the first history of Kentucky.

Filson came to Kentucky in 1782 or 1783 as a surveyor, keeping a journal as he travelled about. One of the first narrators of border Indian warfare, he was himself killed by Indians along the Miami River in 1788. Of Imlay, T. D. Clark writes that he was "a man who left Kentucky without settling his obligations, who seems to have been involved in efforts to organize a French expedition to take the lower Mississippi Valley, and who treated Mary Wollstonecraft shamelessly." He certainly was involved in an attempt to seize Louisiana, and his liaison with Mary Wollstonecraft, although she called herself his wife, was apparently maintained by him primarily to secure her financial aid. When he neglected her and their daughter, she twice attempted suicide. He died in justified obscurity in 1828.

ADVERTISEMENT.

WE the Subfcribers, inhabitants of Kentucky, and well acquainted with the country from its firft fettlement; at the requeft of the author of this book, have carefully revifed it, and recommend it to the Public as an exceeding good performance, containing as accurate a defcription of our country as we think can poffibly be given: much preferable to any in our knowledge extant; and think it will be of great utility to the Public. Witnefs our hands this 12th day of May, Anno Domini 1784.

DANIEL BOON,

LEVI TODD,

JAMES HARROD.

1794 [Keystone Laws]

AN ACT TO PROHIBIT THE CARRYING ON THE SLAVE-TRADE FROM THE UNITED STATES TO ANY FOREIGN PLACE OR COUNTRY.

Broadsheet, 2pp., folio. Philadelphia, March 22, 1794. Fine, large, entirely untrimmed copy. Third Congress, First Session. Signed in type by F. A. Muhlenberg as Speaker of the House, John Adams as Vice President, and approved by George Washington as President. Evans 27839 locates only one other known copy. This is the *first Federal law dealing with slavery.* (34) 500.00

RESOLVED . . . THE JUDICIAL POWER OF THE UNITED STATES SHALL NOT BE CONSTRUED TO EXTEND . . .

Broadside, 1p., folio, Philadelphia, [Jan. 2], 1794. Fine, large, entirely untrimmed copy. Third Congress, First Session. Signed in type by Muhlenberg and Adams. Not in Evans. Bristol 8911, locating three known copies. This is *first printing of the 11th Amendment* to the Constitution. (35) 1000.00

AN ACT MAKING FURTHER PROVISION FOR SECURING AND COLLECTING THE DUTIES ON FOREIGN AND DOMESTIC DISTILLED SPIRITS, STILLS, WINES AND TEAS.

Folded broadsheet, 4pp., folio. Philadelphia, June 5, 1794. Fine, large, entirely untrimmed copy. Signed in type by Muhlenberg, Ralph Izard, and George Washington. Evans 27868, locating only two other known copies. This and another act on the same day comprise *the first separate Federal law taxing liquor,* resulting in the Whiskey Rebellion. (36) 250.00

THE PROCEEDINGS OF THE EXECUTIVE OF THE UNITED STATES, RESPECTING THE INSURGENTS, 1794.

Philadelphia: John Fenno, Feb. 21, 1795. 130pp. Half morocco. Howes P624. Evans 29738. Sabin 65844. *First edition of the first work on the Whiskey Rebellion,* containing numerous official documents and proclamations by Pres. Washington. (37) 185.00

Congress passed some of its most important and far-reaching legislation in 1794, especially the first law dealing with the slave trade, the Whiskey Rebellion law and proclamations, and the 11th Amendment curbing the judiciary.

SLAVE TRADE. The Constitution (Art. I, Sec. 9) prohibited Congress from passing any law affecting the importation of slaves until 1808. This 1794 act, the first Federal law dealing with the subject, prohibits any citizen of the United States from engaging in the slave trade in any fashion, even if the activity took place entirely outside the U.S., such as slave trading between two foreign countries.

ELEVENTH AMENDMENT. In 1793 in Chisholm v. Georgia the Supreme Court upheld the right of a citizen of one state to sue another state. The 11th Amendment overturned the Court and declared that states were exempt from suits by citizens of other states and of foreign countries. It took from the Supreme Court all jurisdiction in controversies between states and individuals.

WHISKEY REBELLION. The excise law of 1791 included distilleries, but without sufficient teeth, so in June of 1794 Congress passed its first separate whiskey tax act. Distillers in Western Pennsylvania rebelled. President Washington acted aggressively and sent in the Federal militia. The rebellion was put down and some of the insurgents were convicted of treason, but pardoned by Washington. The affair was the first test of the power of the Federal government and an important milestone in its firm establishment throughout the country.

Hamilton, Alexander

REPORT OF THE SECRETARY OF THE TREASURY CONTAINING A PLAN FOR THE FURTHER SUPPORT OF PUBLIC CREDIT.

Philadelphia: John Fenno, 1795. 90pp., plus 10 large folding charts. Half morocco. *First edition* of these important and far-reaching proposals, equal in importance to his manufactures report, and considerably rarer. Only five other known copies have been located. Howes H122. Evans 29772. Ford #267.   (38) 750.00

Original Letter Signed by Alexander Hamilton, as Secretary of the Treasury, to Nathaniel Appleton, Commissioner of Loans, Treasury Department, Sept. 27, 1791, 2pp., 4to. ''. . . You have misapprehended a late instruction of the Comptroller, directing you to continue to receive subscriptions to the several loans. . . . But this was not meant to alter the preceeding instruction . . . to make up your dividends of interest according to the then State of the Stock on your books. Any deviation from this . . . will be particularly unfortunate. . . .'' Signed clearly with his full signature.   (39) 475.00

Issued only two weeks before Hamilton's retirement from office, these proposals were so innovative and perspicacious that they were reprinted and studied in England, making the report one of the few official government documents so honored. The document stands as a cornerstone of Federalist principles, and of sound and practical economics.

Hamilton became first Secretary of the Treasury in 1789, whereupon ''though he had no practical experience with the management of finances, his labors were marked by his usual rapidity. . . . He created as from a void a firm public credit; he strengthened the government by not merely placing it on a sure financial foundation, but also uniting great propertied interests behind it; and he gave the country a stable circulating medium, more adequate banking facilities, and important new industries. He saw the importance of what he called 'energy in the administration' and . . . must rank as one of the boldest and most far-sighted of the founders of the nation. . . . He was the virtual premier of Washington's administration.''

This 1795 *Plan for the Further Support of Public Credit,* along with his more common and better known 1791 *Report on the Subject of Manufactures,* are great American state papers, and reflect Hamilton's unique genius in the highest degree.

1796 [The Fur Trade]

AN ACT TO REGULATE TRADE AND INTERCOURSE WITH THE INDIAN TRIBES, AND TO PRESERVE PEACE ON THE FRONTIERS.

Philadelphia, May 19, 1796. 6pp. Folio. Fine, large, untrimmed, copy. Fourth Congress, First Session. Signed in type by Jonathan Dayton as Speaker, Samuel Livermore as President of the Senate, and George Washington as President. Evans 31347, mistakenly citing it as 4pp. and showing no locations.   (40) 1500.00

This exceedingly rare document delineates the boundaries between the United States and the Indian tribes of the west, and establishes regulations governing the fur trade. The act specifies in great detail the procedures for trading licenses and for all forms of intercourse with the Indian tribes.

Fur traders are placed under the regulations of a licensing superintendent, under penalty of fines, forfeiture of their goods and imprisonment. Without a trading license, fur and other traders are forbidden to enter any Indian territory, to buy horses, to buy or sell any other goods. Travellers are required to have government passports.

The boundary between the United States and the Indian lands is set along the Ohio and Miami ''to the tract of 150,000 acres near the rapids of the Ohio, which has been assigned to General Clark, for the use of himself and his warriors,'' and between the Cumberland and Tennessee ''to a point forty miles above Nashville'' and then to the border of the Carolinas, provided that ''the boundary line between the said Indian tribes and the United States shall . . . be varied by any treaty which shall be made . . .''

The document forbids encroachment and settlement by pioneers on Indian lands, and forbids any surveying thereon. It specifies ''that no purchase, grant, lease, or other conveyance of lands, or of any title or claim thereto, from any Indian, or nation or tribe of Indians . . . shall be of any validity, in law or equity, unless the same be made by treaty'' with the U.S. government.

Specifics are given to allow government gifts and programs ''to promote civilization among the friendly Indian tribes, and to secure the continuance of their friendship.'' It also provides penalties and procedures when Indians ''come over or cross the said boundary line, into any state or territory . . . and there take, steal or destroy any . . . property . . . or shall commit any murder, violence, or outrage upon any such citizen or inhabitant.'' Court procedures and capital punishment regulations are established, and procedures to be followed by ''the military force of the United States.''

This keystone act of 1796, issued at the time of the surrender of the British northwest posts to the United States, virtually created the American fur trade and opened and regulated the extensive trading that followed. It was a sensible and visionary law, and shows that in the beginning at least, the error of the Americans in regard to the Indians lay not in the law but in its deliberate avoidance.

Morse, Jedidiah

THE AMERICAN GAZETTEER, A . . . FULL AND ACCURATE ACCOUNT OF THE . . . AMERICAN CONTINENT, ALSO OF THE WEST-INDIA ISLANDS . . . WITH A PARTICULAR DESCRIPTION OF THE GEORGIA WESTERN TERRITORY . . .

Boston: S. Hall and Thomas & Andrews, 1797. [8],619pp. Seven folding maps. Thick octavo. Contemporary full mottled calf. *First edition.* Howes M839.   (41) 250.00

Jedidiah Morse, "the father of American geography," published the first American school geography in 1784 and saw it through numerous changes and editions. In 1797, he published this first important gazetteer of maps of the United States and North America. The work went through numerous editions and was still in use thirty years later.

According to W. Randall Waterman, "during their author's lifetime the Morse geographies virtually monopolized their field in the United States. He was essentially a compiler, drawing his information from the best American and European sources available, as well as from letters and documents sent him from all parts of the country in response to widely published requests for geographical information." Timothy Dwight said Morse was "as full of resources as an egg is of meat." One of his sons was Samuel F. B. Morse, inventor of the telegraph.

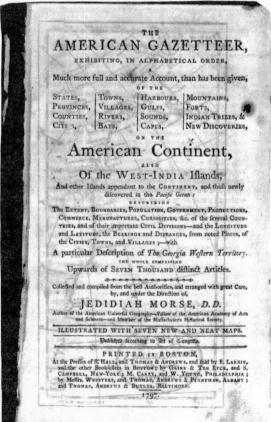

MESSAGE FROM THE PRESIDENT . . . ACCOMPANYING A COMMUNICATION FROM THE ENVOYS EXTRAORDINARY TO THE FRENCH REPUBLIC.

Philadelphia: Printed by Joseph Gales, June 18, 1798. 72pp. Sewn. Evans 34824. *First edition.* Contains the official dispatches and correspondence on the XYZ Affair between John Marshall, Elbridge Gerry, C. C. Pinckney, and Tallyrand in France.   (42) 150.00

Same, a variant printing. Bristol 10641.   (43) 150.00

Adams, John

MESSAGE FROM THE PRESIDENT . . . ACCOMPANYING SUNDRY PAPERS RELATIVE TO THE AFFAIRS OF THE UNITED STATES WITH THE FRENCH REPUBLIC.

Philadelphia, January 18, 1799. 123pp. *First edition.* Sewn. Evans 36551. Contains full reports and documents on the XYZ Affair between Pinckney, Gerry, Marshall, and Tallyrand.   (44) 125.00

Pickering, Timothy

REPORT . . . CONTAINING OBSERVATIONS ON SOME OF THE DOCUMENTS, COMMUNICATED BY THE PRESIDENT, ON THE 18TH INSTANT.

Philadelphia: John Ward Fenno, Jan. 21, 1799. [2],45,[2]pp. *First edition.* Sewn. Evans 36546.   (45) 125.00

The XYZ Affair was the most dramatic episode in the important dispute between the U.S. and France that caused an undeclared war between the two nations during the late 1790's. Tallyrand, the new French foreign minister, was incensed at the American treaty with Britain made by John Jay in 1794. When Pres. Adams sent a peace-making team of three eminent Americans—John Marshall, Elbridge Gerry, and C. C. Pinckney—they were met by three secret agents of Tallyrand and identified in these official reports as X, Y, and Z. The agents suggested that the best way to Tallyrand lay through a quarter million dollar bribe, which was refused.

Tallyrand rejected all the American demands and two of the commissioners returned home. Adams sent the reports to Congress, which released them publicly. ''The publication of its ministers' despatches by the American Government created such a stir in this country that the affair acquired a unique place in the public mind.'' Most of America was hot for war with France.

Some hostilities on the high seas did occur, but the most significant outcome was that on June 18, the same day Adams transmitted the reports, Congress passed the first of the Alien and Sedition Acts, and the rest within the next few weeks. The infamous acts allowed arrest and imprisonment of anyone who wrote or spoke against the President, Congress, or Government.

The French quickly changed their attitude and ultimately an amicable settlement and peace were achieved by a special convention in September, 1800. Within a few years the Alien and Sedition Acts were retracted.

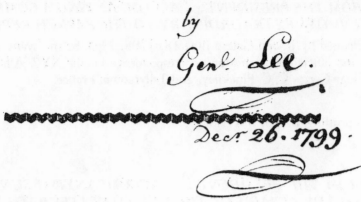

Funeral Oration.

by

Genl. Lee.

Decr. 26. 1799.

1799 [Death of Washington]

Lee, Henry

FUNERAL ORATION [ON THE DEATH OF WASHINGTON, DELIVERED DECEMBER 26, 1799, AND PUBLISHED BY ORDER OF CONGRESS].

[Philadelphia, 1799 or 1800]. 17pp. Sewn. Small hole on cover, not affecting text. *First edition.* Evans 37797. The famous address in which Lee said of Washington: "First in war—first in peace— and first in the hearts of his countrymen . . ." (46) 800.00

MESSAGE FROM THE PRESIDENT TRANSMITTING AN ORIGINAL LETTER FROM MRS. WASHINGTON, IN ANSWER TO A LETTER . . . REQUESTING HER ASSENT TO THE INTERMENT OF THE REMAINS OF GENERAL WASHINGTON IN THE CAPITOL, AT THE CITY OF WASHINGTON.

Phila., Jan. 8, 1800. 3pp. Evans 38780. Includes a letter of assent from Martha Washington dated Mount Vernon, Dec. 31, 1799. (47) 125.00

Morris, Gouverneur

AN ORATION UPON THE DEATH OF GENERAL WASHINGTON, DELIVERED AT THE REQUEST OF THE CORPORATION OF THE CITY OF NEW-YORK, ON THE 31ST DAY OF DECEMBER, 1799.

N.Y.: John Furman, 1800. 24pp. Errata. Sewn. Evan 38002. (48) 85.00

WASHINGTON'S POLITICAL LEGACIES, TO WHICH IS ANNEXED AN APPENDIX, CONTAINING AN ACCOUNT OF HIS ILLNESS, DEATH, AND THE NATIONAL TRIBUTES OF RESPECT PAID TO HIS MEMORY, WITH A BIOGRAPHICAL OUTLINE OF HIS LIFE AND CHARACTER.

Boston, 1800. 208,xivpp. Original calf. *First edition.* Howes W149. Evans 38998.(49) 125.00

There is little doubt that we killed the Father of our Country. Forced to bed by a neglected cold, Washington's strength was sapped to the limit by doctors who forced repeated blood-lettings upon him until on December 14, 1799, he died. "All the remedies, which their united counsel could devise, were used. . . ."

Few men were more famous, or more deservedly so, in their own time. C. C. Robin wrote on a tour here that the Americans, "that cool and sedate people, are roused, animated, and inflamed at the very mention of his name." His character was unique, far from the exalted and barren picture usually painted of him, and very human. One lady wrote to a friend that when he turned on his charm and became "the chatty agreeable companion, he can be down right impudent sometimes; such impudence, Fanny, as you and I like."

When news of his death arrived, Congress adjourned for special services, at which Gen. Henry Lee coined the immortal phrase, "first in war, first in peace, and first in the hearts of his countrymen."

1800   [Gallatin on Finance]

Gallatin, Albert
VIEWS OF THE PUBLIC DEBT, RECEIPTS, AND EXPENDITURES OF THE UNITED STATES.
N.Y.: M. L. & W. A. Davis, 1800. 61,[5]pp. Half morocco. *First edition.* Evans 37485. Kress B4135. "His works are mines of information for the student of history and economics."— Michael Ginsberg.   (50) 175.00

Albert Gallatin possessed an unrivaled grasp of constitutional and economic law, great power of argument, and a calmness of temper unruffled by the frequent attacks of the New England Federalists, who sneered at his foreign birth and French accent. During the 1790's he exerted a profound influence in Congress on the financial affairs of the new country, countering many of what he considered to be Hamilton's excesses. He was responsible for the creation of what is now the Ways and Means Committee. Throughout the period he argued for a balanced budget and for fiscal accountability.

This famous treatise, issued just prior to his becoming Secretary of the Treasury under Jefferson, consolidates and expounds his views on the subject. He served as Secretary of Treasury for thirteen years, the longest term ever served in that office. David S. Muzzey writes: "The labor which he devoted to the details of the office was the most arduous of his life . . . for Gallatin was not content, as he wrote to Jefferson, 'to act the part of a mere financier, to become a contriver of taxes, a dealer of loans . . . fattening contractors, pursuers and agents.' He was a statesman first, shaping his policy to further the political and social ends which he envisaged as the destiny of the United States. . . . The services of this great financier, diplomat, and statesman have never been adequately recognized. . . . In intellect he was the peer of any of his contemporaries — as constructive as Hamilton, as astute as Jefferson, as logical as Adams, as comprehensive as Webster."

ALEXANDER MACKENZIE Esq.

1801   [The First Overland Account]

Mackenzie, Sir Alexander

VOYAGES FROM MONTREAL, ON THE RIVER ST. LAURENCE, THROUGH THE CONTINENT OF NORTH AMERICA, TO THE FROZEN AND PACIFIC OCEANS . . . WITH A PRELIMINARY ACCOUNT OF THE RISE, PROGRESS, AND PRESENT STATE OF THE FUR TRADE OF THAT COUNTRY . . .

London: Printed for T. Cadell, Jun. and W. Davies, 1801. viii,cxxxii,412,[2]pp. Portrait. 3 folding maps. Superb, large-paper copy in original boards, printed paper label. Slipcased. *First edition of the first overland account.* Wagner-Camp #1. Howes M133. Jones 682. Smith 6382. Graff 2630. (51) 1250.00

   This volume is the first account of a coast-to-coast journey across the North American continent. The narrative is of exceptional importance because Mackenzie was the first civilized man known to have crossed the continent. The account also contains the first printed account of the development and growth of the fur trade in the Northwest. Henry R. Wagner states: ''Besides being the discoverer of the Mackenzie River, which in 1789 he descended to the Arctic Ocean, Mackenzie, according to our best knowledge, was the first man to cross the continent north of Mexico, and his journal of this expedition from May 9, 1793, to his arrival at the Pacific Coast, July 30, 1793, and return to the fort on the Peace River, August 24, is of surpassing interest.''

   No writer has given a more careful or interesting description of the Indian tribes encountered on the journeys. The folding map is of great cartographic interest, described by Carl I. Wheat as one of the most ''beautifully executed'' maps of the region ever done.

42

LETTER FROM THOMAS WORTHINGTON [SPECIAL AGENT], INCLOSING AN ORDINANCE PASSED BY THE CONVENTION OF THE STATE OF OHIO, TOGETHER WITH THE CONSTITUTION FORMED AND AGREED TO BY THE CONVENTION . . .

[Wash.], Dec. 23, 1802. 35pp. Sewn. Half-morocco slipcase. Kuhlman, p. 63. Library of Congress Ohio Exhibit #7. Shaw & Shoemaker 3331. This printing is preceded only by the near-unique Chillicothe printing, and is extremely rare, being the only known copy in private hands. (52) 1250.00

ACTS OF THE STATE OF OHIO, PASSED AND REVISED . . . ALSO, THE CONSTITUTION OF THE U.S., ORDINANCE, CONSTITUTION OF THE STATE OF OHIO . . .

Chillicothe: Printed by N. Willis, 1805. [76],491pp. Full calf, morocco label. *First edition.* Wilkie 63. Ohio Imprints Inventory 44. Shaw and Shoemaker 9051. (53) 350.00

The 35 members of the Ohio Constitutional Convention completed their work in 25 days, signing the document on November 29, 1802. Delegate Thomas Worthington, who became first U.S. Senator from the new State, was appointed special agent to present the petition to Congress. It was approved by Congress and President Jefferson on February 19, 1803, and two weeks later Ohio entered the Union as the seventeenth State.

The convention was in such a hurry to gain admittance that the constitution was not submitted to the people of the territory for approval. The document was nevertheless highly democratic, with a long Bill of Rights, a weak veto-less governor, and a powerful legislative assembly. Slavery was prohibited.

CONSTITUTION

ᵒᶠ THE

STATE ᴏꜰ OHIO;

DONE IN CONVENTION, BEGUN AND HELD AT CHILLICOTHE, ON MONDAY THE FIRST DAY OF NOVEMBER, A. D. ONE THOUSAND EIGHT HUNDRED AND TWO, AND OF THE INDEPENDENCE OF THE UNITED STATES THE TWENTY-SEVENTH.

MESSAGE

FROM THE

PRESIDENT

OF THE

UNITED STATES,

TO BOTH

HOUSES OF CONGRESS,

AT THE COMMENCEMENT OF THE SESSION.

———

17th October, 1803.

Referred to the Committee of the whole House on
the State of the Union.

MESSAGE FROM THE PRESIDENT OF THE UNITED STATES, TO BOTH HOUSES OF CONGRESS.

Wash., 17th October, 1803. 10pp. Full morocco slipcase. *First announcement of the Louisiana Purchase,* also requesting measures for its occupation, temporary government, and "for ascertaining the geography of the country acquired." Exceedingly rare, one of only a few known copies. Shaw & Shoemaker 5364, locating only two copies.   (54) 2500.00

TREATY BETWEEN THE UNITED STATES OF AMERICA AND THE FRENCH REPUBLIC [IN] ACTS PASSED AT THE FIRST SESSION OF THE EIGHTH CONGRESS OF THE UNITED STATES ... IN THE YEAR 1803.

Wash., 1803-04. 225,[6]pp. Original wrappers. Contains the entire treaty in French and in English, as well as the "Convention between the United States of America and the French Republic" of April 30, 1803, and five acts relating to the transfer of Louisiana to the United States.   (55) 650.00

Pendergast, Garrett, of Natchez

A PHYSICAL AND TOPOGRAPHICAL SKETCH OF THE MISSISSIPPI TERRITORY, LOWER LOUISIANA, AND A PART OF WEST FLORIDA.

Phila., 1803. Half morocco. *First edition.* Howes P197: "Based on the author's own travels, and on information contributed by William Dunbar." Shaw & Shoemaker 4831, locating three copies. This book constitutes the first scientific description of the lower Mississippi valley.   (56) 1500.00

On October 17, 1803, President Thomas Jefferson announced to a specially called session of Congress that "matters of great public concernment have rendered this call necessary." He then announced that in secret negotiations, for fifteen million dollars, "the enlightened government of France saw, with just discernment, the importance to both nations of such liberal arrangements as might best and permanently promote the peace, friendship and interests of both: and the property and sovereignty of all Louisiana . . . has, on certain conditions, been transferred to the United States."

Jefferson then pointed out the value of his purchase: "Whilst the property and sovereignty of the Mississippi [*sic*] and its waters secure an independent outlet for the produce of the western states . . . the fertility of the country, its climate and extent, promise, in due season, important aids to our treasury, and ample provision for our posterity." He stated the need "for the immediate occupation, and temporary government of the country, for its incorporation into our union. . . ."

Napoleon had hoped to create a colonial empire in the heart of North America, but by 1803 his plans had gone awry. So when the American envoys, Robert R. Livingston and James Monroe, arrived in Paris, Napoleon had Tallyrand and Francois Barbe-Marbois open negotiations for the sale of Louisiana, which included nearly a million square miles in the heart of America. The American envoys exceeded their instructions, but the deal they transacted was approved by Congress three days after Jefferson's October 17 message; needless to say, it was one of the best deals ever struck for the United States.

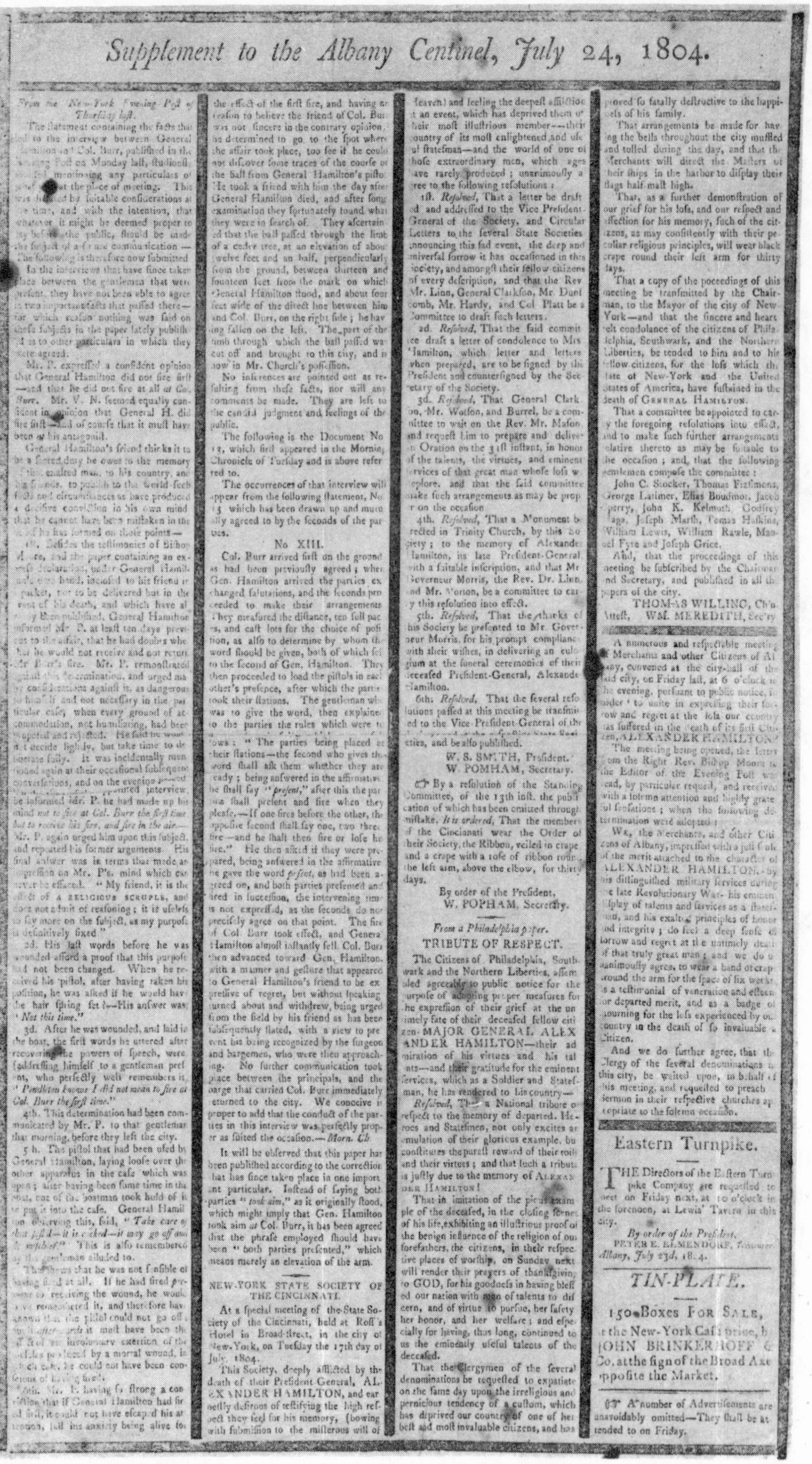

Supplement to the Albany Centinel, July 24, 1804.

From the New-York Evening Post of Thursday last.

The statement containing the facts that led to the interview between General Hamilton and Col. Burr, published in the Evening Post on Monday last, studiously avoided mentioning any particulars of what past at the place of meeting. This was dictated by suitable considerations at the time, and with the intention, that whatever it might be deemed proper to lay before the public, should be made the subject of a future communication — The following is therefore now submitted.

In the interviews that have since taken place between the gentlemen that were present, they have not been able to agree in two important facts that passed there — for which reason nothing was said on those subjects in the paper lately published as to other particulars in which they were agreed.

Mr. P. expressed a confident opinion that General Hamilton did not fire first — and that he did not fire at all *at Col. Burr*. Mr. V. N. seemed equally confident in opinion that General H. did fire first — and of course that it must have been *at* his antagonist.

General Hamilton's friend thinks it to be a sacred duty he owes to the memory of that exalted man, to his country, and his friends, to publish to the world such facts and circumstances as have produced a decisive conviction in his own mind that he cannot have been mistaken in the belief he has formed on those points —

1st. Besides the testimonies of Bishop Moore, and the paper containing an express declaration, under General Hamilton's own hand, inclosed to his friend in a packet, not to be delivered but in the event of his death, and which have already been published, General Hamilton informed Mr. P. at least ten days previous to the affair, that he had doubts whether he would not receive and not return Mr Burr's fire. Mr. P. remonstrated against this determination, and urged many considerations against it, as dangerous to himself and not necessary in the particular case, when every ground of accommodation, not humiliating, had been proposed and rejected. He said he would not decide lightly, but take time to deliberate fully. It was incidentally mentioned again at their occasional subsequent conversations, and on the evening preceding the time of the appointed interview, he informed Mr. P. he had made up his mind *not to fire at Col. Burr the first time, but to receive his fire, and fire in the air*.— Mr. P. again urged him upon this subject, and repeated his former arguments. His final answer was in terms that made an impression on Mr. P's. mind which can never be effaced. "My friend, it is the effect of A RELIGIOUS SCRUPLE, and does not admit of reasoning; it is useless to say more on the subject, as my purpose is definitively fixed."

2d. His last words before he was wounded afford a proof that this purpose had not been changed. When he received his pistol, after having taken his position, he was asked if he would have the hair spring set?—His answer was, "*Not this time.*"

3d. After he was wounded, and laid in the boat, the first words he uttered after recovering the powers of speech, were, (addressing himself to a gentleman present, who perfectly well remembers it, "*Pendleton knows I did not mean to fire at Col. Burr the first time.*"

4th. This determination had been communicated by Mr. P. to that gentleman that morning, before they left the city.

5th. The pistol that had been used by General Hamilton, laying loose over the other apparatus in the case which was open; after having been some time in the boat, one of the boatman took hold of it to put it into the case. General Hamilton observing this, said, "*Take care of that pistol—it is cocked—it may go off and do mischief.*" This is also remembered by the gentleman alluded to.

This shews that he was not sensible of having fired at all. If he had fired *previous* to receiving the wound, he would have remembered it, and therefore have known that the pistol could not go off; but if *afterwards* it must have been the effect of an involuntary exertion of the muscles produced by a mortal wound, in which case, he could not have been conscious of having fired.

6th. Mr. P. having so strong a conviction that if General Hamilton had fired first, it could not have escaped his attention, (all his anxiety being alive for the effect of the first fire, and having no reason to believe the friend of Col. Burr was not sincere in the contrary opinion, he determined to go to the spot where the affair took place, too see if he could not discover some traces of the course of the ball from General Hamilton's pistol. He took a friend with him the day after General Hamilton died, and after some examination they fortunately found what they were in search of. They ascertained that the ball passed through the limb of a ceder tree, at an elevation of about twelve feet and an half, perpendicularly from the ground, between thirteen and fourteen feet from the mark on which General Hamilton stood, and about four feet wide of the direct line between him and Col. Burr, on the right side; he having fallen on the left. The part of the limb through which the ball passed was cut off and brought to this city, and is now in Mr. Church's possession.

No inferences are pointed out as resulting from these facts, nor will any comments be made. They are left to the candid judgment and feelings of the public.

The following is the Document No 12, which first appeared in the Morning Chronicle of Tuesday and is above referred to.

The occurrences of that interview will appear from the following statement, No 13 which has been drawn up and mutually agreed to by the seconds of the parties.

No XIII.

Col. Burr arrived first on the ground as had been previously agreed; when Gen. Hamilton arrived the parties exchanged salutations, and the seconds proceeded to make their arrangements. They measured the distance, ten full paces, and cast lots for the choice of position, as also to determine by whom the word should be given, both of which fell to the second of Gen. Hamilton. They then proceeded to load the pistols in each other's presence, after which the parties took their stations. The gentleman who was to give the word, then explained to the parties the rules which were to [illegible] follows: "The parties being placed at their stations—the second who gives the word shall ask them whether they are ready; being answered in the affirmative he shall say "*present*," after this the parties shall present and fire when they please.—If one fires before the other, the opposite second shall say one, two three fire—and he shall then fire or lose his fire." He then asked if they were prepared, being answered in the affirmative he gave the word *present*, as had been agreed on, and both parties presented and fired in succession, the intervening time is not expressed, as the seconds do not precisely agree on that point. The fire of Col. Burr took effect, and General Hamilton almost instantly fell. Col. Burr then advanced toward Gen. Hamilton, with a manner and gesture that appeared to General Hamilton's friend to be expressive of regret, but without speaking turned about and withdrew, being urged from the field by his friend as has been subsequently stated, with a view to prevent his being recognized by the surgeon and bargemen, who were then approaching. No further communication took place between the principals, and the barge that carried Col. Burr immediately returned to the city. We conceive it proper to add that the conduct of the parties in this interview was perfectly proper as suited the occasion.—*Morn. Ch.*

It will be observed that this paper has been published according to the correction that has since taken place in one important particular. Instead of saying both parties "*took aim*," as it originally stood, which might imply that Gen. Hamilton took aim *at* Col. Burr, it has been agreed that the phrase employed should have been "both parties presented," which means merely an elevation of the arm.

NEW-YORK STATE SOCIETY OF THE CINCINNATI.

At a special meeting of the State Society of the Cincinnati, held at Ross's Hotel in Broad-street, in the city of New-York, on Tuesday the 17th day of July, 1804.

This Society, deeply afflicted by the death of their President-General, ALEXANDER HAMILTON, and earnestly desirous of testifying the high respect they feel for his memory, (bowing with submission to the misterous will of heaven) and feeling the deepest affliction at an event, which has deprived them of their most illustrious member—their country of its most enlightened and useful statesman—and the world of one of those extraordinary men, which ages have rarely produced; unanimously agree to the following resolutions:

1st. *Resolved*, That a letter be drafted and addressed to the Vice President-General of the Society, and Circular Letters to the several State Societies announcing this sad event, the deep and universal sorrow it has occasioned in this Society, and amongst their fellow citizens of every description, and that the Rev Mr. Linn, General Clarkson, Mr. Dunscomb, Mr. Hardy, and Col Platt be a Committee to draft such letters.

2d. *Resolved*, That the said committee draft a letter of condolence to Mrs Hamilton, which letter and letters when prepared, are to be signed by the President and countersigned by the Secretary of the Society.

3d. *Resolved*, That General Clarkson, Mr. Watson, and Burrel, be a committee to wait on the Rev. Mr. Mason and request him to prepare and deliver an Oration on the 31st instant, in honor of the talents, the virtues, and eminent services of that great man whose loss we deplore, and that the said committee make such arrangements as may be proper on the occasion.

4th. *Resolved*, That a Monument be erected in Trinity Church, by this Society; to the memory of Alexander Hamilton, its late President-General, with a suitable inscription, and that Mr Governeur Morris, the Rev. Dr. Linn, and Mr. Morton, be a committee to carry this resolution into effect.

5th. *Resolved*, That the thanks of this Society be presented to Mr. Governeur Morris, for his prompt compliance with their wishes, in delivering an eulogium at the funeral ceremonies of their deceased President-General, Alexander Hamilton.

6th. *Resolved*, That the several resolutions passed at this meeting be transmitted to the Vice-President-General of the [illegible] State Societies, and be also published.

W. S. SMITH, President.
W. POMHAM, Secretary.

☞ By a resolution of the Standing Committee, of the 13th inst. the publication of which has been omitted through mistake, *It is ordered*, That the members of the Cincinnati wear the Order of their Society, the Ribbon, veiled in crape and a crape with a rose of ribbon round the left arm, above the elbow, for thirty days.

By order of the President,
W. POPHAM, Secretary.

From a Philadelphia paper.

TRIBUTE OF RESPECT.

The Citizens of Philadelphia, Southwark and the Northern Liberties, assembled agreeably to public notice for the purpose of adopting proper measures for the expression of their grief at the untimely fate of their deceased fellow citizen MAJOR GENERAL ALEXANDER HAMILTON—their admiration of his virtues and his talents—and their gratitude for the eminent services, which as a Soldier and Statesman, he has rendered to his country—

Resolved, That a National tribute of respect to the memory of departed. Heroes and Statesmen, not only excites an emulation of their glorious example, but constitutes the purest reward of their toils and their virtues; and that such a tribute is justly due to the memory of ALEXANDER HAMILTON!

That in imitation of the pious example of the deceased, in the closing scenes of his life, exhibiting an illustrious proof of the benign influence of the religion of our forefathers, the citizens, in their respective places of worship, on Sunday next will render their prayers of thanksgiving to GOD, for his goodness in having blessed our nation with men of talents to discern, and of virtue to pursue, her safety her honor, and her welfare; and especially for having, thus long, continued to us the eminently useful talents of the deceased.

That the Clergymen of the several denominations be requested to expatiate on the same day upon the irreligious and pernicious tendency of a custom, which has deprived our country of one of her best and most invaluable citizens, and has proved so fatally destructive to the happiness of his family.

That arrangements be made for having the bells throughout the city muffled and tolled during the day, and that the Merchants will direct the Masters of their ships in the harbor to display their flags half-mast high.

That, as a further demonstration of our grief for his loss, and our respect and affection for his memory, such of the citizens, as may consistently with their peculiar religious principles, will wear black crape round their left arm for thirty days.

That a copy of the poceedings of this meeting be transmitted by the Chairman, to the Mayor of the city of New-York—and that the sincere and heartfelt condolance of the citizens of Philadelphia, Southwark, and the Northern Liberties, be tended to him and to his fellow citizens, for the loss which the state of New-York and the United States of America, have sustained in the death of GENERAL HAMILTON.

That a committee be appoited to carry the foregoing resolutions into effect, and to make such further arrangements relative thereto as may be suitable to the occasion; and, that the following gentlemen compose the committee:

John C. Stocker, Thomas Fitzsimons, George Latimer, Elias Boudinot, Jacob Sperry, John K. Kelmuth, Godfrey Haga, Joseph Marsh, Tomas Haskins, William Lewis, William Rawle, Manuel Fyre and Joseph Grice.

And, that the proceedings of this meeting be subscribed by the Chairman and Secretary, and published in all the papers of the city.

THOMAS WILLING, Ch'n.
Attest, WM. MEREDITH, Sec'ry

A numerous and respectable meeting of Merchants and other Citizens of Albany, convened at the city-hall of the said city, on Friday last, at 6 o'clock in the evening, persuant to public notice, in order to unite in expressing their sorrow and regret at the loss our country has suffered in the death of its first Citizen, ALEXANDER HAMILTON.

The meeting being opened, the letter from the Right Rev. Bishop Moore to the Editor of the Evening Post was read, by particular request, and received with a solemn attention and highly grateful sensations; when the following determination were adopted:

WE, the Merchants, and other Citizens of Albany, impressed with a just sense of the merit attached to the character of ALEXANDER HAMILTON, by his distinguished military services during the late Revolutionary War, his eminent display of talents and services as a statesman, and his exalted principles of honor and integrity; do feel a deep sense of sorrow and regret at the untimely death of that truly great man; and we do unanimously agree, to wear a band of crape around the arm for the space of six weeks as a testimonial of veneration and esteem for departed merit, and as a badge of mourning for the loss experienced by our country in the death of so invaluable a Citizen.

And we do further agree, that the Clergy of the several denominations in this city, be waited upon, in behalf of this meeting, and requested to preach a sermon in their respective churches appropriate to the solemn occasion.

☞ A number of Advertisements are unavoidably omitted—They shall be attended to on Friday.

1804   [Hamilton-Burr Duel]

NEW-YORK SPECTATOR.

N.Y.: J. Mills, July 12-14, 1804. 4pp. Large folio. Black-bordered. ''Thursday, July 12. We stop the press to announce the melancholy intelligence that GENERAL HAMILTON IS DEAD!—He expired about half past 2 o'clock. . . .'' Gov. John Jay's copy, with his name in ink at top; from his private papers.   (57) 300.00

SUPPLEMENT TO THE ALBANY CENTINEL.

Broadside, 1p., large folio, black-bordered, Albany, July 24, 1804, containing a full and detailed account of the Burr-Hamilton duel. Not in Shaw & Shoemaker, which cites a similar item of April 10 relating to Burr's nomination.   (58) 200.00

Coleman, William

A COLLECTION OF THE FACTS AND DOCUMENTS, RELATIVE TO THE DEATH OF MAJOR-GENERAL ALEXANDER HAMILTON . . .

N.Y.: Hopkins and Seymour, 1804. 238pp. Half morocco. *First edition.* Howes C572. Shaw & Shoemaker 6041. Bound with J. M. Mason, *AN ORATION,* N.Y., 1804, 40pp., which includes Hamilton's will, and with Harrison G. Otis, *EULOGY,* N.Y., 1804, 23pp. Shaw & Shoemaker 6731 and 6977.   (59) 175.00

The duel between Aaron Burr and Alexander Hamilton was the culmination of the intense partisan political struggles in the young nation, particularly in New York. The acerbic Hamilton made some cracks about Burr, who was running for governor of New York. A few weeks after being defeated, Burr demanded an explanation.

Hamilton evaded the issue, and Burr sent a peremptory challenge. Although Hamilton was opposed on principle to duelling, then a common method of settling personal quarrels, he felt that ''peculiar necessity'' forced him to accept, else he would be ineffective politically in the future.

The two men, both in their late forties, met across from New York (where duelling was illegal) at Weehawken, N.J., on July 11, 1804. The outcome was fatal to both. Hamilton deliberately fired into the air, and Burr shot to kill. Hamilton died the next day, and Burr, ever after a political outcast, suffered a slower and more painful fate of disgrace.

and shall be compelled to give evidence against himself, in the presence of an assembled universe. To his Omniscient Judge, at that awful hour, he now appeals for the rectitude and purity of his conduct, as to all the matters of which he is this day accused.

He hath now only to adjure each member of this honorable court, by the living GOD, and in his holy name, to render impartial justice to him, according to the constitution and laws of the United States. He makes this solemn demand of each member, by all his hopes of happiness in the world to come, which he will have voluntarily renounced by the oath he has taken; if he shall wilfully do this respondent injustice, or disregard the constitution or laws of the United States, which he has solemnly sworn to make the rule and standard of his judgment and decision.

SAMUEL CHASE.

A true copy,

ATTEST, SAMUEL A. OTIS, *Secretary.*

= Judge Chase was acquitted on the 1st day of March 1805 - The House of Representatives then passed a Bill for paying the witnesses for the prosecution. The Senate unanimously amended it by adding of the witnesses for Judge Chase. This the other House would not agree to, so the whole Bill failed - Randolph then proposed an amendment to the Constitution of the US. that Judges should be removed on the address of a Majority of both Houses of Congress, & Nicholson proposed another that Senators should be recallable by the State Legislatures. all these things passed within two Days after the acquittal of Chase -

ARTICLES, EXHIBITED BY THE HOUSE OF REPRESENTATIVES, IN THE NAME OF THEMSELVES, AND OF ALL THE PEOPLE OF THE UNITED STATES, AGAINST SAMUEL CHASE . . . IN SUPPORT OF THEIR IMPEACHMENT AGAINST HIM, FOR HIGH CRIMES AND MISDEMEANORS.

[Washington:] 1805. 8pp. Unrecorded and apparently unique.

Bound with:

THE ANSWER AND PLEAS OF SAMUEL CHASE, ONE OF THE ASSOCIATE JUSTICES OF THE SUPREME COURT OF THE UNITED STATES, TO THE ARTICLES OF IMPEACHMENT . . . FOR HIGH CRIMES AND MISDEMEANORS . . .

Washington City: William Duane, 1805. 84pp. Shaw & Shoemaker 8172, locating only one copy. Sabin 12203.

Bound with:

REPLICATION BY THE HOUSE OF REPRESENTATIVES . . . TO THE ANSWER OF SAMUEL CHASE . . .

[Washington:] Printed by Order of the Senate, 1805. 4pp. Shaw & Shoemaker 9591, locating only two copies. Sabin 12207. All bound together in half morocco.

    This volume belonged to the noted jurist, Chancellor James Kent, and contains his signature and lengthy notes in his hand about the trial, which he apparently witnessed, and with three unrecorded printed notices listing the outcomes of the various votes on impeachment tipped in.   (60) 850.00

Another copy of the *ANSWER AND PLEAS*, sewn with the *REPLICATION.*   (61) 450.00

    Revolutionary War leader, Signer of the Declaration of Independence, and Justice of the U.S. Supreme Court, Samuel Chase was always a controversial figure. Joseph Story described him as "the living image" of Samuel Johnson "in person, in manners, in unwieldy strength, in severity of reproof, in real tenderness of heart; and above all in intellect."

    His unwavering support of the Federalist philosophy brought him afoul of President Jefferson, who engineered the impeachment proceedings on rather trumped-up charges. The trial became the major test of Jefferson's attempt to curb the power of the Supreme Court. In spite of the fact that 25 of the 34 Senators were Jeffersonians, Chase was acquitted. E. S. Corwin, in *D.A.B.*, calls the event "of fundamental importance in our constitutional history."

the precious metals, but has seen a mineral which he supposes might yield copper. From the top of the high mountain the view is bounded by a curve as upon the ocean, and extends over the most beautiful prairies, which seem to be unbounded, particularly towards the east. The finest of the lands he has seen are on the Missouri; no other can compare in richness and fertility with them.

This Canadian, as well as Le Fevre, speak of the Osages of the tribe of Whitehairs, as lawless and unprincipled: and the other Indian tribes hold them in abhorrence as a barbarous and uncivilized race: and the different nations who hunt in their neighbourhood, have their concerting plans for their destruction. On the morning of the 11th, the party passed the petit ecor a Fabri. The osier which grows on the beaches above, is not seen below upon this river; and here they began to meet with the small tree called 'charnier,' which grows only on the water side, and is met with all the way down the Washita. The latitude of 33° 40' seems the northern boundary of the one, and the southern boundary of the other of those vegetables. Having noticed the limit set to the long moss, (Telandsia) on the ascent of the river, in latitude 33°, Mr. Dunbar made inquiry of Mr. Le Fevre, as to its existence on the Arkansa settlement, which is known to lie in about the same parallel; he said, that its growth is limited about ten miles south of the settlement, and that as remarkably, as if a line had been drawn east and west for the purpose; as it ceases all at once, and not by degrees. Hence it appears, that nature has marked with a distinguishing feature, the line established by congress, between the Orleans and Louisiana territories. The cypress is not found on the Washita higher than thirty-four degrees of north latitude.

In ascending *[descending]* the river, they found their rate of going to exceed that of the current about six miles and a half in twenty-four hours; and that on the 12th, they had passed the apex of the tide or wave, occasioned by the fresh, and were descending along an inclined plane; as they encamped at night, they found themselves in deeper water the next morning, and on a more elevated part of the inclined plain than they had been in the preceding evening, from the progress of the apex of the tide during their repose.

At noon, on the 16th, they reached the post of the Washita.

Mr. Dunbar being anxious to reach the Natches as early as possible, and being unable to procure horses at the post, took a canoe with one soldier and his own domestic, to push down to the Catahoola, from whence to Concord there is a road of thirty miles across the low grounds. He set off

1806 [Lewis and Clark Expedition]

Jefferson, Thomas

MESSAGE ... COMMUNICATING DISCOVERIES MADE IN EXPLORING THE MISSOURI, RED RIVER, AND WASHITA, BY CAPTAINS LEWIS AND CLARK, DOCTOR SIBLEY, AND MR. DUNBAR; WITH A STATISTICAL ACCOUNT OF THE COUNTRIES ADJACENT, READ IN CONGRESS, FEBRUARY 19, 1806.

New York: Printed by Hopkins and Seymour, 1806, 128pp. Folding chart. Original wrappers. Slipcased. Fine and interesting copy, with a few ink notations and corrections in an unknown contemporary hand in the text. *First trade edition,* preceded only by the exceedingly rare government printing. Howes L319: ''The first book giving any of their activities.'' Wagner-Camp 5: ''Abundant and valuable information regarding the trans-Mississippi, much of it the first reliable and authentic information on this region.''   (62) 3500.00

Same, London, 1807. 116pp. Half calf. *First English edition.* (63) 350.00

Jefferson, Thomas
MESSAGE CONTAINING HIS COMMUNICATION TO BOTH HOUSES OF CONGRESS . . . 3d DECEMBER, 1805.
Wash.: A&G Way, 1805. 11pp. Full morocco slipcase. *Contains the first reference to the Lewis and Clark Expedition.* See Wagner-Camp 4 and 5. Shaw & Shoemaker 9571, locating only one copy. (64) 650.00

Lewis, Meriwether, and William Clark
HISTORY OF THE EXPEDITION UNDER THE COMMAND OF CAPTAINS LEWIS AND CLARK, TO THE . . . PACIFIC OCEAN.
Philadelphia: Bradford and Inskeep, 1814. 2 volumes. Five charts and one folding map, the latter supplied from a later edition. Half morocco. Nice set. *First edition.* Howes L317: "First authorized and complete account of the most important western exploration and the first of many overland narratives to follow." Wagner-Camp 13. Field 928. Jones 771. Graff 2477. Church 1309. Grolier American Hundred 30: "Most important of all overland narratives." Streeter, Americana Beginnings #52. (65) 2500.00

Lewis, Meriwether, and William Clark
TRAVELS TO THE SOURCE OF THE MISSOURI RIVER, AND ACROSS THE AMERICAN CONTINENT TO THE PACIFIC OCEAN.
London: Longman, Hurst, 1814. 663pp. Charts and folding map. Large quarto. Contemporary half calf. Fine copy. *First English edition.* (66) 650.00

This expedition was sent at the special instigation of President Jefferson. Lewis was his personal secretary and Clark was a close friend. The goal was to travel overland and discover a route to the Pacific Ocean, making as many scientific discoveries as possible in the process.

The party assembled in St. Louis in 1803, immediately after the close of the Louisiana Purchase negotiations, and set out up the Missouri the next spring. The winter of 1804 was passed in the Dakotas, and the winter of 1805 at the Pacific. The expedition arrived back in St. Louis in September of 1806.

Their journals comprise a great epic in human achievement. "Thousands of miles of wilderness had been traversed; an important impulse to the further extension of American trade and settlement had been supplied; important additions to the existing body of geographical and scientific knowledge had been made; in the person of humble, patient, loyal Sacajawea a precious addition to the world's roster of heroines had been disclosed."

Jefferson, Thomas

MESSAGE FROM THE PRESIDENT OF THE UNITED STATES TRANSMITTING INFORMATION TOUCHING AN ILLEGAL COMBINATION OF PRIVATE IN-DIVIDUALS AGAINST THE PEACE AND SAFETY OF THE UNION, AND A MILITARY EXPEDITION PLANNED BY THEM AGAINST THE TERRITORIES OF A POWER IN AMITY WITH THE UNITED STATES.

[Washington:], January 22, 1807. 16pp. Half morocco. Tompkins 51. Sabin 9428. Streeter Sale III-1686. Shaw & Shoemaker 13999. (67) 450.00

THE TRIAL OF COL. AARON BURR, ON AN INDICTMENT FOR TREASON... INCLUDING THE ARGUMENTS AND DECISIONS ON ALL THE MOTIONS MADE DURING THE EXAMINATION AND TRIAL, AND ON THE MOTION FOR AN ATTACHMENT AGAINST GEN. WILKINSON... TAKEN IN SHORT-HAND BY T. CARPENTER.

Washington City: Printed by Wescott & Co., 1807-1808. 3 volumes. Tompkins 18. Sabin 9433. Graff 506. Eberstadt 134-68: *"Probably the rarest and best account of the trial."* (68) 350.00

THE TWO PRINCIPAL ARGUMENTS OF WILLIAM WIRT, ESQUIRE, ON THE TRIAL OF AARON BURR, FOR HIGH TREASON, AND ON THE MOTION TO COMMIT AARON BURR AND OTHERS, FOR TRIAL IN KENTUCKY.

Richmond: Samuel Pleasants, Jun., 1808. 221pp. Half morocco. Tompkins 112. Sabin 104883. Streeter Sale III-1692. Shaw & Shoemaker 16753. Howes W587. (69) 350.00

REPORTS OF THE TRIALS OF COLONEL AARON BURR (LATE VICE PRESI-DENT OF THE UNITED STATES,) FOR TREASON ... IN PREPARING THE MEANS OF A MILITARY EXPEDITION AGAINST MEXICO ... TO WHICH IS ADDED, AN APPENDIX, CONTAINING THE ARGUMENTS AND EVIDENCE ... TAKEN IN SHORT HAND BY DAVID ROBERTSON.

Philadelphia: Hopkins and Earle, 1808. 2 volumes. Original boards, printed paper labels. Large, untrimmed set. Tompkins 87. Sabin 9434. Howes B1013. (70) 225.00

The Burr Conspiracy is one of the most mysterious and complicated events in American history. Whether Burr intended to wrest part of Louisiana away from the U.S., and to invade and conquer Texas will probably never be known for sure, although it is highly likely that he did. Its seed lay in his downfall resulting from the duel with Alexander Hamilton, after which Burr laid secret plans and considerable overt preparations for what Jefferson took to be an invasion army. Since the United States was at peace with Spain, which then owned Texas, Jefferson had Burr arrested and brought to trial.

The trial itself was presided over by Chief Justice John Marshall. Burr was acquitted, but the "conspiracy" was stopped and Burr never again gained a position of power. Colton Storm calls the event "the most exciting trial held in this country during the first half of the nineteenth century. Chief Justice Marshall's rulings on aspects of treason had far-reaching effects; their influence was observable in trials held during and after World War II."

A DIGEST OF THE CIVIL LAWS NOW IN FORCE IN THE TERRITORY OF ORLEANS, WITH ALTERATIONS AND AMENDMENTS ADAPTED TO ITS PRESENT SYSTEM OF GOVERNMENT.

New-Orleans: Printed by Bradford & Anderson, Printers to the Territory, 1808. 491pp. Folio. Half calf. *First edition, large-paper copy on laid paper.* English and French texts on facing pages. McMurtrie #128. Shaw & Shoemaker 15814, locating only two copies. This is the only known copy in private hands.   (71) 1500.00

AN EXPOSITION OF THE CRIMINAL LAWS OF THE TERRITORY OF ORLEANS: THE PRACTICE OF THE COURTS OF CRIMINAL JURISDICTION, THE DUTIES OF THEIR OFFICERS...

New-Orleans: Bradford & Anderson, 1806. xxi,241,lviiipp.plus errata. Bound with: *COLLECTION CONTAINING THE DECLARATION OF INDEPENDENCE, THE CONSTITUTION OF THE UNITED STATES AND ITS AMENDMENTS, THE TREATY OF CESSION BETWEEN THE U.S. AND THE FRENCH REPUBLIC, AS ALSO, THE LAWS AND ORDINANCES OF THE TERRITORY OF ORLEANS,* New-Orleans: Thierry & Dacquency, 1810, [4],122pp. Calf. McMurtrie #87 and #158. Shaw & Shoemaker 10674 and 19798, each locating only one copy. The latter item contains the first Louisiana printing of the Declaration of Independence and the second of the Constitution. Both are the only known copies in private hands.   (72) 1500.00

ACTS PASSED AT THE SECOND SESSION OF THE FIRST LEGISLATURE OF THE TERRITORY OF ORLEANS.

New-Orleans: Bradford & Anderson, Printers to the Territory, 1807. [9],207pp. Half morocco. Foote, p.3. McMurtrie #98. Text in French and English on facing pages. Manuscript notes and corrections in a contemporary hand. Shaw & Shoemaker 13297, locating only three copies. This is the only known copy in private hands.   (73) 850.00

CONSTITUTION OF THE STATE OF LOUISIANA.

Baltimore: Supplement to Niles Register, 1813, 8pp. Contains the complete constitution as passed, and an ordinance relating to Louisiana land claims, both as passed by the Constitutional Convention of 1812.   (74) 45.00

These are the cornerstone documents on the Territory of Orleans, which became the State of Louisiana in 1812. In 1804 Louisiana was divided into the Territory of Orleans and the District of Louisiana. After the apparent attempt by Burr and perhaps by Wilkinson to detach part of the area from the U.S., the Territory of Orleans gradually organized towards statehood. Ultimately some fourteen states came from the 500,000,000 acres purchased from France.

These documents are also cornerstones of American law, since they intermixed with American common law great portions of French civil law. Louisiana, Arkansas, Texas, and other states still retain many elements of the French legal system.

SUNDRY PAPERS, IN RELATION TO CLAIMS, COMMONLY CALLED THE YAZOO CLAIMS.

City of Washington: A. and G. Way, Printers, 1809. 195pp. *Only 300 copies were printed.* Howes Y4. Shaw & Shoemaker 19074. De Renne, p.339: ''This convenient collection includes the Constitution of Georgia, 1789 [and of 1798]'' and many other documents.

(75) 385.00

STATE OF FACTS, SHEWING THE RIGHT OF CERTAIN COMPANIES TO THE LANDS LATELY PURCHASED BY THEM FROM THE STATE OF GEORGIA.

United States, Printed in the Year 1795. 64pp. Half morocco. *First edition.* Evans 28745. De Renne, p.270: ''Probably printed in Philadelphia.'' Sabin 27112. Vail 1027. Howes G126. This important tract is the company's demonstration of the legitimacy of its claims.

(76) 350.00

REPORT FROM THE COMMITTEE TO WHOM WERE REFERRED THE . . . MEMORIALS OF THE NEW ENGLAND LAND COMPANY AND UPPER MISSISSIPPI COMPANY.

Washington: Duane & Son, 1805. 20pp. De Renne, p.324. Report advising that the compromise settlement be received and adjusted.

(77) 150.00

MEMORIAL OF THE DIRECTORS OF THE NEW-ENGLAND MISSISSIPPI LAND COMPANY.

Washington: R. C. Weightman, 1814. 20pp. Not in De Renne. Shaw & Shoemaker 33299. Includes an outline of the history of the claims. The memorialists received four million dollars redress.

(78) 150.00

In 1795 the Georgia Legislature had passed an act granting several Yazoo companies the right to buy thirty million acres of land, over forty thousand square miles, for a cent and a half per acre. The land consisted of what is now most of Alabama and Mississippi. What resulted was probably the most stupendous land fraud in American history.

It was soon discovered that ''all who voted for the law, with one exception, were bribed in one way or another to support the measure.'' The next legislature rescinded the act and held a public burning ceremony of the Yazoo bill. In 1802 Georgia released all her western claims to the United States. The New England Mississippi Land Company and other Yazoo purchasers denied Georgia's right to rescind the act and petitioned Congress for redress. Finally the Supreme Court in 1809-1810 decided in Fletcher v. Peck that the rescinding law was indeed unconstitutional, and in 1814 the Yazoo ''owners'' were paid four million dollars for their claims.

Pike, Zebulon
AN ACCOUNT OF EXPEDITIONS TO THE SOURCES OF THE MISSISSIPPI, AND THROUGH THE WESTERN PARTS OF LOUISIANA, TO THE SOURCES OF THE ARKANSAW, KANS, LA PLATTE, AND PIERRE JUAN RIVERS.
Philadelphia: John Binns, 1810. [8],106,[106,[10],107-278,[4],66,53,87pp. Portrait. Maps and plates. Collates absolutely complete. Contemporary calf. *First edition.* Streeter Texas #1047. Howes P373. Raines, p.164. Graff 3290. Field 1217. Jones 743. Braislin 1474. Rittenhouse 467. Wagner-Camp 9.   (79) 850.00

This important expedition was made as a part of a concerted effort by President Jefferson to explore the newly acquired territory west of the Mississippi. Leaving the St. Louis area in July, 1806, Pike explored Kansas, Oklahoma, northern Texas, and Colorado until captured by the Spanish. Conducted through Santa Fe to Chihuahua, he was returned through Texas to Louisiana.

All Pike's papers were confiscated, but he managed to save his precious journals by secreting them amongst his men. When published in 1810, the narrative offered the first accurate description of the great Southwest. "Few in number, and with the scantiest of material equipment," writes T. C. Cochrane, Pike and his men "braved the treachery of the savages, the perils of starvation, the awful exposure of the Colorado Rockies in midwinter, and the prospect of perpetual confinement in a foreign land. They wrote a new chapter in the annals of human daring and devotion, and added a volume of abiding worth to the literature of New World exploration."

RECAPITULATION.

NAMES OF THE NATIONS.	No. of Warriors.	No. of Women.	No. of Children.	No. of Villages.	Probable number of Souls.	No. of Lodges of the Roving Bands.	No. of Fire Arms.
SAUKS,	700	750	1400	3	2850		700
FOXES,	400	500	850	3	1750		400
IOWAS,	300	400	700	2	1400		250
WINEBAGOS,	450	500	1000	7	1950		450
MENOMENES,	300	350	700	7	1350		300
SUES,	3835	6430	11800	3	21675	1270	1265
CHIPEWAYS,	2049	3185	5944		11177	603	2049
Total	8034	12114	22394	25	45152	1873	5414

STATISTICAL ANALYSIS.	Population in 1803.	Extent of Surface in square Leagues.	No. of Inhabitants to the square League.
XIII. Province of Nuevo Mexico.	40,200	5,709	7

STATISTICAL ANALYSIS.	Population in 1803.	Extent of Surface in square Leagues	No. of Inhabitants to the square League.
XIV. Province of Old California.	9,000	7,295	

1811   [Mapping the Spanish Southwest]

Humboldt, Baron Alexander von

ESSAI POLITIQUE SUR LE ROYAUME DE LA NOUVELLE-ESPAGNE . . . AVEC UN ATLAS PHYSIQUE ET GEOGRAPHIQUE.

Paris, 1811. Two large quarto volumes and elephant folio atlas. *First edition.* A masterpiece on the American Southwest and Mexico. Howes H786: "Of superlative California interest." Streeter Texas 1042: "The map is without question the best representation of Texas [and the Southwest] that had thus far appeared." Wheat, 302-305, calls it one of the most important works ever issued on the American West: "The first authoritative work on the subject, and the basis of all later physical descriptions of New Spain." Griffin 2296: "His account is the most valuable single description of the late colony."   (80) 2850.00

POLITICAL ESSAY ON THE KINGDOM OF NEW SPAIN.

N.Y., 1811. 2 volumes. Calf. *First American edition.* Shaw & Shoemaker 23066.

(81) 250.00

Alexander von Humboldt set out as a young man to join Napolean in Egypt, but while enroute in Madrid decided instead to make a tour of the Spanish colonies in the Americas. The young scientist ended up exploring and studying for five years, and the outcome was the most remarkable and trustworthy record of the period — a record almost without error of that area in his era.

Simon Bolivar once said that "Baron Humboldt did more for the Americas than all the conquistadors." The report of his explorations revealed whole new sections of America, and his maps, which Carl Wheat called some of the world's "truly magnificent cartographic achievements," were the very best of the early 19th century. *Encyc. Brit.* states that "his studies, which his rare combination of parts enabled him to render at once multifarious, rapid, and profound, were directed with extraordinary insight."

JUNE 1st, 1812.

Referred to the Committee on Foreign Relations.

JUNE 3d, 1812.

Bill reported, declaring War against Great Britain, accompanied with a manifesto of the causes leading
to that event.

1812 [Declaration of War]

Madison, James

MESSAGE FROM THE PRESIDENT OF THE UNITED STATES, RECOMMEND-ING AN IMMEDIATE DECLARATION OF WAR AGAINST GREAT BRITAIN.

Washington City: Printed by Roger C. Weightman, June 3, 1812. 12pp. Shaw & Shoemaker 27216.   (82) 250.00

REPORT, OR MANIFESTO OF THE CAUSES AND REASONS OF WAR WITH GREAT BRITAIN, PRESENTED TO THE HOUSE OF REPRESENTATIVES BY THE COMMITTEE OF FOREIGN RELATIONS.

Washington: A. & G. Way, Printers, June 3, 1812. 17pp. Shaw & Shoemaker 27350.
                                                                   (83) 175.00

Monroe, James

MESSAGE . . . CORRESPONDENCE OF THE MINISTER PLENIPOTENTIARY OF G. BRITAIN WITH THE SECRETARY OF STATE.

Washington City: Printed by R. C. Weightman, 1812. 27pp. Timothy Pitkin's copy, signed
by him. Shaw & Shoemaker 27243, locating only three copies.   (84) 185.00

The War of 1812 was provoked primarily by England's maritime policies during the
Napoleanic wars and by her overfriendly relations with American border Indians. At the same
time, however, American designs on Canada and Florida also played a role in the troubles
leading to war.

The largest specific cause was the English policy of denying the rights of neutral ships
and of impressing seamen on the high seas from American ships. In 1807 the U.S.S. Chesa-
peake was fired upon and boarded by the British. Finding negotiated settlement impossible,
Jefferson responded with the Embargo Act of 1807, which was repealed in 1809 and replaced
with an act forbidding trade with England. These led to calls for war, which was approved by
Congress in June of 1812 after months of acrimonious debate. It was not a wise decision on
the part of the United States.

1813   [Unique War of 1812 Broadside]

CARTEL FOR THE EXCHANGE OF PRISONERS OF WAR, BETWEEN GREAT BRITAIN, AND THE UNITED STATES OF AMERICA.

Elephant folio broadside, 17x23 inches, Wash., May 14, 1813, signed in type by John Mason and Thomas Barclay, commissioners, and approved by James Monroe as President. *Unlisted and unique.* (85) 850.00

Historian Wayne Andrews sums up the beginning events of the War of 1812 succinctly, stating that Congress had not made "adequate military, naval or financial preparation for war. The consequence of congressional trifling, of insufficient and ill-trained troops, of military incompetence in high command and of defective strategy was a series of military disasters which, had not England's hands been tied in Europe, might have spelled national calamity."

The early days of the war "witnessed the surrender of Gen. William Hull at Detroit, the failure of Generals Van Rensselaer and Smyth on the Niagara River and of Dearborn at the foot of Lake Champlain. The year 1813 saw the recovery of Detroit and the defeat of the British at the Thames by Gen. Harrison, but closed with the complete failure of Gen. James Wilkinson's campaign against Montreal, and with the capture of Fort Niagara and the burning of Buffalo by the British." All the Americans seemed able to accomplish was the exchange of prisoners of war.

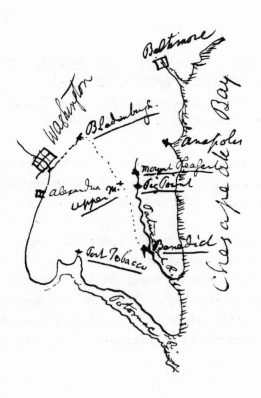

REPORT OF . . . THE CAUSES AND PARTICULARS OF THE INVASION OF THE CITY OF WASHINGTON, BY THE BRITISH FORCES IN THE MONTH OF AUGUST, 1814.

Wash., Nov. 29, 1814. 370pp. Half calf, boards. Chancellor James Kent's copy, signed by him and with extensive notes in his hand and an original manuscript map in his hand of Washington and vicinity. Shaw & Shoemaker 33404.   (86) 1500.00

Another copy, without notes.   (87) 450.00

MESSAGE . . . INFORMATION AS MAY TEND TO EXPLAIN THE CAUSES OF THE FAILURE OF THE ARMS OF THE UNITED STATES, ON THE NORTHERN FRONTIER.

Albany: Websters and Skinners, and H. C. Southwick, 1814. 2 vols. in 1. Chancellor James Kent's copy, with extensive notes in his hand. Shaw & Shoemaker 33305.   (88) 450.00

Another copy, without notes.   (89) 150.00

Key, Francis Scott

THE STAR SPANGLED BANNER [THE DEFENCE OF FORT M'HENRY]

Philadelphia: Analectic Magazine, November, 1814. Bound volume containing one of the earliest printings of what later became the national anthem.   (90) 450.00

THE STAR SPANGLED BANNER, WITH AN ADDITIONAL VERSE BY DR. O. W. HOLMES.

Boston: Oliver Ditson & Co., 1861. Sheet music, 5pp., large folio, pictorial covers in color. Currier and Tilton, Holmes Biblio., pp.519-23, devote a whole chapter to this first printing with an additional 8-line verse by Oliver Wendell Holmes. B.A.L. 8806: *first state.*

(91) 85.00

Napoleon's collapse left the British free to step up the war in America. They attacked on several fronts, and in August temporarily occupied Washington, burning the Capitol and many government buildings. But most of their actions were stalemated; nevertheless, the British were present in such overwhelming force that all the Americans could hope for was to hold their own.

The British bombarded Ft. McHenry in September without success, as described by eyewitness Francis Scott Key in the poem that became our national anthem. Although the song was from that time on used as an anthem, it was not officially adopted by Congress until March 3, 1931.

As the most important judge in New York and one of the most eminent jurists of the period, Chancellor James Kent was eyewitness to many of the events of the war on a high level. His copy of the volumes on the fall of Washington and the northern campaigns contain his valuable notes, clippings, and manuscript map.

Treaty of Peace

1815   [Treaty of Ghent]

TREATY OF PEACE

Broadside, 1815, large folio, printed in four columns on each side. Shaw & Shoemaker 32957, locating only one copy. Extremely rare.   (92) 650.00

Madison, James
MESSAGE . . . TRANSMITTING THE TREATY OF PEACE AND AMITY BE-TWEEN THE UNITED STATES AND HIS BRITANNIC MAJESTY.
Wash., 1815. 16pp. Uncut. *First official printing.* Shaw & Shoemaker 36335.   (93) 250.00

TREATIES MADE BETWEEN GREAT BRITAIN AND THE UNITED STATES . . .
Troy: Printed by Parker and Bliss, 1815. 47pp. Half calf. Shaw & Shoemaker 36414, locating only two copies.   (94) 225.00

ACTS PASSED AT THE THIRD SESSION OF THE THIRTEENTH CONGRESS OF THE UNITED STATES.
Wash.: Printed by Rapine and Elliot, 1815. [2],202,[30]pp. Contains the Treaty. Shaw & Shoemaker 36158.   (95) 80.00

Having warred to exhaustion, Britain and America agreed to meet at Ghent to work out terms of peace. The American delegation was star-studded, including Albert Gallatin, Henry Clay, and John Quincy Adams, but they were unable to effect any of their goals. They even found it necessary to drop their demands for concessions in regard to neutral rights and impressments. About all that was accomplished was British agreement to stop the war, give up its demands for territorial concessions, and return to the status quo ante bellum.

The treaty was signed on December 24, 1814; two weeks later Andrew Jackson, unaware of the treaty, inflicted an overwhelming defeat on the British at New Orleans, which almost surely would have resulted in some concessions to the Americans had it been a factor in the negotiations. Some good did come out of this miserable war, in a sense, because the exhausted British were thereafter powerless to check the American immigration push westward, and American lust for Florida was soon accomplished by Jackson without significant British or Spanish interference.

Morrow, Mr.

IN SENATE . . . FROM THE COMMITTEE TO WHOM WAS REFERRED THE BILL ENTITLED "AN ACT TO ENABLE THE PEOPLE OF INDIANA TERRITORY TO FORM A CONSTITUTION AND STATE GOVERNMENT, AND FOR THE ADMISSION OF SUCH STATE INTO THE UNION . . ."

Wash., 1816. 2pp. Morrow was on the committee considering the act for admitting Indiana; the document is the certified Census of the Indiana Territory, by counties, totalling 63,897. Shaw & Shoemaker 39444, locating two copies. (96) 125.00

CONSTITUTION OF THE STATE OF INDIANA, ADOPTED IN CONVENTION, AT CORYDON . . .

Baltimore, Niles' Register, October 4, 1817, entire issue, containing the complete Indiana Constitution and statehood petition. (97) 35.00

Courtauld, George

ADDRESS TO THOSE WHO MAY BE DISPOSED TO REMOVE TO THE UNITED STATES OF AMERICA, ON THE ADVANTANGES OF EQUITABLE ASSOCIA-TIONS OF CAPITAL AND LABOUR, IN THE FORMATION OF AGRICUL-TURAL ESTABLISHMENTS IN THE INTERIOR COUNTRY.

Sudbury: J. Burkitt, 1820. 40pp. Original wrappers, bound in half morocco. *First edition.* Howes C806. An account of Harmony, Indiana, based on a visit there in 1819, along with a plan for uniting capital and labor in a colonization company. (98) 1250.00

Until 1763 Indiana formed part of the French colonial empire, after which it spent twenty years under nominal British control. George Rogers Clark captured Vincennes in 1778, and in 1787 it became a part of the Northwest Territory. In 1800 Indiana Territory was created, with William Henry Harrison as governor.

Settlement was slow, primarily due to persistent Indian troubles. The United States did not truly bring the area under control until the War of 1812. In the meantime Michigan Territory and Illinois Territory had been carved from Indiana. After the war colonization began to speed up, and the population report, showing over 60,000 inhabitants, induced Congress to grant statehood to Indiana on December 11, 1816, as the nineteenth state.

STATUTES

OF THE

MISSISSIPPI TERRITORY;

THE

CONSTITUTION OF THE UNITED STATES, WITH THE

SEVERAL AMENDMENTS THERETO;

THE ORDINANCE

FOR THE GOVERNMENT OF THE TERRITORY OF THE

UNITED STATES, NORTH-WEST OF THE

RIVER OHIO;

THE

ARTICLES OF AGREEMENT AND CESSION, BETWEEN THE

UNITED STATES AND THE STATE OF GEORGIA;

AND

SUCH ACTS OF CONGRESS

AS RELATE TO THE

MISSISSIPPI TERRITORY.

DIGESTED BY THE AUTHORITY OF THE GENERAL ASSEMBLY.

NATCHEZ:

PRINTED BY PETER ISLER, PRINTER TO THE TERRITORY.

::::::::::::::

1816.

LETTER FROM HIS EXCELLENCY DAVID HOLMES, GOVERNOR OF THE STATE OF MISSISSIPPI, TRANSMITTING A COPY OF THE CONSTITUTION AND FORM OF GOVERNMENT OF THE SAID STATE.

Wash.: Printed by E. de Krafft, 1817. 23pp. Fine copy, uncut. Library of Congress Mississippi Exhibit #98: ''Contains the full text of the Constitution, together with Holmes' letter of Nov. 6, 1817, transmitting a copy to the Speaker of the House, Henry Clay.''   (99) 225.00

CONSTITUTION—STATE OF MISSISSIPPI

Baltimore, Niles' Register, Sept. 20, 1817, complete issue containing the entire Constitution of Mississippi.   (100) 35.00

STATUTES OF THE MISSISSIPPI TERRITORY; THE CONSTITUTION OF THE UNITED STATES, WITH THE SEVERAL AMENDMENTS THERETO: THE ORDINANCE FOR THE GOVERNMENT OF THE TERRITORY OF THE UNITED STATES NORTH-WEST OF THE RIVER OHIO; THE ARTICLES OF AGREEMENT AND CESSION, BETWEEN THE UNITED STATES AND THE STATE OF GEORGIA, AND SUCH ACTS OF CONGRESS AS RELATE TO THE MISSISSIPPI TERRITORY.

Natchez: Printed by Peter Isler, Printer to the Territory, 1816. 495,[28]pp. Full original calf. McMurtrie 96: ''Digested by Edward Turner and known as 'Turner's Code' . . . Contains the laws from 1798 through the session . . . of 1816.'' Shaw & Shoemaker 38269.   (101) 475.00

CONSTITUTION OF THE STATE OF ALABAMA

Wash.: Printed by Gales & Seaton, 1819. 24pp. Shaw & Shoemaker 49746.   (101A) 150.00

Mississippi Territory was organized in 1798, with a territorial government similar to that of Ohio under the Northwest Ordinance of 1787, except that slavery was permitted. Mississippi pressed early for statehood, but for a number of years agreement could not be reached over the boundaries.

These were extremely complicated because of the Spanish occupation of the southeastern area, French interests in the west, and the Yazoo Fraud throughout the whole area. The Louisiana Purchase, War of 1812, and Supreme Court helped solve these problems, and on March 1, 1817, Congress passed an enabling act for the western half of the territory. The convention met in July and August to form a constitution, and Mississippi was admitted on December 10, 1817, at the same time creating Alabama territory out of the eastern half and became a state in 1819.

Birkbeck, Morris
NOTES ON A JOURNEY IN AMERICA, FROM THE COAST OF VIRGINIA TO THE TERRITORY OF ILLINOIS.
London: Severn & Redington, 1818. 144pp. Original boards, untrimmed. *First English edition.* Howes B468.   (102) 75.00

Fearon, Henry B.
SKETCHES OF AMERICA: A NARRATIVE OF A JOURNEY OF 5000 MILES THROUGH THE EASTERN AND WESTERN STATES . . . WITH REMARKS ON MR. BIRKBECK'S NOTES . . .
London, 1818. 462pp. Half calf. *First edition.* Howes F65: "Unflattering picture of the western frontier." Buck 98. Clark II-22. Hubach, p. 49. Thomson 406. Graff 1301: "The chief value of the work lies in the information Fearon gathered about the problems of making a living in the United States."   (103) 125.00

Cobbett, William
A YEAR'S RESIDENCE IN THE UNITED STATES OF AMERICA, TREATING OF THE FACE OF THE COUNTRY . . . OF THE MANNERS AND CUSTOMS OF THE PEOPLE . . .
London, 1818-1819. 610pp. Half calf. Folding map. Three parts in one volume, the third devoted to a discussion of Birkbeck's narratives. *First edition.* Howes C525. Buck 112. Matthews, p.231. Sabin 14021. Graff 778.   (104) 100.00

Birkbeck, Morris
EXTRACTS FROM A SUPPLEMENTARY LETTER FROM THE ILLINOIS: ADDRESS TO BRITISH EMIGRANTS ARRIVING IN THE EASTERN PARTS . . . REPLY TO WILLIAM COBBETT.
N.Y.: C. Wiley and Co., 1819. 29pp. Half morocco. *First edition.* Buck 134. Rusk II-129. Howes B466. Shaw & Shoemaker 47365, locating two copies. One of the earliest printed records of daily life in frontier Illinois. Graff 302: "The interesting part of this pamphlet is Birkbeck's temperate reply to Cobbett's intemperate attack."   (105) 550.00

Flower, Richard
LETTERS FROM ILLINOIS, 1820-1821: CONTAINING AN ACCOUNT OF THE ENGLISH SETTLEMENT AT ALBION AND ITS VICINITY, AND A REFUTATION OF VARIOUS MISREPRESENTATIONS . . . OF MR. COBBETT, WITH A LETTER FROM MR. BIRKBECK.
London: James Ridgway, 1822. 76pp. Half calf. *First edition.* Buck 165. Bradford 1715. Jones 839. Sabin 24911. Graff 1367. Howes F220. A glowing account of English life in southern Illinois, with much about immigration.   (106) 450.00

Morris Birkbeck was born at Settle, England, in 1764, where he was a shepherd and writer, and at 40 the widowed father of seven children. George H. Genzmer writes of him: "A liberal in politics and religion, he found it increasingly irksome to be taxed by a government that denied him a vote and tithed by a church whose doctrines he disapproved, and in 1817, with a party consisting chiefly of his children, he emigrated to the United States.''

During 1817 and 1818 Birkbeck, for himself and others, entered 26,400 acres of public land in Illinois Territory, which became a state on December 3, 1818. While colonists were being raised in England for his settlement, he published his excellent *Notes on a Journey,* which ran through twelve editions in two years. It ''exercised a widespread influence, and incidentally brought down . . . the hearty vituperation of William Cobbett, who was in the pay of eastern land speculators.''

Birkbeck's writings became the center around which were written a notable group of books and tracts on Illinois and on immigration to America in general. Birkbeck became a leader in the new state, and helped consolidate the anti-slavery forces which kept Illinois a free state. He drowned in the Fox River in 1825 returning home from a visit to Robert Dale Owen in Indiana. Genzmer writes: ''He was one of the ablest, most cultured, and most public-spirited men on the frontier. His services to his adopted country were ill requited and soon forgotten.''

1819 [Adams–Onis Treaty]

Monroe, James
MESSAGE . . . AT THE COMMENCEMENT OF THE FIRST SESSION OF THE SIX-TEENTH CONGRESS.
Wash.: Gales & Seaton, 1819. 96pp. Sewn. The Adams–Onis Treaty, ceding East Florida to the U.S., is on pages 52-59; also includes preliminary drafts and other related documents. *First edition.* Sabin 49876. Streeter Texas 1076.   (107) 275.00

Onis, Luis de
MEMOIR UPON THE NEGOTIATIONS BETWEEN SPAIN AND THE UNITED STATES OF AMERICA, WHICH LED TO THE TREATY OF 1819, WITH A STATISTICAL NOTICE OF THAT COUNTRY.
Baltimore: Fielding Lucas, Junr., 1821. 152pp. Original boards. *First edition in English.* Sabin 57356. Raines, p.160. Streeter Texas 1079B. Howes O98: ''Official correspondence concerning the Floridas and the disputed western boundary of Louisiana.'' Shoemaker 6348.   (108) 550.00

The Adams–Onis Treaty was heavily in favor of the United States. Spain, weakened by European wars and American colonial revolutions, was obliged to sacrifice her interests in Florida to the United States, especially after Andrew Jackson's seizure of Spanish property in the area of 1818. Ferdinand VII's own ministers at first refused to ratify the treaty, but after several evasions ratification was accomplished in February, 1821.

The treaty, negotiated by John Quincy Adams and Luis de Onis, ceded East Florida and abandoned West Florida, giving the United States clear title to everything south of her old border and east of Louisiana. About the only thing Spain gained was temporary recognition of the Sabine River as the Texas border. Within a few years, however, Spain lost Texas, Mexico, and South America, and was never again a great international power in the old world or new.

CONSTITUTION OF THE STATE OF MISSOURI.
Wash.: Gales & Seaton, 1820. 25pp. Shoemaker 3636, locating three copies.   (109) 300.00

Bell, Samuel
MESSAGE FROM HIS EXCELLENCY THE GOVERNOR, COMMUNICATING SUNDRY RESOLUTIONS OF THE LEGISLATURE OF VIRGINIA, ON THE MISSOURI QUESTION.
Concord, 1820. 35pp. Sewn. Uncut. *First edition.* One of 300 copies printed, this work offers the full text of the preamble and resolutions of Virginia deploring the prohibition of slavery in the Missouri issue. Shoemaker 2439, locating three copies.   (110) 85.00

King, Sen. Rufus
THE SUBSTANCES OF TWO SPEECHES ON THE MISSOURI BILL.
Jamaica, Long Island, Nov. 22, 1819. 32pp. Wrappers. *Numerous holograph textual corrections in ink in King's hand.* Shaw & Shoemaker 48430.   (111) 150.00

CONSTITUTION OF MISSOURI.
Baltimore, Niles' Register, Sept. 23, 1820, complete issue containing the entire Missouri Constitution.   (112) 25.00

THE DEBATES, RESOLUTIONS, AND OTHER PROCEEDINGS OF THE CONVENTION . . . FOR THE PURPOSE OF FORMING A CONSTITUTION FOR THE STATE OF MAINE, TO WHICH IS PREFIXED THE CONSTITUTION.
Portland: A. Shirley, 1820. 300pp. plus errata. Original printed boards. Untrimmed. Edited by Jeremiah Perley. *First printing of the Maine Constitution and of the convention debates.*   (113) 250.00

In 1819 there were an equal number of free and slave states, resulting in a balanced Congress. When Missouri petitioned for admission as a slave state, a storm erupted in Congress. It came, said Thomas Jefferson, "like a fire bell in the night," and the sectional struggle threatened the Union.

Maine also was petitioning for statehood. In March, 1820, the House passed a bill admitting Missouri, but only as a free state. The Senate took up debate, then agreed to admit Missouri as a slave state and at the same time Maine as a free state, with the provision that henceforth no slave state would be admitted north of 36°30'. The House concurred, and this Missouri Compromise was "respected and regarded as almost sacred" until a new debate in the 1850's arose over the far western territories.

Schoolcraft, Henry R.

JOURNAL OF A TOUR TO THE INTERIOR OF MISSOURI AND ARKANSAW, FROM POTOSI, OR MINE A BURTON, IN MISSOURI TERRITORY, IN A SOUTH-WEST DIRECTION, TOWARD THE ROCKY MOUNTAINS.

London: Printed for Sir Richard Phillips, 1821. 102pp. Folding map. Half morocco. *First edition.* Wagner-Camp 21A. Howes S185.   (114) 165.00

Schoolcraft, Henry R.

NARRATIVE OF AN EXPEDITION THROUGH THE UPPER MISSISSIPPI TO ITASCA LAKE . . . EMBRACING AN EXPLORATORY TOUR THROUGH THE ST. CROIX AND BURNTWOOD (OR BROULE) RIVERS.

N.Y.: Harper & Brothers, 1834. 307pp. Maps. Original cloth. *First edition.* Howes S187: ''On this trip was discovered what later proved to be the real source of the Mississippi.'' Bradford 4848. Field 1367. Graff 3698. Sabin 77863.   (115) 150.00

Schoolcraft, Henry R.

SUMMARY NARRATIVE OF AN EXPLORATORY EXPEDITION TO THE SOURCES OF THE MISSISSIPPI RIVER IN 1820: RESUMED AND COMPLETED, BY THE DISCOVERY OF ITS ORIGIN IN ITASKA LAKE IN 1832 . . . WITH APPENDICES . . . WITH ALL THE OFFICIAL REPORTS AND SCIENTIFIC PAPERS OF BOTH EXPEDITIONS.

Phila.: Lippincott, Grambo, and Co., 1855. 598pp. Illus. Original cloth, spine restored. Howes S192: ''A fusion of his 1821 and 1834 Narratives, with additions.''   (116) 75.00

In 1817 Henry R. Schoolcraft, then 24, began researching for a book on glass-making, his father having reared him in that trade. He made a tour into Missouri from his home in Albany, and decided instead to become an explorer-scientist. In 1820 he was allowed to accompany the Lewis Cass expedition up the Mississippi to the Lake Superior copper region. His book on that expedition, published in 1821, became a classic.

In 1832 he made another expedition to discover the source of the Mississippi, which was still unknown. His writings on his travels were read with much interest, as were his numerous writings on Indian culture. He had married a part Chippewa girl in 1823, and worked from that time on mainly in the field of ethnology, although he wrote on many subjects, of which about the best that has been said is that ''his literary remains are of impressive bulk.'' In the 1850's he published with Seth Eastman an important multi-volume set on the Indian tribes of the United States.

PUBLIC DOCUMENTS,

RELATING TO THE

NEW-YORK CANALS,

WHICH ARE TO CONNECT

THE WESTERN AND NORTHERN LAKES,

WITH THE

ATLANTIC OCEAN;

WITH AN

INTRODUCTION.

❖

PRINTED UNDER THE DIRECTION OF THE NEW-YORK CORRES-
PONDING ASSOCIATION, FOR THE PROMOTION OF
INTERNAL IMPROVEMENTS.

❖

NEW-YORK:

WILLIAM A. MERCEIN, PRINTER,

No. 93, Gold-Street.

. . . .

1821.

DOCUMENTS RELATING TO THE WESTERN TERMINATION OF THE ERIE CANAL...

Black Rock: Lewis C. Hoffman, 1822. 60pp. Folding map. Sewn. *First edition.* Howes E167. Shoemaker 8092.   (117) 175.00

PUBLIC DOCUMENTS RELATING TO THE NEW-YORK CANALS, WHICH ARE TO CONNECT THE WESTERN AND NORTHERN LAKES, WITH THE ATLANTIC OCEAN.

N.Y.: Wm. A. Mercein, 1821. [52],484,[2]pp. Huge color folding map: "A New Map and Profile of the Proposed Canal from Lake Erie to Hudson River . . ." *First edition.* Howes H18, attributing this to the editorship of Charles G. Haines. Shoemaker 6265.   (118) 375.00

AN EXAMINATION OF THE LINE OF THE GREAT ERIE CANAL, AS ADOPTED BY THE COMMISSIONERS...

N.p.: Printed for the Publisher, 1822. 32pp. Sewn. Shoemaker 8650, locating only one other known copy.   (119) 175.00

Randel, John
DESCRIPTION OF A DIRECT ROUTE FOR THE ERIE CANAL, AT ITS EASTERN TERMINATION.

Albany: G. J. Loomis, 1822. 72pp. Sewn. *First edition.* Shoemaker 10063.   (120) 125.00

FACTS AND OBSERVATIONS IN RELATION TO THE ORIGIN AND COMPLETION OF THE ERIE CANAL.

N.Y.: N. B. Holmes, 1825. 36pp. *First edition.* Howes E168. Shoemaker 20456. (121) 85.00

From the time of the Revolution there was a movement for an artificial canal to connect the Great Lakes with the settlements in eastern New York. The legislature set up a canal commission in 1810, which settled upon Lake Erie for the western terminus. The major mover behind the project was De Witt Clinton, who was canal commissioner and later governor. Construction was finally authorized in 1817.

It was a major engineering feat for the technology of the period. The ditch was 363 miles long with 83 locks lifting the vessels a total of over 600 feet. On October 27, 1822, a 280-mile section of the canal was opened, and by 1825 a boat could travel the entire 550 miles from New York City to Lake Erie.

Monroe, James
MESSAGE FROM THE PRESIDENT OF THE UNITED STATES, TO BOTH HOUSES OF CONGRESS, AT THE COMMENCEMENT OF THE FIRST SESSION OF THE EIGHTEENTH CONGRESS.
Wash.: Gales & Seaton, 1823. 16;206pp. Charts. Original calf. *First edition, first issue,* of the Monroe Doctrine. Howes M724: "In addition to containing the notable first enunciation of the Monroe Doctrine, one of the accompanying documents gives General Gaines' report on the upper Missouri campaign against the Arikaras." Grolier American Hundred #33.   (122) 650.00

Monroe, James
PRESIDENT'S MESSAGE . . . DECEMBER 2, 1823.
Washington, National Intelligencer, Dec. 3, 1823. 4pp. Elephant folio. Full text of the Monroe Doctrine message. The first newspaper printing, quite possibly preceding the official printing.   (123) 175.00

Both Washington in his Farewell Address and Jefferson in his first inaugural address had warned against any deep involvement of America in European affairs. But it was the message of James Monroe to Congress on December 2, 1823, that set the unique policy now known as the Monroe Doctrine. Monroe said, quoting almost verbatim from words recommended by his Secretary of State John Quincy Adams: "The American continents, by the free and independent condition which they have assumed and maintained, are henceforth not to be considered as subjects for future colonization by any European powers."

Although at first Monroe's statement that any such attempt would be considered a "manifestation of an unfriendly disposition toward the United States" was largely viewed with contempt by European nations, it was used many times afterwards by the United States to prevent interference in the Western Hemisphere, the most notable example being that of the Cuban Missile Crisis in 1961.

WYOMING,

No. I.

The Next President

AND

GENERAL ANDREW JACKSON.

1824   [Jackson–Adams Election]

*THE LETTERS OF WYOMING, TO THE PEOPLE OF THE UNITED STATES, ON
THE PRESIDENTIAL ELECTION, AND IN FAVOUR OF ANDREW JACKSON.*
Phila.: S. Simpson & J. Conrad, 1824. 104pp. Shoemaker 19341. Traces Jackson's career and
emphasizes the Battle of New Orleans and the Florida campaign.   (124) 125.00

NATIONAL INTELLIGENCER.
Wash.: Gales & Seaton, February 10 and March 10, 1825. Two complete issues, the first announcing the election of Adams and describing in fascinating detail the unusual procedure, and
the second announcing that Henry Clay had become Secretary of State.   (125) 45.00

The election of 1824 was one of the most interesting ever held in the United States.
There were four major candidates: Andrew Jackson, the Hero of New Orleans; John Quincy
Adams, Secretary of State, co-author of the Monroe Doctrine, and son of a President; Henry
Clay, Speaker of the House; and William Crawford, former senator and cabinet member.

The campaign was intense, it being ''during this period that the campaigners were able
to arouse the masses throughout the country to an active interest in politics and to a pitch of en-
thusiasm which was more general than anything that had previously affected the people.''
Jackson received the highest vote but only a plurality, and the decision was sent to the House.

Crawford lost support, and Clay forces joined with Adams to give Adams the Presidency. Clay was accused of having made a deal for the office of Secretary of State, and when he
received that office the political history of the country was profoundly affected. Such was the bitterness of the populace that the incumbent Adams was not re-elected in 1828 and Clay was put
under a cloud that probably cost him the presidency several times. It made an even more
popular hero of Jackson, whose forces swamped the subsequent three presidential elections.

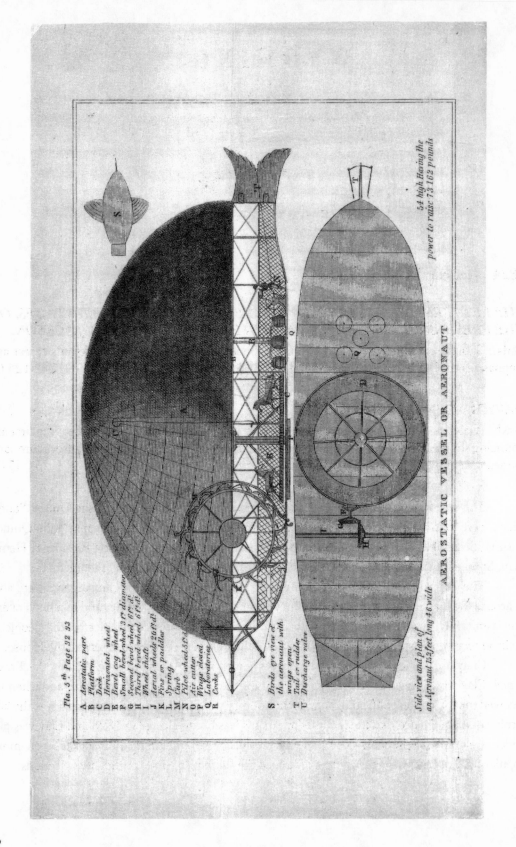

Fig. 5.ᵗʰ Page 92 93

A Aerostatic part
B Platform
C Deck
D Horizontal wheel
E Bevel cog wheel
F Small bevel wheel 3 ft diameter
G Second bevel wheel 6 ft dt
H Third bevel wheel 6 ft dt
I Wheel shaft
J Aerial wheels 20 ft dt
K Fins or paddles
L Spring
M Curb
N Pilot wheel 5 ft d
O Air cutter
P Wings closed
Q Laboratories
R Cocks

S Birds eye view of
the aeronaut with
wings open.
T Trail or rudder
U Discharge valve

54 high Having the
power to raise 7.3 162 pounds

Side view and plan of
an Aeronaut 112 feet long 46 wide

AEROSTATIC VESSEL OR AERONAUT

72

Genet, Edmond Charles
MEMORIAL ON THE UPWARD FORCES OF FLUIDS, AND THEIR AP-
PLICABILITY TO SEVERAL ARTS, SCIENCES, AND PUBLIC IMPROVEMENTS,
FOR WHICH A PATENT HAS BEEN GRANTED BY THE GOVERNMENT OF
THE UNITED STATES.
Albany: Printed by Packard & Van Benthuysen, 1825. 112pp. Six plates. Folding table. *First edition. With an original leaf of holograph manuscript in Genet's hand* and a short A.L.S. to Genet from E. B. Child, Aug. 26, 1825, both 12mo, inserted. Howes G100. Shoemaker 20645. Aeronautical Americana #9. Bennett, p.59: ''Most important American publication in the field of aviation.''   (126) 1250.00

Edmond Charles Genet, the first minister of the French Republic to the United States, decided to settle in America. He married the daughter of Gov. George Clinton of New York and became a U.S. citizen. For nearly three decades he pursued politics, business, and scientific pursuits as a gentleman farmer.

His *Memorial* is the first American treatise on aviation. Whitman Bennett states: ''From a scientific viewpoint this is the most important American publication in the field of aviation, for it is the first printed suggestion of the correct theory of the heavier than air machine. Plate No. 5 showing a dirigible balloon propelled by two horses on a treadmill has long been the source of much amusement.'' Thomas W. Streeter called it ''extremely rare and important, the first book printed in the United States on practical aeronautics and on the first patent for an aeronautical invention.''

WASHINGTON.

TUESDAY, JULY 4, 1826.

The sentiments contained in the following letters are in every respect so appropriate to the occasion of this day's Celebration, that, in offering them to our readers, it would be supererogation to add a word of comment. If history is philosophy teaching by example, where could a more beautiful example be found, than in that which is afforded by the following Letters from the surviving men of the Revolution?

WASHINGTON, JUNE 14, 1826.

SIR: As Chairman of a Committee appointed by the citizens of Washington, to make arrangements for celebrating the Fiftieth Anniversary of American Independence in a manner worthy of the Metropolis of the Nation, I am directed to invite you, as one of the Signers of the ever-memorable Declaration of the Fourth of July, 1776, to favor the City with your presence on the occasion.

I am further instructed to inform you, that, on receiving your acceptance of this invitation, a special deputation will be sent, to accompany you from your residence to this City, and back to your home.

With sentiments of the highest respect and veneration, I have the honor to be, your most obedient servant,

R. C. WEIGHTMAN,
Mayor of Washington, and Chairman of the Committee of Arrangements.

[The above is a copy of the letter addressed to the surviving signers of the Declaration of Independence: a letter to the same effect was also addressed to the former Presidents of the United States, who were not signers of this instrument. In the letter addressed to Mr. ADAMS there was a slight variation; the shortness of the time, and the distance of his residence from the Seat of Government, making it necessary for the Committee of Arrangement to depute a gentleman to escort him without awaiting his answer. Col. HOUSE, of the Army, most promptly and cheerfully undertook this honorable mission, at the request and on behalf of the committee.]

VOL. XXVII.

PUBLISHED BY
GALES & SEATON,
THREE TIMES A WEEK, ON TUESDAYS, THURSDAYS, AND SATURDAYS.

Price, for a year, six dollars,
For six months, four dollars, } Payable in advance.

WASHINGTON.

FRIDAY, JULY 7, 1826.

Pallida Mors æquo pulsat pede pauperum tabernas,
Regumque turres.

THOMAS JEFFERSON IS NO MORE! His weary sun hath made a golden set, leaving a bright tract of undying fame to mark his path to a glorious immortality.

The illustrious Author of the Declaration of Independence breathed his last at Monticello on the fourth of this month, at 10 minutes before one o'clock. On the Fiftieth Anniversary of the birth of this Nation, with which event his Name and Fame are forever and indissolubly united, at the moment when all tongues throughout the land were engaged in repeating the language of his greatest work—his soul, satisfied with the retrospection of half a century of past events, winged its flight to the realms of immortality! Singular, but felicitous coincidence!

We shall not coolly undertake to indite the memoirs of such a man. His history may be read in a Nation's eyes—his eulogy beams on the surface of every thing that is admirable and peculiar in the principles of our Governments.

For a review of his past life this is not the moment. A more suitable occasion shall be chosen, and perhaps a more able pen than ours.

1826 [Adams and Jefferson Die on July 4, 1826]

Webster, Daniel

A DISCOURSE IN COMMEMORATION OF THE LIVES AND SERVICES OF JOHN ADAMS AND THOMAS JEFFERSON, DELIVERED IN FANEUIL HALL.

Boston: Cummings, Hilliard and Co., 1826. 62pp. Original printed wrappers. Fine, untrimmed copy. *First edition.* Shoemaker 27583.　　　　　(127) 85.00

WASHINGTON NATIONAL INTELLIGENCER.

Wash., July 4, 1826, and July 8, 1826. Two complete issues, each 4pp., elephant folio, the first being the *50th Anniversary of the U.S. issue,* and the second being a black-bordered issue headed "Thomas Jefferson Is No More!" News of John Adams' death had not yet reached the Capital.　　　　　—　　　(128) 45.00

One of the most familiar stories of American history is how John Adams and Thomas Jefferson both died on July 4, 1826, the 50th Anniversary of American Independence. In March of 1826 Jefferson had written to Adams that "it was the lot of our early years to witness the dull monotony of a colonial subservience; and of our riper years, to breast the labors and perils of working out of it." Adams replied that in present times "public affairs go on pretty much as usual, perpetual chicanery and rather more personal abuse than there used to be." Adams died on the evening of July 4th, remarking that Jefferson still lived.

But Jefferson had died earlier that day. As he declined he had asked, "Is it the 4th?" The doctor replied, "It soon will be," and Jefferson said, "Ah," and expired about noon. As James Truslow Adams remarked, "death had struck simultaneously at the two most shining marks in the land, and as the past symbolically went down to the grave, an era was dramatically closed."

As representative of the new era, Congressman Daniel Webster delivered his now-famous eulogy in Fanueil Hall, before President John Quincy Adams and many others, stating that no "two men have ever lived, in one age, who, more than those we now commemorate, have impressed their own sentiments, in regard to politics and government, on mankind, infused their own opinions more deeply into the opinions of others, or given a more lasting direction to the current of human thought. Their work doth not perish with them. . . . Washington is in the clear upper sky. These other stars have now joined the American constellation."

TO

WILLIAM JOHNSON, ESQ.

◆

DEAR SIR,

IN compiling these volumes, (originally intended and now published for the benefit of American students,) I have frequently been led to revisit the same ground, and to follow out the same paths, over which I have so often passed with you as a companion to cheer and delight me.

You have reported every opinion which I gave in term time, and thought worth reporting, during the five and twenty years that I was a Judge at Law and in Equity, with the exception of the short interval occupied by Mr. Caines' Reports. During that long period, I had the happiness to maintain a free, cordial, and instructive intercourse with you; and I feel unwilling now to close my labours as an author, and withdraw myself finally from the public eye, without leaving some memorial of my grateful sense of the value of your friendship, and my reverence for your character.

In inscribing this work to you, I beg leave, sir, at the same time, to add my ardent wishes for your future welfare, and to assure you of my constant esteem and regard.

JAMES KENT.

Kent, Chancellor James
COMMENTARIES ON AMERICAN LAW.
N.Y.: O. Halsted, 1826-1827-1828-1830. 4 volumes. Calf. Van Doren and Adler, p.1065: "The first major systematic work on Anglo-American law." *First edition,* with Kent's own copy of Theron Metcalf's 14-page "Review: Commentaries on American Law" from U.S. Review, May, 1827, with some notes in ink in Kent's hand, and an original Autograph Letter Signed from Aaron Burr, then a New York attorney, remarking ". . . Please to transmit to me by mail a copy of the Chancellor's opinion—it is hoped that he will be induced to expunge that part which . . ." Also inserted is an original Autograph Letter Signed from Kent, Albany, 1822, 1p., 4to, regarding a Phi Beta Kappa Society address.   (129) 650.00

Chancellor James Kent was one of the greatest jurists and legal minds America has produced. Frederick C. Hicks states that he was "practically the creator of equity jurisdiction in the United States," and his great *Commentaries* gained him the unchallenged title of the American Blackstone. It is said that he was the first American jurist to deliver his opinions in writing. Hicks claims the *Commentaries* "still remains the foremost American institutional legal treatise."

Andrew C. McLaughlin wrote of Kent's *Commentaries:* "It has remained an authoritative treatise, and the opinions of the writer have had great weight with courts and lawyers, and influenced the development of American law. The work is marked by a firm grasp of essentials, by explicit statement of fundamental principles, and by a clear, unaffected, straightforward style, which avoids any pedantic exhibition of learning. The four volumes cover in a general way nearly all the main divisions of the law, including international law and constitutional law."

The work, states J. P. Chamberlain, is "superior to any previous treatise on this subject, and a landmark in the history of international law." Thomas R. Powell states that anyone wishing a "review of the foundation stones of our Constitutional jurisprudence can go nowhere else with such profit and pleasure as to the . . . *Commentaries.* In his constitutional principles, he foreshadowed Marshall, and his opinions are worthy of a place beside those of the great Chief Justice."

It was Chancellor Kent, by the way, who made the famous anti-temperance comment: "Gentlemen, I refuse to sign any pledge. I never have been drunk, and, by the blessing of God, I never will get drunk, but, sirs, I have a constitutional privilege to get drunk, and that privilege I will not sign away!"

The words defence, expence, offence, pretence, recompence, are written with c instead of s; but why perplex a learner with such an anomaly? The original words in Latin & French are written with s; & what is of more importance, the derivatives defensive, expensive, offensive, pretension, recompensed, are always written with s. Indeed expense is generally written with s; why not the other words?

So also connection, deflection, inflection, reflection ought to follow the verbs connect, deflect, inflect, reflect. There are some other irregularities of the same kind; but these are in classes, & the correction would be easy. It greatly facilitates the learning of the language by natives as well as by foreigners, to have classes of words of the same origin and the same analogy, as uniform as possible.

In my early publications, I generally adopted the current English orthography, with the common discrepancies. In my quarto dictionary, many such discrepancies appear, although many are corrected. The English edition is, to a good degree, corrected; & if another edition should be published in this country, I trust this fault will be removed.

But in my Spelling Book & small Dictionaries for schools, the orthography is rendered uniform; at least if there is any exception, it must be an oversight or misprint, & will be corrected, when discovered.

Webster, Noah
AN AMERICAN DICTIONARY OF THE ENGLISH LANGUAGE.
N.Y.: S. Converse and H. Howe, 1828. 2 volumes. Large thick quarto. Full calf. *First edition.*
Grolier American Hundred #36. Downs, Famous Books #62. Printing and the Mind of Man
#291. *With an original leaf of manuscript in Webster's hand* inserted, 1p., 4to, 22 lines
of notes on the use of the letter ''c'' in ''the words defence, expence, offence, pretence''
etc.   (130 1850.00

Webster, Noah
A COMPENDIOUS DICTIONARY OF THE ENGLISH LANGUAGE.
New Haven: Sidney's Press, 1806. 400pp. Contemporary calf. Three leaves repaired, with
partial loss of text. *First edition of Webster's first dictionary.*   (131) 275.00

Webster, Noah
OBSERVATIONS ON LANGUAGE...
New Haven: S. Babcock, 1839. 39pp. Half morocco. Sabin 102371.   (132) 150.00

Webster, Noah
MISTAKES AND CORRECTIONS.
New Haven: B. L. Hamlen, 1837, 28pp. Yellow printed wrappers. Corrections to his and
others' works. Very scarce.   (133) 150.00

In 1783 Noah Webster introduced what became known as the Blue-Backed Speller, of
which at least 70 million copies were sold in the century following. Only the McGuffey Readers
can compare with Webster's grammars and readers, which likewise sold in the millions. But
this was not enough for that remarkable man, so 45 years later he gave us Webster's Dictionary. And 61 years after his first publication he was still writing and publishing tracts
improving his original idea that ''as an independent nation, our honor requires us to have a
system of our own in language.''

In 1806 Webster published his first dictionary, listing 5,000 words that had never before
appeared in any dictionary. This was mere prologue, however, to his grand work, on which he
worked unstintingly throughout his career. By 1813, he had learned twenty major languages;
he later added a dozen more. He was seventy years old in 1828 when his dictionary appeared,
and every word in the 70,000-entry manuscript was in his own hand. The published work of
1800 pages contained 12,000 words that had never before appeared. It has justly been called
''the most ambitious publication ever undertaken, up to that time, upon American soil.''

A recent tribute to him states: Webster, in fact, was in his own sphere as much a
founder of his nation as Washington, and consciously so, for he had the vision.... In his own
way Webster was the Pericles of his country....''

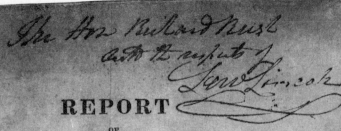

REPORT

OF

THE BOARD OF DIRECTORS

OF INTERNAL IMPROVEMENTS

OF THE

STATE OF MASSACHUSETTS,

ON

THE PRACTICABILITY AND EXPEDIENCY

OF A

RAIL-ROAD

FROM BOSTON TO THE HUDSON RIVER

AND

FROM BOSTON TO PROVIDENCE.

SUBMITTED TO THE GENERAL COURT, JANUARY 16, 1829.

To which are annexed,

The Reports of the Engineers,

CONTAINING THE RESULTS OF THEIR SURVEYS, AND ESTIMATES OF THE
COST OF CONSTRUCTING A RAIL-ROAD, ON EACH
OF THE ROUTES SELECTED.

WITH PLANS AND PROFILES OF THE ROUTES.

Boston:
PRESS OF THE BOSTON DAILY ADVERTISER,
W. L. Lewis, Printer, Congress-street.
1829.

Lincoln, Levi
REPORT OF THE BOARD OF DIRECTORS OF INTERNAL IMPROVEMENTS OF THE STATE OF MASSACHUSETTS, ON THE PRACTICABILITY AND EXPEDIENCY OF A RAIL-ROAD.
Boston, 1829. 76+119pp. Sewn. Six fine large engraved folding maps. *Inscribed and signed from Lincoln to Richard Rush.* Thomson 325. Shoemaker 39503.   (134) 200.00

Redfield, William C.
SKETCH OF THE GEOGRAPHICAL ROUT OF A GREAT RAILWAY, BY WHICH IT IS PROPOSED TO CONNECT THE CANALS AND NAVIGABLE RIVERS OF NEW-YORK, PENNSYLVANIA, OHIO, INDIANA, ILLINOIS, MICHIGAN, MISSOURI, AND THE ADJACENT STATES AND TERRITORIES . . . BETWEEN THE ATLANTIC STATES AND THE GREAT VALLEY OF THE MISSISSIPPI.
N.Y.: G. & C. & H. Carvill, 1830. 48pp. Original printed wrappers. Fine engraved folding map. Second and best edition, tripled in size. Howes R113. Cooper 3253. Inserted is a very important detailed original Autograph Letter Signed, 2pp., 4to, about the project from historian John H. Redfield, son of the author, stating in part: ". . . I have thought that perhaps you would value a copy of my father's first rail road pamphlet — especially as it has a historical interest as being the initial movement towards the establishment of the Erie Rail Road & its western connections. . . ."   (135) 350.00

TO THE CITIZENS OF MASSACHUSETTS.
Broadside, 1p., large wide quarto, Boston, 1829. Issued by Joseph H. Dorr, Henry J. Oliver, and A. J. Allen, committee to raise donations "to aid the construction of a Rail Road." Interesting two-column plea to make Massachusetts the home of the first passenger train in America and not to "be outdone in enterprize by the states of the south!" *Unlisted and unique;* not in Cooper.   (136) 150.00

The earliest railroads in America were short wooden tramways at mines or quarries, with cars pulled by horses. Col. John Stevens in 1812 expounded the idea of using steam engines to pull railway cars by mechanical power and in 1815 received a charter to construct a system in New Jersey, but failed from lack of capital. In 1828 passengers were pulled in railway cars by horses in Maryland.

It was not until 1829-1830, however, that steam locomotives were actually used to pull passengers in cars on railroad tracks, the most famous being Peter Cooper's Tom Thumb. Immediately, railroads were chartered in several states, and throughout the 1830's tracks were laid in various areas of the East and South. With improvements in steam engines, the era of railroads in America was on its way to criss-crossing the country.

Both of the charters listed above became systems that are still in operation—the Boston & Maine, operating 1700 miles of track in New England, and the mighty Erie, with its checkered history, with 2300 miles of track from New York to Chicago.

SUPPLEMENT

TO THE

MILLENNIAL STAR.

AUGUST 1844.

ADDRESS TO THE SAINTS.

BELOVED SAINTS,—In a strange and melancholy garb, we have been led this month to print a supplement to the STAR.

But why these tokens of woe and mourning? Will it be believed in the face of high heaven, in the present age, that men are required to seal their testimony of truth with their blood? Yes; such is the fact. The Prophet of the Lord in the last days, together with his brother Hyrum, have been MURDERED—basely, dastardly murdered—in prison, with the pledged faith of a state of the American union for their protection.

But can it be; is it not a dream—a phantasy of the brain? The land of freedom, boasted freedom, and of equal rights, stained with the blood of martyrs to the principles of the gospel of Christ! "The land of the brave, and the home of the free"—the country that has presented herself as the asylum of the oppressed—as a welcome refuge for the sufferers for conscience' sake, become the altar of sacrifice of the servants of God, by the cruel hands of a bloodthirsty mob! Can such things indeed be? Slumber on, ye mighty fathers of a degenerate race—ye who fought and toiled, who bled and died for liberty, and for conscience' sake. Oh! wake not from your honourable repose, to a consciousness of the dark deeds of your fallen sons, who, not contented with a long career of persecution, even unto death—of spoliation and ravage of the Saints of God, have filled up the cup of their iniquity by one of the most treacherous murders in the annals of time. Columbia! thy glory hath departed—virtue and innocence weep on thy shores—justice has fled from presiding over the deliberations of thy senate, while the hand of lawless violence, over thy wide spread territory, is raised for the destruction of thy subjects.

1830 [The Mormons]

Smith, Joseph, Author and Proprietor
THE BOOK OF MORMON: AN ACCOUNT WRITTEN BY THE HAND OF MOR-MON, UPON PLATES TAKEN FROM THE PLATES OF NEPHI.
Palmyra: Printed by E. B. Grendin, for the Author, 1830. 588,[2]pp. Early full morocco, gilt. Very fine copy. *First edition.* Written on the fly-leaf: "The original copy of this book, in the handwriting of Oliver Condery, is now at Independence, Missouri, as I am informed by William E. McLellan, once one of the 'Twelve ('My Servant William'), as the Lord called him at Kirtland, Ohio, 1876. T. M. Dill." Howes S623: "In the first edition only was Smith designated as author; in all subsequent ones he is designated as translator. The first edition was also the only one carrying his two-page preface." Grolier American Hundred #37. Cooper 579. Downs, Books That Changed America, #3. (137) 2500.00

Smith, Joseph, Translator
THE BOOK OF MORMON.
Liverpool: Printed by J. Tompkins, for Brigham Young, Heber C. Kimball and Parley P. Pratt, 1841. [4],643pp. Contemporary full blind-tooled calf. *First English edition, and first edition outside America.* (138) 550.00

Hardy, John [comp.]
A COLLECTION OF SACRED HYMNS; ADAPTED TO THE FAITH AND VIEWS OF THE CHURCH OF JESUS CHRIST OF LATTER DAY SAINTS.
Boston: Dow & Jackson's Press, 1843. 160pp. Original full calf, morocco label. *First edition.* Of great rarity and importance. Not in N.Y.P.L. Mormon list or any other bibliography consulted. Only three other copies located. (139) 2000.00

Reid, H. T., and J. W. Woods
ADDRESS TO THE SAINTS ... AWFUL ASSASSINATION ...
Supplement to the Millennial Star, August, 1844. 16pp. Sewn. Black-bordered throughout. Full account of the murder of Joseph Smith. (140) 200.00

THE DESERET NEWS.
Salt Lake City, 1850-1863. Volume I no. 1 through Volume XII. Complete except for about twenty issues. *Of superlative rarity, no complete file existing.* "Considered with respect to the conditions under which it was created, the apparently insuperable difficulties encountered and surmounted in its publication ... it may well be described as perhaps the most remarkable and historically interesting newspaper that ever existed." It was printed on a small wrought-iron press hauled across the plains; the first issue was run off by Brigham Young himself. Further details upon request. (141) 11,500.00

CONSTITUTION OF THE UNITED STATES ... ALSO, AN ACT TO ESTABLISH A TERRITORIAL GOVERNMENT FOR UTAH.

Salt Lake City, 1852. 48pp. McMurtrie #12, locating only two copies. (142) 600.00

Young, Brigham
PROCLAMATION BY THE GOVERNOR: CITIZENS OF UTAH, WE ARE INVADED BY A HOSTILE FORCE WHO ARE EVIDENTLY ASSAILING US TO ACCOMPLISH OUR OVERTHROW AND DESTRUCTION ...

Salt Lake City, 1857. Broadside, 1p., folio, silked, laid in half morocco slipcase. Graff 4449. This famous Proclamation by Brigham Young is one of the great documents in Mormon history, the only instance in American history where a Territorial Governor forbade U.S. troops to enter the Territory and declared war on the United States. The proclamation also declared martial law and called upon the people of Utah to arm in preparation for repelling American invasion. Col. Albert Sidney Johnston was sent at the head of the U.S. troops, and by compromises the issue was settled amicably. (143) 5000.00

The Church of Jesus Christ of Latter-day Saints was organized on April 6, 1830, about two weeks after the publication of the *Book of Mormon.* The new church grew rapidly but met with fierce popular opposition. The Mormons, as they were called, founded the town of Nauvoo in Illinois, where Joseph Smith was murdered in 1844. The leadership of the church then fell to Brigham Young.

T. C. Cochran states: "In 1845 hostilities again broke out and the Mormons were forced again from their homes. In the month of February, 1846, the first bands of refugees crossed the Mississippi River, with cannon pointing at them to hasten their flight. In poverty and inclement weather they commenced their journey westward ... in search of a new home." By July of 1847, after futile searching, they finally settled in the Salt Lake Valley. There they made their permanent home and capital of Salt Lake City, and swiftly became a major international religion.

PROCLAMATION

BY THE GOVERNOR.

CITIZENS OF UTAH—

We are invaded by a hostile force who are evidently assailing us to accomplish our overthrow and destruction.

For the last twenty five years we have trusted officials of the Government, from Constables and Justices to Judges, Governors, and Presidents, only to be scorned, held in derision, insulted and betrayed. Our houses have been plundered and then burned, our fields laid waste, our principal men butchered while under the pledged faith of the government for their safety, and our families driven from their homes to find that shelter in the barren wilderness and that protection among hostile savages which were denied them in the boasted abodes of Christianity and civilization.

The Constitution of our common country guarantees unto us all that we do now or have ever claimed.

If the Constitutional rights which pertain unto us as American citizens were extended to Utah, according to the spirit and meaning thereof, and fairly and impartially administered, it is all that we could ask, all that we have ever asked.

Our opponents have availed themselves of prejudice existing against us because of our religious faith, to send out a formidable host to accomplish our destruction. We have had no privilege, no opportunity of defending ourselves from the false, foul, and unjust aspersions against us before the nation. The Government has not condescended to cause an investigating committee or other person to be sent to inquire into and ascertain the truth, as is customary in such cases.

We know those aspersions to be false, but that avails us nothing. We are condemned unheard and forced to an issue with an armed, mercenary mob, which has been sent against us at the instigation of anonymous letter writers ashamed to father the base, slanderous falsehoods which they have given to the public; of corrupt officials who have brought false accusation against us to screen themselves in their own infamy; and of hireling priests and howling editors who prostitute the truth for filthy lucre's sake.

The issue which has been thus forced upon us compels us to resort to the great first law of self preservation and stand in our own defence, a right guaranteed unto us by the genius of the institutions of our country, and upon which the Government is based.

Our duty to ourselves, to our families, requires us not to tamely submit to be driven and slain, without an attempt to preserve ourselves. Our duty to our country, our holy religion, our God, to freedom and liberty, requires that we should not quietly stand still and see those fetters forging around, which are calculated to enslave and bring us in subjection to an unlawful military despotism such as can only emanate [in a country of Constitutional law] from usurpation, tyranny, and oppression.

Therefore I, Brigham Young, Governor and Superintendent of Indian Affairs for the Territory of Utah, in the name of the People of the United States in the Territory of Utah,

1st:—Forbid all armed forces, of every description, from coming into this Territory under any pretence whatever.

2d:—That all the forces in said Territory hold themselves in readiness to march, at a moment's notice, to repel any and all such invasion.

3d:—Martial law is hereby declared to exist in this Territory, from and after the publication of this Proclamation; and no person shall be allowed to pass or repass into, or through, or from this Territory, without a permit from the proper officer.

{ L. S. }

Given under my hand and seal at Great Salt Lake City, Territory of Utah, this fifteenth day of September, A. D. Eighteen hundred and fifty seven and of the Independence of the United States of America the eighty second.

BRIGHAM YOUNG.

Pattie, James Ohio

THE PERSONAL NARRATIVE OF JAMES O. PATTIE, OF KENTUCKY, DURING AN EXPEDITION FROM SAINT LOUIS, THROUGH THE VAST REGIONS BETWEEN THAT PLACE AND THE PACIFIC OCEAN.

Cincinnati, 1831-33, 300pp. 5 plates. Contemporary calf. First edition, first state (1831) of text, with p.251 misnumbered 151 and second state (1833) of title page. Howes P123. Cowan, p.476. BAL 6122. Sabin 59150. Graff 3217. Field 1186. Jones 937. Rader 2619. Wagner-Camp 45. Rittenhouse 452: "A classic on the Southwest." Zamorano Eighty #60: "This book is the first printed narrative of an overland journey to California . . . of extreme rarity." A cornerstone of Western Americana.   (144) 1450.00

Edited by Timothy Flint, this volume contains the first overland trip to California of which there is a written record. Beginning in July, 1824, near present Omaha, Pattie and his father joined an expedition destined for Santa Fe, arriving in November. For three years thereafter they participated in numerous trapping and hunting adventures in the Rockies. In 1828 they reached California, were arrested and imprisoned in San Diego, where the elder Pattie died from brutal treatment. James was released and reached Cincinnati in August, 1830, travelling via Mexico City. There he met Timothy Flint, who helped him prepare his book. Pattie later joined the California gold rush in 1849 and died that winter in the mines.

Henry Wagner states: "Some doubt has been manifested as to the truth of the remarkable wanderings of Pattie through the mountains, but probably in the main the story can be accepted as true." Thomas W. Field writes: "The narrative of Pattie's expedition and captivity has more than the ordinary interest and value. He crossed the continent of America on a route which his party were the first to pursue. He encountered tribes of Indians who then saw a white man for the first time, and his narrative has the merit of being given in a candid, unexaggerated style, which impresses us with its veracity . . . all narrated with spirit and candor."

MESSRS. PATTIE AND SLOVER RESCUED FROM FAMISH.

1832 [My Country, – 'Tis of Thee]

Smith, Samuel F.
AMERICA.
Autograph Manuscript Signed, 1p., large quarto, four verses totaling 28 lines of the famous anthem beginning:

> "My Country, — 'tis of thee,
> Sweet land of liberty
>   Of thee I sing
> Land where my fathers died,
> Land of the pilgrim's pride,
> From every mountain side
>   Let freedom ring."

(145) 450.00

Samuel Francis Smith was a Bostonian who attended the Eliot School, Boston Latin School, and Harvard College. He entered Harvard in 1829 in one of its most distinguished classes, its memory preserved by Oliver Wendell Holmes in "The Boys," in which are the lines: "And there's a nice youngster of excellent pith: / Fate tried to conceal him by naming him Smith." After Harvard, Smith entered Andover Theological Seminary, where he helped earn his way by translating Francis Lieber's *Encyclopedia Americana.*

In 1832 he was asked by Lowell Mason to translate and compose verses for a school song book. Among some samples given him he found a German hymn that appealed to him. Smith later wrote: "Being pleased with its simple and easy movement, I glanced at the German words, and seeing that they were patriotic, instantly felt the impulse to write a patriotic hymn of my own to the same tune. Seizing a scrap of waste paper, I put upon it, within half an hour, the verses substantially as they stand today."

The poem was first published in Mason's *The Choir* in 1832. As William H. Allen has written, "it speedily was popularly adopted as the national hymn, a status never needing the support of political action, but maintained by force of sentiment."

America.

My country 'tis of thee,
Sweet land of liberty—
Of thee I sing;
Land where my father's died,
Land of the pilgrim's pride,
From every mountain side
Let freedom ring.

My native country—thee—
Land of the noble free—
Thy name I love;
I love thy rocks and rills,
Thy woods and templed hills;
My heart with rapture thrills
Like that above.

Let music swell the breeze
And ring from all the trees
Sweet freedom's song;
Let mortal tongues awake;
Let all that breathe partake;
Let rocks their silence break,
The sound prolong.

Our father's God, to thee,
Author of liberty,
To thee we sing;
Long may our land be bright
With freedom's holy light;
Protect us by thy might
Great God, our King.

Written in 1832.

ADDRESS TO THE PEOPLE OF THE UNITED STATES, BY THE CONVENTION OF THE PEOPLE OF SOUTH CAROLINA.

[Columbia, 1832]. 16pp. "We, the people of South Carolina, assembled in Convention, have solemnly and deliberately declared, in our paramount sovereign capacity, that the Acts of Congress [of May 19, 1828, and July 14, 1832] . . . are unconstitutional, and therefore, absolutely void, and of no binding force within the limits of this State. . . ." Issued by James Hamilton, Jr., President of the Convention. (146) 150.00

Jackson, Andrew
MESSAGE . . . TRANSMITTING COPIES OF THE PROCLAMATION AND PROCEEDINGS IN RELATION TO SOUTH CAROLINA.
Wash., Jan. 16, 1833. 112pp. (147) 45.00

THE REPORTS AND ORDINANCES, OF THE CONVENTION OF THE PEOPLE OF SOUTH CAROLINA, ADOPTED AT ITS SESSION IN MARCH, 1833.
Columbia: A. S. Johnston, 1833. 19pp. Sewn. (148) 150.00

PROCLAMATION OF PRESIDENT JACKSON, IN RELATION TO NULLIFICATION; COUNTER-PROCLAMATION OF GOV. HAYNE OF S. CAROLINA; AND MESSAGE OF PRESIDENT JACKSON TO CONGRESS, IN RELATION TO THE NULLIFIERS.
Boston: Beals, Homer & Co., 1833. 108pp. Sewn. (149) 45.00

MR. CLAY'S BILL.
Broadsheet, 3pp., folio, printed in two columns, n.p., 1833. "The following is a copy of Mr. Clay's Bill in the form in which it was passed in the Senate. . . . A Bill to modify the act . . . imposing duties on imports." This extremely important event cleared the way for a peaceful settlement of the Nullification controversy. (150) 150.00

STATE PAPERS ON NULLIFICATION.
Boston: Dulton and Wentworth, 1834. 381pp. Calf. (151) 30.00

The theory of nullification was expounded as early as 1798-99 by Virginia and Kentucky, based on the theory that the Union was simply a compact among sovereign states. In the Webster-Hayne debate of 1830, the theoretical lines were clearly drawn; the issue for testing came in South Carolina under the leadership of John C. Calhoun. In 1832, Congress enacted a tariff act and South Carolina called a nullifcation convention which declared the act null and void in South Carolina.

President Andrew Jackson responded by denouncing nullification as treason and a Force Bill was passed by Congress enabling him to send troops to enforce the law. At the same time, the tariff was revised in a compromise manner to placate the Southerners and the Ordinance of Nullification was rescinded by a new convention. The final test of the theory would not come until the Civil War.

BLACK HAWK

Pendleton,Boston

Wakefield, John A.

HISTORY OF THE WAR BETWEEN THE UNITED STATES AND THE SAC AND FOX NATIONS OF INDIANS, AND PARTS OF OTHER DISAFFECTED TRIBES OF INDIANS.

Jacksonville, Ill.: Calvin Goudy, 1834. 142pp. *First edition.* Very fine copy in original half morocco, marbled boards. Howes W19. Bennett, p.75: "The records concerning this uprising are so vague that Wakefield's History, compiled from . . . a journal kept at the time, is very important."   (152) 350.00

Patterson, J. B. [ed.]

LIFE OF BLACK HAWK, EMBRACING THE . . . INDIAN WARS IN WHICH HE HAS BEEN ENGAGED . . . WITH AN ACCOUNT OF THE CAUSE AND GENERAL HISTORY OF THE LATE WAR, HIS SURRENDER AND CONFINEMENT AT JEFFERSON BARRACKS, AND TRAVELS THROUGH THE UNITED STATES: DICTATED BY HIMSELF.

Boston, 1834. 155pp. Original boards. Howes P120. "A classic statement of Indian resentment against white interlopers."—Charles Van Doren.   (153) 75.00

Another dismal chapter in American Indian relations, the Black Hawk War was fought with the Sauk and Fox Indians in Illinois and Wisconsin. In 1804 some self-appointed spokesmen for the two tribes traded for a pittance their tribes' title to over fifty million acres of land, consisting of the northeastern half of Illinois and much of Wisconsin and Missouri. In 1831, Chief Black Hawk's own village was pre-empted under this treaty and Black Hawk and a faction of the tribes threatened resistance.

Militia forced him across the Mississippi into Iowa, but in 1832 Black Hawk and several hundred Indians crossed back into Illinois to join the Winnebagoes in raising a corn crop. The American forces ordered him out, he refused, and the war began. A series of skirmishes followed, ending with a free-for-all battle at Bad Axe River, where the Black Hawk forces were virtually annihilated. The next month the United States compelled the Winnebago, Sauk, and Foxes to cede the rest of their lands in Wisconsin and eastern Iowa as a punishment. In 1833 Black Hawk was taken to meet President Jackson and in 1834 put in the custody of his rival, Chief Keokuk. He died in 1838.

EXPLORING EXPEDITION.

CORRESPONDENCE

Between J. N. REYNOLDS and the Hon. MAHLON DICKERSON, under the respective signatures of "Citizen" and "Friend to the Navy," touching the South Sea Surveying and Exploring Expedition; wherein the objects of the enterprise, and the causes which have delayed its departure, are canvassed. Originally published in the "New-York Times" of July, August, and September, 1837, and in the "New-York Courier and Enquirer" of December and January, 1837–38.

1835 [Reynolds and Wilkes Expeditions]

Reynolds, J. N.

VOYAGE OF THE UNITED STATES FRIGATE POTOMAC, UNDER THE COMMAND OF COMMODORE JOHN DOWNES, DURING THE CIRCUMNAVIGATION OF THE GLOBE IN THE YEARS, 1831-1834.

N.Y.: Harper & Brothers, 1835. 560pp. Original folding map. 9 plates, 5 of which are folding. Half morocco. Sabin 70434. Harbeck, p.121. Hill Collection, p.252. The Hill copy had the map in facsimile. Not in Howes. (154) 150.00

A BILL TO PROVIDE FOR AN EXPLORING EXPEDITION.

Broadside, 1p., folio, [Wash.], S. 175, March 21, 1836, lines numbered along left side. Original bill providing for the Wilkes Expedition. *Possibly unique;* no other recorded copy. (155) 125.00

Reynolds, J. N., and Mahlon Dickerson

EXPLORING EXPEDITION: CORRESPONDENCE . . . TOUCHING THE SOUTH SEA SURVEYING AND EXPLORING EXPEDITION.

[N.Y., 1838?] 151pp. Harbeck, p.121. (156) 125.00

EXPLORING EXPEDITION: LETTERS, DOCUMENTS, AND COMMUNICATIONS.

Wash., HED 147, 1838. 611pp. Uncut and unopened. The most important document on the beginnings of the Wilkes Expedition. Haskell 230. (157) 75.00

Wilkes, Charles

NARRATIVE OF THE UNITED STATES EXPLORING EXPEDITION, DURING THE YEARS 1838-1842.

Phila.: Lea and Blanchard, 1845. 5 volumes and Atlas volume. Illus. Color maps. Original cloth. Large octavo. Very nice set. *With an original Autograph Letter Signed, 1p., 4to, from Wilkes laid in.* Harbeck, p.114. Howes W414: "The first U.S. scientific expedition by sea. Wilkes sailed along and surveyed the whole Northwest coast and his exploring parties penetrated into the interior at many points." Hill, p.325: "This is the full text of the expedition's report. The atlas is much valued." Day #49. Taylor, p.13. Wheat 457, re Oregon map: "This map was in many respects the most detailed of this extensive area yet published . . . an accurate, really quite extraordinary map." (158) 325.00

Beginning in 1827, Jeremiah Reynolds began lobbying for a government-sponsored naval exploring expedition. His proposals met with considerable interest but protracted delays. In the early 1830's he accompanied the U.S. frigate Potomac on a world circumnavigation, publishing his report in 1835. Jonathan A. Hill states that "during her course of duty, the Potomac visited Rio de Janeiro, Cape Town, Quallah-Battoo, Sumatra, Batavia, Macao, Canton, Hawaii, Tahiti, Callao and Lima, the Galapagos Islands, and the Falkland Islands."

After his return, there were still further delays and political complications. Finally, the expedition was approved, but with Charles Wilkes as commander. Wilkes sailed in 1838 on the first official United States naval exploring expedition. Mortimer Adler writes: "Setting out in August with six ships, he was accompanied by a team of scientists in various fields. After stops in South America, islands of the South Pacific, and Australia, the squadron sailed through the Antarctic Ocean and made several successive sightings of land. Wilkes claimed on the basis of these observations to have discovered Antarctica as a Continent; though long disputed, his claim was later substantiated and the large region he had seen named Wilkes Land. The expedition sailed northward, visiting the Fiji and Hawaiian Islands, and made explorations along the North American coast that served to bolster U.S. claims to the Oregon Territory. After circling the globe westward, Wilkes and his party returned to America in 1842." The expedition was a tremendous success, having explored 280 islands in the Pacific, having discovered and laid out 1600 miles of Antarctica, having surveyed 800 miles of coast and rivers in the Pacific Northwest, and having presented concrete evidence of American prominence on the high seas.

TO THE CITIZENS OF TEXAS.

———※———

COMMANDANCY OF THE ALAMO, BEJAR, FEB. 24, 1836.

FELLOW-CITIZENS,

I am besieged by a thousand or more of the Mexicans, under Santa Ana. I have sustained a continual bombardment and cannonade, for twenty-four hours, and have not lost one man. The enemy have demanded a surrender at discretion, otherwise the garrison is to be put to the sword, if the fort is taken. I have answered the demand with a cannon shot, and our flag still waves proudly from the walls. *I shall never surrender nor retreat:* then I call on you, in the name of liberty, of patriotism, and of every thing dear to the American character, to come to our aid, with all possible despatch. The enemy are receiving reinforcements daily, and will, no doubt, increase to three or four thousands, in four or five days. Though this call may be neglected, I am determined to sustain myself as long as possible, and die like a soldier who never forgets what is due to his own honor and that of his country.

VICTORY OR DEATH.

W. BARRET TRAVIS,
Lieutenant-Colonel Commandant.

P. S. The Lord is on our side. When the enemy appeared in sight, we had not three bushels of corn; we have since found, in deserted houses, eighty or ninety bushels, and got into the walls twenty or thirty head of beeves.   T.

94

1836 [Fall of the Alamo]

Travis, William Barret

TO THE CITIZENS OF TEXAS.

Broadside, 1p., 4to, Commandancy of the Alamo, Bejar, Feb. 24, 1836. Streeter Texas 185: "This is the first separate printing of a great Texas document." The most famous document in Texas history: "Fellow-Citizens, I am besieged by a thousand or more of the Mexicans. . . . I shall never surrender nor retreat. . . . Victory or Death, W. Barret Travis."　(159) 5500.00

In the garrison of the Alamo in San Antonio de Bexar, Texas, a group of 187 men, including David Crockett and James Bowie, found themselves surrounded by an army of some six thousand men under the personal direction of Santa Anna, President of Mexico. Jim Bowie and William B. Travis were joint commanders, but Bowie was sick and incapacitated. On February 24, Travis sent out his appeal for help, in what has been called the most heroic letter ever written in America.

Dr. A. P. McDonald writes of the Travis letter that printed copies were not only distributed in Texas but also "the letter was read in New Orleans and it helped the recruiters organize more troops; it travelled on and was printed in newspapers as far away as New York, Philadelphia and Boston in a matter of weeks, and it brought enough help to have more than made the difference. . . . It is a letter of defiance, a letter of enduring fineness that made Travis more than an obscure garrison commander in a remote and hopeless outpost in a forgotten war. It made him a genuine personality of the American frontier, helped bring thousands of people to Texas, helped turn a war around that a decade later led into another conflict that added one quarter of the present territory of the United States. . . . The letter spoke to the American character . . . a fighting character. . . . Wherever man read it or heard about it, some of them began to get ready to answer the call."

A week later, on March 2, 1836, Sam Houston and a convention met at Washington-on-the-Brazos, declared Texas independent of Mexico, and founded the Republic of Texas. On March 6, Santa Anna stormed the Alamo, losing nearly 2000 men — nearly ten for one — and every single defender was massacred, heaped in a pile, and burned to ashes.

Irving, Washington

THE ROCKY MOUNTAINS; OR, SCENES, INCIDENTS, AND ADVENTURES IN THE FAR WEST; DIGESTED FROM THE JOURNAL OF CAPTAIN B. L. E. BONNEVILLE.

Phila.: Carey, Lea, & Blanchard, 1837. 2 volumes. Original cloth, printed paper labels. Two folding maps. *First edition, with an autographed slip from Irving laid in, dated New York, 1837.* B.A.L. 10151. Graff 2160. Rader 2028. Smith 5056. Larned 2020: ''An entertaining narrative of early travel and adventure in the West.'' Howes I85: ''The first account of the trapping expedition over the Sierras to California.'' Wagner-Camp 67: ''This book contains an account of the famous Walker expedition, presumably furnished by Bonneville himself.''   (160) 300.00

    Benjamin Louis Eulalie de Bonneville was born in Paris in 1796 in a home that was frequented by Lafayette, Condorcet, and Thomas Paine. Moving to America in 1802, Bonneville attended West Point, graduating in 1815. W. J. Ghent states: ''The fur trade had long interested him, and . . . in the fall of 1830 he interested several capitalists . . . in a project for a thorough exploitation of the fur country. . . . With an imposing force of 110 men, he left Fort Osage, Mo., for Green River. He spent more than three years in the mountains, sending detachments of trappers and hunters in every direction.'' John Jacob Astor was a backer of the enterprise.

    Meanwhile, the great American author, Washington Irving, had left for the West in 1832 and produced two books on his trips, *A Tour of the Prairies* and *Astoria.* When he produced *The Rocky Mountains* from Bonneville's journals, the result was a volume that was immensely successful.

ANCIENT AND MODERN REPUBLICS.

Tocqueville, Alexis de
DEMOCRACY IN AMERICA.
DEMOCRACY IN AMERICA, PART THE SECOND.
N.Y., 1838 and 1840. 2 volumes. Original cloth, one spine reinforced. Nice set. *First American edition.* Howes T278 and T279. Downs, Books That Changed America #5: "One of the most influential works of the 19th century — a monument in the intellectual history of the West." Printing and the Mind of Man 358n: "One of the most important texts in political literature."   (161) 400.00

Trollope, Frances M.
DOMESTIC MANNERS OF THE AMERICANS.
London: Whittaker, Treacher & Co., 1832. 2 volumes. Contemporary half morocco. *First edition.* Howes T357. Sadleir 3218.   (162) 175.00

Same, *first American edition.* N.Y., 1832. [18],325pp. With the rarely found 8 satirical plates. Original cloth, paper label. Contemporary review tipped in. Unusually fine copy of a fragile book. Sadleir 3218b.   (163) 125.00

Alexis de Tocqueville's reflections on his American tour have been called "the greatest work ever written on one country by a citizen of another." Daniel C. Gilman called it flatly "the best philosophical discussion of democracy." Tocqueville came to America in 1831, in fact, not to study it but to study democracy, feeling that in America he would find the political system destined to spread throughout the world.

His reflections have remained pertinent to our own times, and have helped us understand our system and ourselves. He said, "I know of no country, indeed, where the love of money has taken a stronger hold on the affections of men," and "I have never been more struck by the good sense and the practical judgment of the Americans than in the manner in which they elude the numberless difficulties resulting from their Federal Constitution."

Mrs. Trollope came to America in 1827 and stayed for nearly four years. When she returned to England she published one of the most scathing indictments of the United States ever written. "The author frankly discloses her dislike for this country, and the work so angered the American people that it stood for a half century as typical of English judgment of American life," writes Davis R. Dewey, who states that her "style is excellent and in spite of its prejudiced tone is of value to those who can bear criticism, with a calm temper." As H. T. Tuckerman was forced to admit, "the truth is, that Mrs. Trollope's powers of observation are remarkable. What she sees, she describes with vivacity, and often with accurate skill."

It was Tocqueville who made that most startling prediction: "The American relies upon personal interest to accomplish his ends, and gives free scope to the unguided exertions and common sense of the citizens; the Russian centers all the authority of society in a single arm: the principal instrument of the former is freedom; of the latter, servitude. Their starting point is different, and their courses are not the same; yet each of them seems to be marked out by the will of Heaven to sway the destinies of half the globe."

H. R. 557.

DECEMBER 17, 1846.

Read, and made the special order for Monday next.

Mr. DOUGLASS, from the Committee on the Territories, reported the following bill:

A BILL

For the admission of the State of Iowa into the Union.

Whereas the people of the Territory of Iowa did, on the eighteenth day of May, anno Domini eighteen hundred and forty-six, by a convention of delegates called and assembled for that purpose, form for themselves a constitution and State government—which constitution is republican in its character and features—and said convention has asked admission of the said Territory into the Union as a State, on an equal footing with the original States, in obedience to "An act for the admission of the States of Iowa and Florida into the Union," approved March third, eighteen hundred and forty-five, and "An act to define the boundaries of the State of Iowa, and to repeal so much of the act of the third of March, one thousand eight hundred and forty-five, as relates to the boundaries of Iowa," which said last act was approved August fourth, anno Domini eighteen hundred and forty-six: Therefore—

1   *Be it enacted by the Senate and House of Representatives*
2   *of the United States of America in Congress assembled,* That
3   the State of Iowa shall be one, and is hereby declared to be one,
4   of the United States of America, and admitted into the Union
5   on an equal footing with the original States in all respects
6   whatsoever.

Plumbe, John

SKETCHES OF IOWA AND WISCONSIN, TAKEN DURING A RESIDENCE OF THREE YEARS IN THOSE TERRITORIES.

St. Louis: Chambers, Harris & Knapp, 1839. 103pp. Folding map. Full morocco. *First edition.* The first book printed west of the Mississippi to propose a transcontinental railroad to the Pacific Coast. Missouri Imp. Inv. 250. Bradford 4430. Graff 3309. Howes P426: "Covers Iowa only; Wisconsin part was planned but never appeared."　　　　　(164) 2500.00

THE STATUTE LAWS OF THE TERRITORY OF IOWA, ENACTED BY THE FIRST SESSION OF THE LEGISLATIVE ASSEMBLY OF SAID TERRITORY, HELD AT BURLINGTON, 1838-39.

DuBuque: Russell and Reeves, 1839. 597,[1]pp. Half morocco. *First edition of the famous "Old Blue Book,"* which was for many years the law of all the Country West of the Rocky Mountains between the 42nd and 45th parallels. Not in Moffit. Fitzpatrick, p.19. Very rare and early Iowa imprint being preceded only by five others: two broadsides, a pamphlet, and two sets of 1838 laws.　　　　　(165) 475.00

CONSTITUTION FOR THE STATE OF IOWA.

Wash., SD3, Dec. 9, 1844. 15pp. This constitution was rejected because of boundaries proposed.　　　　　(166) 40.00

CONSTITUTION FOR THE STATE OF IOWA, ADOPTED IN CONVENTION, MAY 18, 1846.

Iowa City: Printed by Abraham H. Palmer, 1846. 20pp. Half calf. Harvard Tercent. Exh. 18: *First printing of the first constitution accepted by the voters."* Fitzpatrick, p.24. Not in Kuhlman. The main change is in area, which is cut to 56,147 square miles, of which Eberstadt 166:58 states: "Maybe that ain't hay, but it's one whale of a lot of corn!" Iowa was admitted under this constitution. Exceedingly rare.　　　　　(167) 1500.00

A BILL FOR THE ADMISSION OF THE STATE OF IOWA INTO THE UNION.

Broadsheet, 2pp., long folio, Wash., H.R. 557, Dec. 17, 1846, lines numbered along left side. In half morocco slipcase. Bill admitting Iowa into the Union, accomplished on Dec. 28. Possibly unique; no other copy located.　　　　　(168) 475.00

　　　　John Plumbe was born in Wales in 1809 and came to America in 1821, settling in Dubuque, Iowa in 1836. G. H. Genzmer says in *D.A.B.* that he "appears to have been the first responsible and effective advocate of a railway to the Pacific." He was also a pioneer photographer, starting a photography company in 1840, growing by 1845 to branches in fourteen cities. But he is best remembered for his book on Iowa, of which Genzmer states: "It is an enthusiastic description of the country, with much detailed information, and is now [1946] a rare book." In 1849 Plumbe went to California, returned in 1855, and committed suicide in Dubuque in 1857.

I . D. ƚ refused with full knowledge

(a) refund acc + attach = £1069 . H— told D. it was Mary

⧺ Thomas remembers the send   H. ƚ let h.

(b) H — o full inf. p. H.   Declaration.

[D. cannot see decl— & knew full act. de]

Sister knew acc . but care than decl?

Hutchins D. called after, Saw ye decl—. Told D. was

for money H. ƚ him to stop proc. of H. o Bird

when no such prosecution started.

No condition . D. very little.

D. called he to see Wh. Wh 2° contradict — agreed

the was dies[?]table .   D. but by assured in

her character — understood all round —

Began in Aug. & had the day q entry —

(c) Ag. advice of Mr. Garston.

(d) with recent recollection of those; can

(e) No attempt to explain to H —.

(f) Secret to be kept. Decl— off files

but here it to Reg —

Dana, Richard Henry, Jr.

TWO YEARS BEFORE THE MAST: A PERSONAL NARRATIVE OF LIFE AT SEA.

New York: Harper & Brothers, 1840. 483pp. Original tan muslin, a nice copy with some slight chipping to extremities of spine. *First edition,* binding issue with 121 titles listed on back cover. *With an original Autograph Letter Signed from Dana* to A. B. Merrill, Old State House, Aug. 5, 1841, 2pp., about Dana's brother, loosely inserted, and with *an original leaf of manuscript in Dana's hand,* 1p., 4to, including lists of words, synonyms, definitions, and notes. Cowan, p.156. Howes D49. Sabin 18448. Graff 998. Zamorano Eighty #26. B.A.L. 4434. Grolier American Hundred #46. Adams Herd #642. Peter Parley to Penrod, p.144. Dobie, p.101. Downs, Famous American Books #14.   (169) 850.00

Although accounts of sea voyages were frequently issued, few if any before this were written from the viewpoint of the common sailor. Dana sailed on the crew of the brig Pilgrim in 1834, but he took literary credentials along — scion of a famous Boston family, son of an author and editor, and student at Harvard, he made the trip hoping the hard work of a seaman would help restore his poor health. There was certainly plenty of hard work on the two years' tour to California and back; he wrote of the typical week: "Six days shall thou labor and do all thou art able, And on the seventh — holystone the decks and scrape the cable."

The book has been praised in many quarters. D. H. Lawrence called it "a very great book: contains a great extreme of knowledge, knowledge of the great element." Fullerton calls it "the greatest of American sea sagas." Cowan calls it "probably the most widely read book relating to California." J. Frank Dobie praised it as a cattle book, calling it "a classic on the hide and tallow trade."

When Dana returned he was just past twenty years old, and he went on to graduate at the top of his class at Harvard the next spring, as though he had never been away. He wrote his great classic and sent it to his friend William Cullen Bryant, who with difficulty sold it for $250 to Harper. It has seldom since been out of print, and of all 19th century books it ranks among the top for being as fascinating and gripping a tale today as when it first appeared.

Emerson, Ralph Waldo
ESSAYS.
ESSAYS: SECOND SERIES.
Boston: James Munroe and Company, 1841 and 1844. 2 volumes. Original cloth. Very good set. *First edition of each,* binding state with ''First Series'' and ''Second Series'' on the spines. B.A.L. 5189 and 5198. Grolier American Hundred #47. Downs, Famous Books #72. Johnson, High Spots of American Literature, p.32.   (170) 275.00

Emerson, Ralph Waldo
SOCIETY AND SOLITUDE.
Boston: Fields, Osgood, & Co., 1870. 300pp. Original green cloth. Very fine, bright copy, inscribed: ''William Henry Channing with affectionate regards of R. W. Emerson, June, 1870.'' *First edition, first state.* The C. W. Barrett copy, slipcased. B.A.L. 5260.   (171) 350.00

Ludwig Lewisohn said of Emerson that ''his mind and his perceptions were among the most lucid and unerring in the world.'' This same feeling was phrased by James Russell Lowell as: ''Emerson had a Greek head on right Yankee shoulders.'' Whittier claimed that Emerson told him that he thanked God every morning because he lived so near Boston. This came, of course, from a man who never saw Texas.

Of his *Essays,* Matthew Arnold called them ''the most important work done in prose'' in the 19th century. In them we find many phrases that are a part of the educated American's soul, particularly in the chapter on Self-Reliance. ''A foolish consistency is the hobgoblin of little minds.'' ''In every work of genius we recognize our own rejected thoughts.'' ''To be great is to be misunderstood.'' ''All history resolves itself into the biography of a few stout and earnest men.'' ''Whoso would be a man, must be a nonconformist.''

Emerson dominated the intellectual world in America during and after his prime. He gently slid into senility in the 1870's, but *Society and Solitude,* written ten years earlier, contains some of his best essays. In it he wrote: ''Hitch your wagon to a star.'' ''Every genuine work of art has as much reason for being as the earth and the sun.'' ''Can anybody remember when times were not hard and money not scarce?''

We owe much of our comprehension of civilized life to Emerson and his writings. It was he himself who said: ''In the highest civilization the book is still the highest delight. He who has once known its satisfaction is provided with a resource against calamity.''

DRAFT OF CONSTITUTION OF RHODE ISLAND . . . AS REVISED BY A COMMITTEE APPOINTED BY THE CONVENTION, ASSEMBLED AT PROVIDENCE, NOVEMBER, 1841.

Providence: Knowles & Vose, 1841. 26pp. Sewn. Working draft, lines numbered along left of each page, some pencilled alterations. Signed by N. Bullock on title. The Landholder's Constitution.   (172) 200.00

CONSTITUTION OF THE STATE OF RHODE ISLAND . . . AS ADOPTED BY THE CONVENTION, ASSEMBLED AT PROVIDENCE, NOVEMBER, 1841.

Providence: Knowles & Vose, 1842. 27pp.   (173) 200.00

THE CONSTITUTION OF THE STATE OF RHODE-ISLAND . . . AS ADOPTED BY THE CONVENTION, ASSEMBLED AT NEWPORT, SEPTEMBER, 1842.

Providence: Knowles and Vose, 1842. 24pp. Sewn. *First edition.* Kuhlman, p.70. The final reform constitution, which was adopted.   (174) 250.00

CHARTERS AND LEGISLATIVE DOCUMENTS, ILLUSTRATIVE OF RHODE-ISLAND HISTORY, SHOWING . . . THE RIGHTS OF SELF-GOVERNMENT . . .

Providence: Knowles & Vose, 1844. 68,[2]pp. Sewn. Uncut. Contains materials on the People's Constitution and the Landholder's Constitution.   (175) 60.00

Incredible as it may seem, up until 1841 Rhode Island was still using as its constitution the charter granted by Charles II in 1663. It limited the vote to landowners and their eldest sons, thus disfranchising more than half the adult male population. Under the leadership of Thomas W. Dorr, the discontented called a convention in October of 1841 and drew up a new "People's Constitution." A month later another crew met and framed a "Landholders' Constitution." In December a vote allowing all adult males accepted the first and in March, 1842, another vote rejected the second.

The regular state government continued to function, ignoring both, but in the spring of 1842 a new government was organized with Dorr as governor. The regular governor sent state troops to attack the Dorrites, stopped the movement, and imprisoned Dorr for awhile. Then a third constitution was drawn up and accepted, granting much wider male suffrage and other reforms.

Nicollet, I. N., and John C. Fremont

REPORT INTENDED TO ILLUSTRATE A MAP OF THE HYDROGRAPHICAL BASIN OF THE UPPER MISSISSIPPI RIVER.

Wash.: Blair and Rives, 1843. 170pp. Sen. Doc. 237, 26th Cong., 2nd Sess. Slipcased. Large folding map, prepared by John C. Fremont, slipcased separately. *First edition.* Howes N152. Wagner-Camp 98. Buck 339. Graff 3022. Wheat p.180 "a great map." Holliday 820: "Scarce and most interesting."   (176) 225.00

Fremont, John C.

A REPORT ON AN EXPLORATION OF THE COUNTRY LYING BETWEEN THE MISSOURI RIVER AND THE ROCKY MOUNTAINS.

Wash., SD243, 1843. 207pp. 6 plates. Map. *First edition.* Howes F371. Graff 1437. Wagner-Camp 95.   (177) 175.00

Fremont, John C.

REPORT OF THE EXPLORING EXPEDITION TO THE ROCKY MOUNTAINS IN THE YEAR 1842, AND TO OREGON AND NORTH CALIFORNIA IN THE YEARS 1843-44.

Wash., 1845. 693pp. 22 plates. Five maps, four folding. Original blind-stamped cloth, spine gilt. Fine copy. *First edition, first issue, Francis Parkman's copy,* signed twice by him and dated 1847, while he was writing his own great classic, with the Harvard–Francis Parkman Library bookplate, dated 1894, with release stamp. Grolier American Hundred #49. Wagner-Camp 115. Howes F370. Zamorano Eighty #39. Cowan, p.233. Rittenhouse 229. Larned 2036. Field 565. Graff 1436. A remarkable association copy of a great classic. (178) 1500.00

Parkman, Francis

THE CALIFORNIA AND OREGON TRAIL.

N.Y.: George P. Putnam, 1849. 448pp. plus adv. Original cloth. Very good copy. *First edition, with a short third person Autograph Letter Signed from Parkman inserted.* Howes P97. Field 1177. Wagner-Camp 170. Grolier American Hundred #58: "The classic account of the emigrant journey to the Rockies."   (179) 375.00

THE KNICKERBOCKER MAGAZINE [VOLS. 29-33].

N.Y., 1847-1849. Five complete volumes. Excellent set in contemporary half morocco. Contains the full text in 22 issues of the first appearance of Parkman's work, beginning in February, 1847, as "The Oregon Trail: or a Summer's Journey Out of Bounds, by a Bostonian" and ending in February, 1849.   (180) 225.00

Francis Parkman *ii 4j*

REPORT

OF

THE EXPLORING EXPEDITION

Fremont's first taste of the West came as a lieutenant under J. N. Nicollet in the exploration of the area between the Mississippi and the Missouri. Fremont helped prepare the map, which is one of the most superb cartographic achievements of the era. After returning, Fremont met Thomas Hart Benton and in a celebrated courtship married his daughter Jessie. Benton thereafter helped Fremont obtain government aid on his famous exploring expeditions.

In 1842 Fremont led the important exploration to the Wind River chain of the Rockies. He explored the Oregon Trail and South Pass, with the assistance of Kit Carson. His report, in which Jessie Fremont's literary hand is clearly seen, brought him immense popularity and was an important influence in the negotiations with the British over Oregon.

His most important expedition began in May, 1843, and was again accompanied by Kit Carson. They explored the Salt Lake Valley and much of the Oregon and California area. He returned in August, 1844, and "his return was one of the sensations of the day. His second report was as detailed, vivid, and readable as the first report, with much careful scientific observation, and it showed that the Oregon Trail was not difficult and that the Northwest was fertile and desirable."

One of the many people influenced by Fremont's activities was a young man named Francis Parkman, Jr. Even in college, stated his classmate Edward Wheelwright, he "showed symptoms of 'Injuns' on the brain." In April of 1846 Parkman began one of the truly great adventures ever taken by an educated man in the West, travelling along the Oregon Trail and returning in October, 1846. He began publishing in February, 1847, his *The California and Oregon Trail,* reissued many times under the shorter title of *The Oregon Trail.* W. M. Davis wrote of it: "This is one of the classics of western narratives. . . . No other book on the West has enjoyed equal popularity." Bernard DeVoto called it "one of the exuberant masterpieces of American literature."

The works of Fremont and Parkman encouraged literally thousands of settlers to make the trip west on the Oregon Trail, and many a pioneer cursed these two great adventurers along the way and blessed them after the dangerous trip was over.

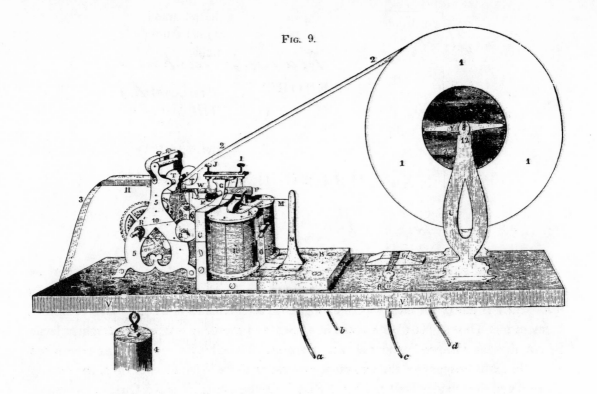

FIG. 9.

1844 [The Telegraph]

Morse, Samuel F. B.

THE TELEGRAPH: A LETTER FROM PROFESSOR MORSE, RELATIVE TO THE MAGNETIC TELEGRAPH.

Wash., HD24, 1844. 18pp. Describes the telegraph and proposes establishment of a national chain of telegraph wires. (181) 45.00

Vail, Alfred

DESCRIPTION OF THE AMERICAN ELECTRO MAGNETIC TELEGRAPH, NOW IN OPERATION BETWEEN THE CITIES OF WASHINGTON AND BALTIMORE.

Wash., J. & G. S. Gideon, 1845. 24pp. Illus. Includes the *first appearance of the Morse Code.* Morse assisted in writing this pamphlet. (182) 75.00

Jones, Alexander
HISTORICAL SKETCH OF THE ELECTRIC TELEGRAPH: INCLUDING ITS RISE AND PROGRESS IN THE U.S.
N.Y.: George P. Putnam, 1852. 194pp. Original cloth. *First edition, inscribed by the author.*   (184) 85.00

HISTORY GETTING RIGHT, ON THE INVENTION OF THE AMERICAN ELECTRO-MAGNETIC TELEGRAPH.
N.p., 1872. 21pp. Sewn. Controversy over who invented the telegraph, with letter of and much on Prof. L. D. Gale, who assisted Morse. With an original Autograph Letter Signed, 1p., small 4to, May 28, 1872, from Prof. Gale about the pamphlet.   (185) 150.00

THE DECISION OF THE GREAT TELEGRAPH SUIT OF SAMUEL F. B. MORSE AND ALFRED VAIL VS. FRANCIS O. J. SMITH, IN THE SUPERIOR COURT OF THE STATE OF NEW YORK.
N.Y., [1858]. 30pp. Original printed wrappers. ''One of the most remarkable cases to be found in the judicial records of any State, or country.''   (183) 125.00

Group of five early telegrams, 1848-1853, each in original printed telegram envelope and on printed telegraph stationery. The earliest, Providence, 1848, has 20 printed lines of telegraphic regulations. Another, ''Morse's Line, New-York and Boston Telegraph Assn.,'' 1851, has 29 lines of rules and regulations. Interesting and rare.   (186) 125.00

Samuel F. B. Morse was by profession an artist, but ''at the cost of twelve years of hard work and miserable poverty, produced the first practicable telegraph instrument.'' After years of promotion, Morse finally got Congress to appropriate funds for an experimental line between Washington and Baltimore. On May 24, 1844, the line was formally opened when Morse sent his partner Alfred Vail the message, ''What hath God wrought!''

After several years Congress declined to acquire the patent for the government, mostly on the advice of Cave Johnson, who showed the perspicacity of most other Postmasters General by announcing that the telegraph had no future. Morse finally received fortune and worldwide fame as telegraph lines gradually came into use everywhere. He was tormented by litigation over the patents, especially by F. O. J. Smith, a former Congressman who had helped in the early promotion; Smith ''proved the most unscrupulous and implacable, pursuing the inventor even to his death-bed. Morse's rights were upheld in the courts, and . . . otherwise he enjoyed the acclaim, honors, and emoluments of a great inventor and public personage.''

ALPHABET.

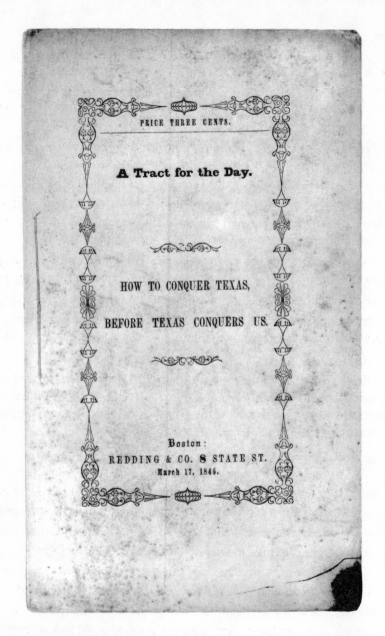

PRICE THREE CENTS.

A Tract for the Day.

HOW TO CONQUER TEXAS,

BEFORE TEXAS CONQUERS US.

Boston:
REDDING & CO. 8 STATE ST.
March 17, 1845.

1845 [Texas Annexation]

JOINT RESOLUTION DECLARING THE TERMS ON WHICH CONGRESS WILL ADMIT TEXAS INTO THE UNION AS A STATE.

Wash., Senate Res. 10, Jan. 13, 1845. 3pp. Folio. In half morocco slipcase.   (187) 3000.00

Hale, Edward Everett
HOW TO CONQUER TEXAS, BEFORE TEXAS CONQUERS US.

Boston: Redding & Co., March 17, 1845. 16pp. Original printed wrappers. Streeter Texas 1583.   (188) 285.00

108

LAWS PASSED AT THE EXTRA SESSION OF THE NINTH CONGRESS, OF THE REPUBLIC OF TEXAS.

Washington-on-the-Brazos: Miller & Cushney, 1845. 22, [5]pp. Special session to consider transferring Texan sovereignty to the U.S. Includes "Joint Resolution Giving Consent . . . to the Annexation of Texas to the United States," June 23, 1845, and other related acts. Streeter Texas 652.   (189) 450.00

THE CONSTITUTION OF THE STATE OF TEXAS.

Wash., HED16, Dec. 9, 1845. 28pp. Half morocco. Streeter Texas 1613. The first state constitution of Texas.   (190) 125.00

For ten years Texas maintained its independence as a successful republic, establishing treaties with Britain, France, the Netherlands, and other nations. But the Texans from the beginning had desired to join the Union, and continued to petition for annexation in spite of British guarantees to aid in sustaining Texan independence. By 1842, Texas was claiming that her boundaries extended to the Pacific Ocean and northwest almost to Canada.

In 1844 an annexation treaty was rejected by the U.S. Senate, but in 1845, after Democratic victories in the Congressional elections the previous fall, Congress offered statehood to Texas. Texas accepted the terms offered, formed a constitution, and was admitted to the Union by Joint Resolution.

New England generally opposed the measure and was furious over the action. John Quincy Adams fought annexation for many years, and his grandson later explained: "Texas, it must be remembered, was the American Botany Bay. It was filled with speculators, adventurers, fugitives from debt and the law, and ruffians generally. . . . G.T.T. in those days had a well understood significance — Gone (absconded) to Texas. The New England element was, therefore wholly justified in exerting its every effort to prevent such a community association and moral partnership. It failed, and the results of its failure are writ large in our subsequent annals. . . . Judging by your narrative, one would suppose that when we introduced Texas into the Union we introduced a community at least respectable. Such was not the fact. It was immoral, lawless, pro-slavery, uneducated, grasping, and generally brutal, — in a word, half-civilized. . . ."

The uneducated and grasping Texans entered the Union on terms that were little short of incredible. Texas was allowed to divide itself into five states any time it chose to do so. It was allowed to keep all of its extensive public lands, which even after New Mexico, Colorado, and other areas had been chiseled off amounted to more than a hundred million state-owned acres. Its entire public debt as a nation was paid off in the settlement over its boundaries. Since it was a nation when it entered, it claimed, and in the famous Tidelands Act of 1953 maintained, its ownership of offshore minerals for 10½ miles instead of 3 miles for other coastal states.

In return, the United States got Texas in all its glory — although she soon had to fight a war with Mexico in order to sustain that ownership. Sam Houston negotiated this deal for Texas, and we thank him every time tax season approaches.

29th CONGRESS,
1st SESSION.

H. R. 5.

IN THE HOUSE OF REPRESENTATIVES.

JANUARY 26, 1846.

On motion of Mr. THOMAS BUTLER KING,

Ordered, That the following joint resolution, (No. 5,) and all amendments heretofore proposed to the same, be printed.

JOINT RESOLUTION

Of notice to Great Britain to "annul and abrogate" the convention between Great Britain and the United States of the sixth of August, eighteen hundred and twenty-seven, relative to the country "on the northwest coast of America, westward of the Stony mountains," commonly called Oregon.

1   *Resolved by the Senate and House of Representatives of*

2   *the United States of America in Congress assembled,* That

3   the President of the United States forthwith cause notice to be

4   given to the government of Great Britain that the convention

5   between the United States and Great Britain, concerning the

6   territory of Oregon, of the sixth of August, eighteen hundred

7   and twenty-seven, signed at London, [shall be annulled and ab-

8   rogated twelve months after the expiration of the said notice,

9   conformably to the second article of the said convention of the

10   sixth of August, eighteen hundred and twenty-seven

AMENDMENTS PENDING.

Mr. C. J. INGERSOLL proposes to strike out the portion enclosed in brackets, and insert the following :

1   *Shall be annulled and abrogated at the expiration of the*

2   *term of twelve months from and after said notice shall be given,*

TREATY

BETWEEN

HER MAJESTY

AND THE

UNITED STATES OF AMERICA,

FOR THE

SETTLEMENT OF THE OREGON BOUNDARY.

Signed at Washington, June 15, 1846.

Presented to both Houses of Parliament by Command of Her Majesty.
1846.

LONDON:
PRINTED BY T. R. HARRISON.

(106)

JOINT RESOLUTION OF NOTICE TO GREAT BRITAIN TO ANNUL AND ABROGATE THE CONVENTION ... RELATIVE TO ... OREGON.

Wash., 1846. 5pp. Large folio, lines numbered along left side. Extremely rare. Unrecorded.
(191) 750.00

TREATY BETWEEN HER MAJESTY AND THE UNITED STATES OF AMERICA, FOR THE SETTLEMENT OF THE OREGON BOUNDARY, SIGNED AT WASHINGTON, JUNE 15, 1846.

London: Printed by T. R. Harrison, 1846. [4]pp. Large folio. Presented to both Houses of Parliament by Command of Her Majesty. Signed by Richard Parkenham for Britain and James Buchanan for the United States.
(192) 3750.00

CORRESPONDENCE RELATIVE TO THE NEGOTIATION OF THE QUESTION OF DISPUTED RIGHT TO THE OREGON TERRITORY, ON THE NORTH-WEST COAST OF AMERICA; SUBSEQUENT TO THE TREATY OF WASHINGTON OF AUGUST 9, 1842.

London: Printed by T. R. Harrison, 1846. iv,71pp. Large folio. Presented to both Houses of Parliament by Command of Her Majesty. Official documents from November 15, 1842, to March 3, 1846. Howes C105. Smith 1496.
(193) 1750.00

Browne, Peter Arnell
A LECTURE ON THE OREGON TERRITORY: THE TITLE OF THE UNITED STATES TO ITS SOVEREIGNTY, ITS CAPABILITIES AND VALUE TO OUR COUNTRY, AND THE NECESSITY OF AN IMMEDIATE SETTLEMENT OF IT FROM THE STATES.

Phila., 1843. 20pp. Half morocco. *First edition.* Howes B879. Smith 1197.   (194) 650.00

Wilkes, George
THE HISTORY OF OREGON, GEOGRAPHICAL AND POLITICAL . . . A THOROUGH EXAMINATION OF A NATIONAL RAILROAD . . . TO WHICH IS ADDED A JOURNAL OF THE EVENTS OF THE CELEBRATED EMIGRATING EXPEDITION OF 1843. . . .

N.Y.: William H. Colyer, 1845. 127,[1]pp. Folding map. *First edition.* Graff 4657. Smith 11005. Wagner-Camp 119. Howes W418.
(195) 1250.00

Robertson, Wyndham
OREGON, OUR RIGHT AND TITLE: CONTAINING AN ACCOUNT OF THE CONDITION OF THE OREGON TERRITORY.

Wash., 1846. 203,[24]pp. Folding map. Contemporary half morocco. *First edition.* Cowan, p.192. Smith 8705. Howes R359. One of the best and rarest earliest histories of the Pacific Northwest, with much source material unavailable elsewhere.
(196) 1250.00

A BILL TO ESTABLISH THE TERRITORIAL GOVERNMENT OF OREGON.
Wash., 1848. 16pp. Large folio, lines numbered along left side. Extremely rare. Unrecorded. (197) 500.00

CONSTITUTION FOR THE STATE OF OREGON, PASSED BY THE CONVENTION, SEPT. 18, 1857.
Salem: Asahel Bush, Printer, 1857. 23pp. Sewn, as issued. In half morocco slipcase. Last leaf in facsimile. Kuhlmann, p.66. McMurtrie 134. A great document in the history of the Pacific Northwest, this is the first official printing of Oregon Constitution, covering an area that included all of Idaho and western Montana, and part of Washington. (198) 1250.00

Each year after 1842 saw large numbers of pioneers travelling the Oregon trail to settle in Oregon. Since 1818, the territory south of 50°40' and west of the Rockies had been held jointly by England and the United States. Frequent negotiations failed to settle the boundary, until in 1844 the question became a prime issue in the Presidential campaign. Polk was elected under the slogan "Fifty-four Forty or Fight." When the Treaty was finally agreed to in June, 1846, a compromise at the 49th parallel settled the vexing problem once and for all. The United States got the rich area south of the line and England got Vancouver Island and the area to the north — a friendly treaty without starting another war between Britain and America. It covered the area now including Washington, Oregon, Montana, and Idaho. In 1848 Oregon Territory was created, in 1857 a constitution was written, and in 1859 statehood was granted.

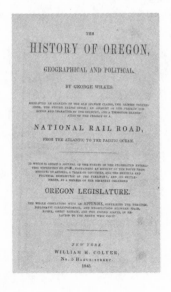
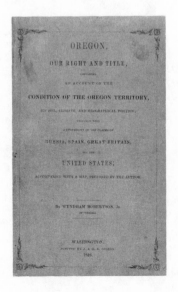
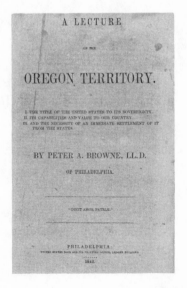

Washington 19 January 1849.

My dear Sir /

I have received your letter of the 19th Instant & would most gladly serve your son in the manner which you indicate, if this were in my power. The President has no power to appoint a Notary Public in California or to make any other civil appointments in that territory; & I very much fear that Congress will adjourn without establishing a territorial Government there. For this we are indebted to the Wilmot proviso & the free soil agitation.

If the President possessed the power I should urge the appointment of Dr. Guier strongly as it would afford me peculiar pleasure to afford you some token of my regard before the close of the present administration.

from your friend
very respectfully
James Buchanan

George Guier Esq

SPEECH OF MR. WILMOT, OF PENNSYLVANIA, ON HIS AMENDMENT RESTRICTING SLAVERY FROM TERRITORY HEREAFTER ACQUIRED . . .
Bound with:
THE WILMOT PROVISO: BILL AND EXPLANATION, BY PRESTON KING.
Wash., 1847. 8pp. and 8pp. Bound together in half morocco, Wilmot's speech contained the original address leaf, *signed and franked by Wilmot,* and the other also containing the original address leaf, *signed and franked by King.*   (199) 250.00

Buchanan, James
[LETTER ABOUT THE WILMOT PROVISO AND CALIFORNIA].
Original Autograph Letter Signed, 1p., 4to, as Secretary of State, Washington, January 19, 1849. The future President states his inability to appoint officials, ''in California or to make any other civil appointments in that territory: & I very much fear that Congress will adjourn without establishing a Territorial Government there. For this we are indebted to the Wilmot Proviso & the free soil agitation. If the President [Polk] possessed the power I would urge the appointment . . . to afford you some token of my regard before the close of the present administration. . . .'' Congress failed to create a territorial government for California, leading to great civil disorder and to the formation of the notorious Vigilance Committees there.
                    (200) 385.00

Foreseeing a successful conclusion to the Mexican War, Congress began to plan for accepting territories to be acquired from Mexico. David Wilmot, an obscure Pennsylvania Congressman, prompted and guided by the powerful Congressman, Preston King, introduced a bill requiring that ''neither slavery nor involuntary servitude shall ever exist in any part of said territory.'' The result was a national debate that shook the country. The House passed the Proviso, but the Senate debated and adjourned without taking a vote. The next session brought another fight over the matter, in which the House again passed the Proviso but the Senate voted it down. Nevertheless, the principle enunciated in the Proviso polarized sectional debate thereafter. The modern Republican Party was founded upon the principle, and Abraham Lincoln was nominated on a platform pledged to carry it out.

The fight was especially hard on the settlers in the far west, after the conquest of California. Unable to enter the Union as a state because of the long debate over the Proviso, anarchy prevailed as no constituted California government could obtain Congressional approval. Vigilance committees and mob violence were the result. In San Francisco, a murderer named John Jenkins was captured by a mob and within an hour ''tried by a jury of the highest respectability'' and hanged immediately in the Plaza, after being given a brandy and cigar.

1848 [Treaty of Guadalupe Hidalgo]

THE TREATY BETWEEN THE UNITED STATES AND MEXICO, THE PRO-CEEDINGS OF THE SENATE THEREON . . . WITH CORRESPONDENCE . . . AND OTHER PAPERS . . . FROM WHICH THE INJUNCTION OF SECRESY [SIC] HAS BEEN REMOVED.

Wash., Sen. Exec. Doc. 52, 30th Cong., 1st Sess., May 31, 1848. 384pp. Howes M565. *First edition in English.* (201) 150.00

MESSAGE FROM THE PRESIDENT OF THE UNITED STATES, COMMUNICATING A COPY OF THE TREATY WITH THE MEXICAN REPUBLIC, OF FEBRUARY 2, 1848, AND OF THE CORRESPONDENCE IN RELATION THERETO, AND RECOMMENDING MEASURES FOR CARRYING THE SAME INTO EFFECT.

Wash., Sen. Exec. Doc. 60, 30th Cong., 1st Sess., July 6, 1848. 74pp. (202) 85.00

When Mexico refused to acknowledge Texas' annexation to the United States, war began in 1846. After victories by Gen. Zachary Taylor in northern Mexico and the capture of Mexico City by Gen. Winfield Scott, Mexico sued for peace. The Treaty of Guadalupe Hidalgo, lopsided in favor of the United States, not only ended the Mexican War but secured Texas and added to our national domain Arizona, New Mexico, and California. The boundaries of the United States now consisted of the whole middle section of the North American continent.

The treaty included payment of fifteen million dollars for California, bargained away by Mexico almost at the very moment gold was being discovered there.

1849 [California Gold Rush]

Robinson, Fayette

CALIFORNIA AND ITS GOLD REGIONS, WITH A . . . VIEW OF THE COUNTRY . . . THE U.S. MAIL STEAM PACKETS TO CALIFORNIA, ALSO THE VARIOUS OVERLAND ROUTES.

N.Y.: Stringer & Townsend, 1849. 138,[6]pp. Folding map. Original yellow printed wrappers, bound in half morocco. *Large paper, untrimmed copy. First edition, first issue.* Cowan, p.537. Graff 3527. Howes R366. Jones 1215. Wheat Gold Rush 168: "One of the best of the earliest books on California printed for sale to goldseekers." (203) 350.00

Eckfeldt, J. R., and W. E. DuBois

NEW VARIETIES OF GOLD AND SILVER COINS, COUNTERFEIT COINS, AND BULLION, WITH MINT VALUES.

Phila.: Published by the authors, and for sale . . . at Panama and San Francisco, 1850. 60,[1]pp. Two plates, one in color. In half morocco slipcase. *Contains a packet of original gold nuggets* to be used for telling real from fool's gold. Cowan, p.76. Wheat, Gold Rush

#67: "Actual samples of California gold . . . render this little book an extraordinary and colorful souvenir of the Gold Rush." (204) 1850.00

M'Collum, Dr. William
CALIFORNIA AS I SAW IT: ITS NEW CITIES AND VILLAGS [SIC], ITS RAPID ACCESSION OF POPULATION, ITS SOIL, CLIMATE, AND PRODUCTIONS: PENCILLINGS BY THE WAY OF ITS COLD AND GOLD DIGGERS! AND INCIDENTS OF TRAVEL BY LAND AND WATER.
Buffalo: George H. Derby & Co., 1850. 72pp. Original printed front wrapper. In half-morocco slipcase. Cowan, p.146. Wheat, Gold Rush #131. Howes M55: "One of the most authentic contemporary narratives of California in the first year of the gold rush." *One of only six known copies.* (205) 6500.00

Delavan, James
NOTES ON CALIFORNIA AND THE PLACERS: HOW TO GET THERE AND WHAT TO DO AFTERWARDS.
N.Y.: H. Long & Brother, 1850. 128pp. Two lithographic plates. Boards. *First edition.* One of Henry R. Wagner's "Twenty Rarest and Most Important Books on California." Cowan, p.66. Graff 1044. Howes D237. Wheat, Gold Rush #58: "Lively account by a returned Californian of his experience in the American River diggings." (206) 1500.00

Kip, Leonard
CALIFORNIA SKETCHES, WITH RECOLLECTIONS OF THE GOLD MINES.
Albany: Erastus H. Pease & Co., 1850. 57pp. Half morocco. *First edition.* Graff 2343. Cowan, p.331. Wheat, Gold Rush #119: "A rare and interesting pamphlet." Howes K174. By the brother of the Bishop of California. (207) 850.00

Benton, J. A.
CALIFORNIA AS SHE WAS: AS SHE IS: AS SHE IS TO BE.
Sacramento: Placer Times Press, 1850. Original printed wrappers. Wagner California Imprints #46: "Second book printed in Sacramento." Greenwood 161. Cowan, p.48. A superlatively rare historical discourse. (208) 2250.00

From newly-won California came the cry of "gold, gold!" and the rush was on. Forty-niners headed for California in 1849 to make their fortunes. Both of the two routes — around the Horn or across the Rockies — were treacherous and lengthy journeys, taking months of hardships to accomplish. Thousands made the trip; many survived the journey and staked a claim; a few struck it rich.

To aid both the novice prospector and the experienced miner, guides were issued that are now great rarities. In the Eckfeldt volume were placed a few nuggets of the real thing — precious relics of some of the first gold discovered in the fabulous California Gold Rush.

formly, but appears in specks or clots through the mass of metal. The amount of platinum in the case mentioned, was 47 parts per thousand.

The alloy of the gold ordinarily, is wholly silver, with a little iron. It is the coating of the oxide of iron which gives the gold its rich hue, almost resembling that of fine gold. As that is removed in melting, the metal comes out so much paler than before, that persons unacquainted with the matter might suspect a wilful admixture of silver. The people of California understand this, from the comparison of bars and coins made there, with the native grains. We need not send coals to Newcastle; but on our side of the Union, small samples will be interesting.

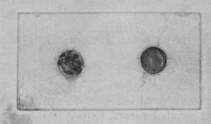

V. RECAPITULATION OF THE NET MINT VALUE OF GOLD AND SILVER COINS, ISSUED WITHIN TWENTY-FIVE YEARS PAST.

N.B. Inquiry has been frequently made at

Clay, Henry

SPEECH OF THE HON. HENRY CLAY, OF KENTUCKY, ON TAKING UP HIS COMPROMISE RESOLUTIONS ON THE SUBJECT OF SLAVERY.

New York: Stringer & Townsend, 1850. 32pp. Yellow printed wrappers, bound in three-quarter calf, with the original address leaf, *signed and franked by Clay.* Includes the text of the Compromise Resolutions. "Mr. President, never on any former occasion have I risen under feelings of such painful solicitude. . . ." (209) 125.00

Webster, Daniel

SPEECH OF MR. WEBSTER ON MR. CLAY'S RESOLUTIONS, DELIVERED IN THE SENATE OF THE UNITED STATES, MARCH 7, 1850.

Wash.: Gideon & Co., 1850. 15pp. Half morocco. *First printing, with the original address leaf signed and franked by Webster.* Dumond p.114. "Mr. President, I wish to speak to-day, not as a Massachusetts man, nor as a Northern man, but as an American. . . . I speak to-day for the preservation of the Union. 'Hear me for my cause.'" (210) 175.00

Webster, Daniel

SPEECH . . . IN REPLY TO MR. HAYNE.

Wash.: Printed by Gales & Seaton, 1830. Sewn. *First edition.* Howes W200: "Most famous American oration of the 19th century." (211) 150.00

Daniel Webster held one goal above all others — the union of the United States. Throughout his long and splendid career he rose many times to quell sectionalism and internal strife; twice he made orations that rose above politics to heights of greatness. The first was in 1830, the second in 1850. Webster's reply to Hayne in 1830 was one of the greatest orations ever delivered on the floor of Congress, and the Webster–Hayne Debate was one of the most significant constitutional arguments ever held in Congress. Robert Y. Hayne of South Carolina argued for states' rights and Daniel Webster argued for the theory of nationalism.

Samuel A. Foot had introduced on December 29, 1829, a resolution for gradual restrictions on the sale of federal lands, and Thomas Hart Benton attacked such a policy as harmful to the West. Hayne hoped for a fusion of southern and western interests to defeat the East, but was led cleverly by Webster into a debate of states' rights, a theory he deplored. He showed the error of each separate state being able to interpret the Constitution as it saw fit, and maintained that the Constitution was the work of the people as a whole.

His ringing close made his speech immortal: "God grant that . . . when my eyes shall be turned to behold for the last time the sun in heaven, may I not see him shining on the broken and dishonored fragments of a once glorious Union. . . . Let their last feeble and lingering glance rather behold the gorgeous ensign of the republic . . . everywhere spread all over in characters of living light, blazing on all its ample folds . . . that sentiment, dear to every true American heart — Liberty *and* Union, now and forever, one and inseparable!''

Henry Clay, returning to Congress after a seven-year absence, introduced his famous set of compromise resolutions on January 29, 1850, in a final effort to remove the slavery issue from contention and resolve the many national problems created by it. The Compromise Measures dealt with California, Texas, Mexican cession territory, slave trade, and the fugitive slave laws, aiming at an equitable settlement and truce. President Zachary Taylor, Jefferson Davis, William H. Seward, Charles Sumner, and John C. Calhoun fought the compromises, while Clay, Sam Houston, Lewis Cass, and Stephen A. Douglas supported them.

On March 7, 1850, Webster rose in the Senate once more to deliver an unforgettable address, ''Mr. President, I wish to speak to-day, not as a Massachusetts man, nor as a Northern man, but as an American. . . . I speak to-day for the preservation of the Union. 'Hear me for my cause.' '' Webster's support carried the measure, a valiant but futile attempt to avoid the dreadful war that was fast approaching.

1851 [Call Me Ishmael!]

Melville, Herman
MOBY DICK; OR, THE WHALE.
N.Y.: Harper & Brothers, 1851. [34],634,[8]pp. Original cloth. *First edition,* issue with sides stamped in blind with heavy rule frame, yellow endpapers, which have ''Thomas Melville'' written in ink on the front flyleaf. A few minor repairs to spine. In half morocco slipcase. B.A.L. 13664. Wright II-1701. Johnson, High Spots of American Literature, p.57. Mumey, Rare Books 374. Grolier American Hundred #60.   (212) 1450.00

Generally considered the most fascinating story of the sea ever written, *Moby Dick* is one of the world's great classics. Melville spent four years in the South Seas, 1841-1844, the great adventure of his life—settling thereafter on a farm near his friend Nathaniel Hawthorne. The year 1851 saw the publication of Hawthorne's *The House of Seven Gables,* which was highly successful, and Melville's *Moby Dick* (dedicated to Hawthorne), which was a flop. *Moby Dick* was misunderstood by the critics and ignored by the public. A short time later, Harpers' warehouse burned, destroying the plates and most copies of the book. Melville died almost forgotten. It was nearly a hundred years before *Moby Dick* was finally recognized as ''the most eminent American novel'' (Herzberg, *Encyc. Amer. Lit.*) and as ''one of the ten greatest novels ever written'' (W. Somerset Maugham). As A. S. W. Rosenbach wrote, ''*Moby Dick* will always remain the masterpiece and the guiding light for all writers of the mystery and lure of the ocean.''

Stowe, Harriet Beecher

UNCLE TOM'S CABIN; OR, LIFE AMONG THE LOWLY.

Boston: John P. Jewett, 1852. 2 volumes. Original cloth. Some wear; spine chipped. *First edition, first issue,* with an original Autograph Quotation Signed by Stowe tipped in, 9 lines, 12 mo. Wright II-2401. Johnson, High Spots of American Literature. Grolier American Hundred #61. Grolier English Hundred #91. Printing and the Mind of Man #519.

(213) 950.00

Same, *first Edinburgh edition,* 1853. Inscribed and signed by Harriet Beecher Stowe and by her husband, Edinburgh, April 19, 1853. Fine copy in original pictorial cloth, gilt extra, all edges gilt, with 130 wood engravings by Matthew Sears. (214) 225.00

Smith, W. L. G.

LIFE AT THE SOUTH; OR, "UNCLE TOM'S CABIN" AS IT IS, BEING NARRA-TIVES, SCENES, AND INCIDENTS IN THE REAL "LIFE OF THE LOWLY."

Buffalo: Geo. H. Derby, 1852. 519pp. Original cloth, gilt. Fine copy. *First edition.* Wright III-2278. Howes S715. (215) 85.00

Ker, Leander

SLAVERY CONSISTENT WITH CHRISTIANITY, WITH AN INTRODUCTION EMBRACING A NOTICE OF THE "UNCLE TOM'S CABIN" MOVEMENT IN ENGLAND.

Weston, Missouri: Finch & O'Gorman, 1853. 36pp. Later boards. Revised edition. "Such productions as 'Uncle Tom's Cabin,' in which romantic fiction and gross misrepresentation occupy the place of truth . . . elicit false sentiments, and set at work false principles, that, in their blind and ignorant career, may result in consequences the most fearful and fatal."

(216) 275.00

Excellent collection of nine original large folio sheet music pieces, some with pictorial covers, all issued in 1852, all by different composers and publishers, as follows:

Uncle Tom's Cabin Song
Uncle Tom's Lament for Eva
Uncle Tom's Song & Chorus
Uncle Tom's Glimpse of Glory
St. Clare to Little Eva in Heaven
I am Going There; or, The Death of Little Eva
The Death of St. Clare
Eva to Her Papa
Eva's Parting

(217) 200.00

When this work was published in March of 1852, the entire edition was sold out in 48 hours. Hundreds of printings followed, and when Harriet Beecher Stowe visited the White House ten years later, Abraham Lincoln leaned down to her and said, "So, you're the little lady who wrote the book that made this big war."

There was more than a little truth in the statement; Kurt Vonnegut recently called Stowe the "only writer in history who had an effect on the course of world affairs." The Civil War may have been and probably was inevitable, but *Uncle Tom's Cabin* made it a certainty. Never before in literary history had a work of fiction so totally grasped a nation, making it in Longfellow's words "one of the greatest triumphs recorded in literary history."

Mrs. Stowe's son later wrote about its appearance: "Like the kindling of a mighty conflagration, the sky was all aglow with the resistless tide of emotion that swept all before it . . . till it seemed as if the whole world scarcely thought or talked of anything else." Its influence was equally great in Europe, where it altered public opinion about slavery and about the approaching American Civil War. In America, it literally made impossible the enforcement of the Fugitive Slave Law, and Charles Sumner wrote: "If *Uncle Tom's Cabin* had not been written, Abraham Lincoln could not have been elected President of the United States."

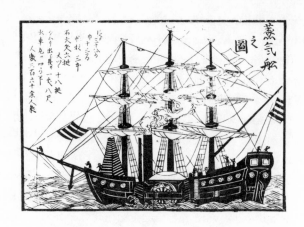

1853   [Perry's Expedition to Japan]

SHINSEI TANOSHIMI SOSHI [BOOK OF NEW INTERESTING THINGS]
Edo, Japan, ca. 1853. 34pp., oriental style. Original paper wrappers. Includes 31 woodcuts deriving from Perry's expedition, incl. Perry and his flagship, some hand-colored.

(218) 750.00

IKOKU OCHIBA [FALLEN LEAVES FROM A FOREIGN COUNTRY].
Tokyo, ca. 1853. 40pp., oriental style. Blue paper wrappers. Slipcased, bone clasps. Illus. Record of M. C. Perry's expedition, including portraits of Commodore Perry, American naval officers, Perry's flagship, etc., some hand-colored.

(219) 750.00

Perry, Matthew C.
CORRESPONDENCE, &c., RELATIVE TO THE NAVAL EXPEDITION TO JAPAN.
Wash., SED34, 1855. 195pp. Original blindstamped cloth, spine gilt.

(220) 75.00

GRAPHIC SCENES OF THE JAPAN EXPEDITION, BY WM. HEINE, ARTIST OF THE EXPEDITION.
N.Y.: G. P. Putnam & Co., 1856. Elephant folio. Original half morocco. Ten lithographed plates and engraved extra title page by Sarony. Eight of the plates are in full color, 15x21 inches.

(221) 2750.00

Hawks, Francis L.
NARRATIVE OF THE EXPEDITION OF AN AMERICAN SQUADRON TO THE CHINA SEAS AND JAPAN . . .. UNDER THE COMMAND OF COMMODORE M. C. PERRY . . . COMPILED FROM ORIGINAL NOTES AND JOURNALS OF COMMODORE PERRY AND HIS OFFICERS, AT HIS REQUEST AND UNDER HIS SUPERVISION.
N.Y.: D. Appleton, 1856. 624pp. Illus. Maps. *First edition.*

(222) 125.00

For almost 250 years Japan had remained sealed to all foreign commerce, except for a trickle of trade granted to the Dutch. The major European powers had tried many times to open trade with Japan but failed; in 1852 the United States began its own attempt. Commodore Matthew C. Perry was despatched with a powerful squadron of seven warships to arrange a treaty and secure the rich trade with the Orient.

He landed at Tokyo in July, 1853, formally delivered letters from the American government to the Emperor, and withdrew for some months to await a reply. In February, 1854, he returned and negotiated at Yokohama a brilliant agreement to open Japan to American trade. The Treaty of Kanagawa, March 31, 1854, was the result; its results were immensely fruitful, and fateful, for Japan and the entire western world. This was in no small part due to Perry's ability and personality, the expedition having justly been called ''the most important diplomatic mission ever intrusted to an American naval officer.''

Perry returned to the United States in January, 1855. C. O. Paullin summed up the expedition thusly: ''As one of the chief diplomatic achievements of the 19th century, the opening of Japan will long make the name of Perry memorable. His expedition marked a departure in Occidental policy respecting Japan, in American policy respecting the Orient, and in Japanese policy respecting the western world.''

THE LANDING OF THE AMERICAN EXPEDITION IN JAPAN.

125

1854 [The Contemplative Life]

Thoreau, Henry David
WALDEN; OR, LIFE IN THE WOODS.
Boston: Ticknor and Fields, 1854. 357pp. Original cloth, gilt, spine repaired. Flyleaf torn, otherwise a clean, tight copy. *First edition,* with the misprints on pages 24, 137, and 217. Ads dated May, 1854. Allen, p.8. Bennett, p.115. Grolier American Hundred #63. Johnson, High Spots of American Literature, p.72. Princeton Hundred.   (223) 600.00

Same, second issue. Fine copy, presentation copy from the publisher inscribed by James T. Fields to Miss M. A. Dodge. Only 280 copies of this rare Boston, 1862, edition were sold. It consisted of the sheets of the first edition with a new title page.   (224) 350.00

Original lead pencil made by Thoreau's famous pencil factory. Stamped ''J. Thoreau & Co.'' ''Concord, 1850. Thoreau worked for his family's private pencil company and was a peddler from Concord to New York. He helped invent a special type of graphite which made the Thoreau pencil the best in the United States.   (225) 150.00

Thoreau searched for five years in vain before he finally found a publisher for *Walden;* when Ticknor and Fields finally signed a contract, it was probably more out of loyalty to the Concord intellectual circle than to expectation for its success. Nevertheless, writes Edward Woks, ''on its appearance in 1854, it was the most powerfully original American book yet written. It vibrates [still] with vitality.'' Few works have had such powerful and varied influence throughout the world, from Tolstoy to Gandhi to Martin Luther King.

E. B. White stated: ''It still seems to me the best youth's companion yet written by an American.'' Whitman Bennett called it ''not only the most famous nature book by an American but probably the most famous since Walton's *Compleat Angler.*'' Ludwig Lewisohn said it is ''one of the most tonic and heartening books in all literature,'' and Frank Magill recently claimed that ''no more original book has been produced in the Western Hemisphere.'' It has certainly become one of the classic statements of the American spirit.

Leaves of Grass.

———————

I CELEBRATE myself,
    And what I assume you shall assume,
For every atom belonging to me as good belongs to you.

I loafe and invite my soul,
I lean and loafe at my ease .... observing a spear of summer grass.

Houses and rooms are full of perfumes .... the shelves are crowded with perfumes,
I breathe the fragrance myself, and know it and like it,
The distillation would intoxicate me also, but I shall not let it.

The atmosphere is not a perfume .... it has no taste of the distillation .... it is
    odorless,
It is for my mouth forever .... I am in love with it,
I will go to the bank by the wood and become undisguised and naked,
I am mad for it to be in contact with me.

The smoke of my own breath,
Echos, ripples, and buzzed whispers .... loveroot, silkthread, crotch and vine,
My respiration and inspiration .... the beating of my heart .... the passing of blood
    and air through my lungs,
The sniff of green leaves and dry leaves, and of the shore and darkcolored sea-
    rocks, and of hay in the barn,
The sound of the belched words of my voice .... words loosed to the eddies of
    the wind,
A few light kisses .... a few embraces .... a reaching around of arms,
The play of shine and shade on the trees as the supple boughs wag,
The delight alone or in the rush of the streets, or along the fields and hillsides,
The feeling of health .... the full-noon trill .... the song of me rising from bed
    and meeting the sun.

———

Whitman, Walt
LEAVES OF GRASS.
Brooklyn, New York: 1855. xii,[13]-95pp. *First edition, first state of text,* with the second state of binding, title stamped in gold on front cover, and with eight pages of adv. inserted inside front cover. *A very fine, bright copy,* with an original 5x7 cabinet photograph of Whitman loosely inserted. Grolier American Hundred #67. Johnson, High Spots of American Literature, p.79. Printing and the Mind of Man #340: "In a sense, it is America's second Declaration of Independence; that of 1776 was political, this of 1855 intellectual."

(226) 3500.00

Longfellow, Henry W.
THE SONG OF HIAWATHA.
Boston: Ticknor and Fields, 1855. 316,[12]pp. Original cloth. Very fine, bright copy. *First edition, with an original Autograph Letter Signed, from the publisher,* J. T. Fields, Boston, Jan. 2, 1856, an interesting letter about the book. BAL 12112. Grolier American Hundred #66. Johnson High Spots, p.53.   (227) 275.00

Bulfinch, Thomas
THE AGE OF FABLE.
Boston: Sanborn, Carter, and Bazin, 1855. 485,[1]pp. Original cloth. *First edition, first state.* Grolier American Hundred #65. Peter Parley to Penrod, p.13. Jenkins, Works of Genius #56.   (228) 185.00

Bartlett, John R.
A COLLECTION OF FAMILIAR QUOTATIONS.
Cambridge: John Bartlett, 1855. 295pp. Original cloth. *First edition, with an original Autograph Letter Signed by Bartlett, 2pp., small 4to, about additions to the work, loosely inserted.* Grolier American Hundred #64: "As essential to the living room as the cook book to the kitchen."   (229) 250.00

An astounding literary bonanza, matched only by the remarkable year 1929, greeted America during 1855. As might be expected, the greatest of the books that year was the least accepted by the public, but all four works made a mighty impact on our literary heritage.

The most popular of the four works was *Hiawatha.* It sold over thirty thousand copies in the first six months, and became perhaps the largest selling American poetry book ever. W. S. Kennedy states that "no other poem in the English language was ever so immediately popular" and Bayard Taylor predicted, shortly after it appeared: "It will be parodied, perhaps ridiculed in many quarters, but it will live long after the Indian race has vanished from our continent."

Bulfinch's *Age of Fable,* with the companion volume *The Age of Chivalry* issued four years later, introduced classical mythology to America in a manner that exerted immeasurable influence. Palmer Bovie called it "a literary work that was to prove more durable and less dated than the works of Lowell, Whittier, and Longfellow," and W. F. Courtney recently said it is still "a delight to read as well as to consult." Bulfinch's *Mythology* has never been out of print since first issued, and Bennett Cerf stated: "So completely has his work entered the consciousness of present-day readers that the mere mention of the word 'mythology' evokes the immediate response, by association, of the name 'Bulfinch.'"

Of *Bartlett's Quotations* there is little that need be said. From the original 295-page edition through eight more in his lifetime through the present 1750-page edition, the work has become, in the words of the Grolier American Hundred Exhibit, "as essential to the American living-room as the cook book to the American kitchen."

The greatest of the four, of course, is *Leaves of Grass.* As the Grolier Exhibit stated, "practically everything that can be said about the significance of this book has been said by its author, and most of it is true." W. Bennett describes Whitman as newspaperman, hack writer, philosopher, patriot, poet, loafer, and enigma, and one of the few towering American literary figures. Whitman issued the book almost single-handedly in a minute edition that now ranks as one of the most prized volumes in the world of rare books. Emerson immediately claimed: "I find it the most extraordinary piece of wit and wisdom that America has yet contributed." Oscar Wilde justly called him "the herald to a new era." But Whitman himself said it all when he remarked, "I am large, I contain multitudes."

SUPREME COURT OF THE UNITED STATES: DRED SCOTT, (A COLORED MAN), VS. JOHN F. A. SANDFORD: ARGUMENT OF MONTGOMERY BLAIR, OF COUNSEL FOR THE PLAINTIFF IN ERROR.
Wash., December, 1856. 40pp. Sewn.   (230) 125.00

REPORT OF THE DECISION OF THE SUPREME COURT OF THE UNITED STATES, AND THE OPINIONS OF THE JUDGES THEREOF, IN THE CASE OF DRED SCOTT VERSUS JOHN F. A. SANDFORD.
Wash.: Cornelius Wendell, 1857. 239pp. Sewn. Corners slightly bumped. *Inscribed by Charles Sumner.* Howes S218.   (231) 85.00

Same, N.Y.: D. Appleton & Co., 1857. Contemporary half calf. Howes S218.   (232) 85.00

A LEGAL REVIEW OF THE CASE OF DRED SCOTT, AS DECIDED BY THE SUPREME COURT OF THE UNITED STATES.
Boston: Crosby, Nichols, and Company, 1857. 62pp. Original printed wrappers. *Inscribed: "Ellis Ames Esq. with the authors' compliments."*   (233) 150.00

In December of 1856 the Supreme Court heard arguments on the case of Dred Scott, a Negro suing for his freedom on the basis of having lived with his former master in the free state of Illinois for several years before resettling in the slave state of Missouri.

In March of 1857 the court released its decision, a broad statement on the entire issue of slavery. Basically, it held (1) that Negroes had never been intended to be considered citizens by the designers of the Constitution, and therefore had no right to sue in Federal courts, (2) the whole Missouri Compromise was unconstitutional, as Congress had no power to enact it, and thus Scott was still a slave, and (3) whatever the effect of his residence in Illinois, Missouri courts had considered him a slave and thus he was not a citizen and had no right to sue.

The conclusions of the court were of tremendous import for the slavery issue. Although the court had hoped the decision would help resolve the issue, it actually only heaped flames on the conflict, and "probably did much to precipitate the Civil War." The destruction of the Missouri Compromise principle was a heavy blow to the anti-slavery forces and the statements of the court about the nature of a slave and of a citizen crushed many of the hopes for a peaceful settlement of the problem. In fact, the court's decision was never overthrown, but was ultimately resolved by the 14th Amendment which declared "all persons" born in the United States were citizens.

Kleber, Henry
THE ATLANTIC TELEGRAPH SCOTTISCH.
N.Y., 1857. 5pp. Large folio sheet music. Elaborate pictorial cover, showing a telegraph set, coiled wire, ships laying cable, etc. Dichter, p.104.   (234) 20.00

Mullay, John
THE LAYING OF THE CABLE; OR, THE OCEAN TELEGRAPH, BEING A COMPLETE AND AUTHENTIC NARRATIVE OF THE ATTEMPT TO LAY THE CABLE ACROSS THE ENTRANCE TO THE GULF OF ST. LAWRENCE IN 1855, AND OF THE THREE ATLANTIC TELEGRAPH EXPEDITIONS OF 1857 AND 1858, WITH A DETAILED ACCOUNT OF THE MECHANICAL AND SCIENTIFIC PART OF THE WORK.
N.Y.: D. Appleton, 1858. 329,[2]pp. Map and plates. Half morocco. *First edition.* By the official historian of the enterprise.   (235) 125.00

Field, Henry M.
THE STORY OF THE ATLANTIC TELEGRAPH.
N. Y.: Charles Scriberner's Sons, 1892. 415pp. Original cloth. *First edition.* Frontis. of Cyrus Field; issued in the year of his death. Business card of Cyrus Field, Grammercy Park, laid inside front cover.   (236) 35.00

The laying of the Atlantic cable, making possible for the first time instant communication with Europe, was due in no small degree to the perseverance of Cyrus W. Field. He organized the original attempt in 1854 and surveyed a route. British and American governments sponsored the project and loaned ships for the expeditions. In 1857 the first laying attempt was made, but was frustrated by a broken cable. The same happened in 1858.

A second attempt was made later in 1858 with success, and a few cables were sent between Pres. Buchanan and Queen Victoria, and great jubilation took place on both sides of the Atlantic. Shortly afterwards, however, the cable ceased to function. Nothing further was done until after the Civil War. In 1865 still another attempt was made and it also broke. Finally, in 1866 a cable was completely installed that remained successful. Thereafter, Field travelled extensively advocating a world-wide telegraph cable communications system. His vision and foresight ultimately succeeded in bringing the farthest reaches of the world closer together through communications.

Buchanan, James

MESSAGE TRANSMITTING TO CONGRESS THE CONSTITUTION OF KANSAS, FRAMED BY THE CONVENTION ASSEMBLED AT LECOMPTON.
Wash., 1858. 8pp. Sewn.   (237) 45.00

Buchanan, James

MESSAGE COMMUNICATING A CONSTITUTION FOR KANSAS AS A STATE, AND PRESENTING HIS VIEWS IN RELATION TO THE AFFAIRS OF THAT TERRITORY.
Wash., SED21, 1858. 32pp. Sewn.   (238) 40.00

HOUSE JOURNAL OF THE LEGISLATIVE ASSEMBLY OF KANSAS TERRITORY, FOR THE YEAR 1858: COMMENCED AT LECOMPTON . . . AND CONCLUDED AT THE CITY OF LAWRENCE.
Lawrence, Kans.: Sam. A. Medary, 1861. 451pp. Half calf. Includes the "Memorial of the Legislative Assembly of the Territory of Kansas to the Congress of the United States" praying for statehood, and the act moving the seat of government to Lawrence.   (239) 450.00

What is known as the Lecompton Constitution was framed by a pro-slavery convention held in Lecompton, which proposed a Kansas Constitution with an article permitting slavery. This constitution was then submitted to the people, who were given the choice of accepting or rejecting the slavery clause; however, if the slavery clause were rejected, then no new slavery would be admitted, but there would be no interference with slave property already held there. This passed a state referendum 6,226 to 569, the anti-slavery forces refusing to vote.

The Free State forces then held their own election, which rejected the proposed constitution, 10,226 to 162.

In spite of this, President Buchanan submitted the constitution to Congress in early 1858, urging its acceptance. After several votes, Congress agreed to re-submit the constitution to the people of Kansas and promised the future state five million acres of land if it were ratified. On August 2, 1858, the people of Kansas rejected it by a vote of 11,300 to 1,788.

Politically, the affair had important national ramifications. For proposing the pro-slavery document, Buchanan lost the support of the North. For fighting it, Stephen A. Douglas lost the South. Kansas was torn bitterly by the affair, but was finally admitted as a free state on January 29, 1861.

Dixie!

God made dis worl in just six days,
An finished it in various ways:
    Chorus — Look away — look away — look away — Dixie Land.
He den made Dixie trim an nice,
When Adam called it "Paradise"
    Chorus — Look away — look away — look away — Dixie Land.
Den I wish I was in Dixie — look 'way — look 'way —
    Chorus — In Dixie Lann, I'll took my stann,
            To lib an die in Dixie!
Away — away — away down South in Dixie!
Away — away — away down South in Dixie!

            Daniel D. Emmett (author.)
                (Aged 84 years,)
        Coshocton, O. Feb'y 22d. 1899

1859   [Songs for the Coming War]

Emmett, Daniel D.
DIXIE!
Autograph Manuscript Signed, 1 page, large 4to, of the famous song of the South. Exceedingly rare holograph version of the 1859 verse which became the national battle song of the Confederacy, written out by Emmett at a later date, along with an account of how he was induced to do so.   (240) 1500.00

Emmett, Daniel D.
I WISH I WAS IN DIXIE'S LAND, WRITTEN AND COMPOSED EXPRESSLY FOR BRYANT'S MINSTRELS.
N.Y.: Firth, Pond & Co., 1860. 6pp. Large folio sheet music. Engraved cover. Dichter, p.105.   (241) 85.00

DIXIE FOR THE UNION.
N.Y., 1861. 6pp. Large folio sheet music. Color cover with crossed American flags. Yankeefied text by F. J. Crosby. Dichter, p.107.   (242) 45.00

Galbreath, C. B.
DANIEL DECATUR EMMETT, AUTHOR OF "DIXIE."
Columbus: Fred J. Heer, 1904. Cloth. *Inscribed by the author.* Story of the writing of the song and its influence.   (243) 45.00

134

Howe, Julia Ward
[BATTLE HYMN OF THE REPUBLIC] GLORY HALLELUJA.
Phila., 1862. 9pp. Large folio sheet music. Dichter, p.111-112.   (244) 65.00

Howe, Julia Ward
[LETTER ON SONG WRITING]
Original Autograph Letter Signed, 3pp., small 4to, Jan. 3, 1852, early in her career, about a musical composition. ''My little poem will at least illustrate the different trains of thought awakened by the same idea. . . . It is all played on one chord — it was spontaneous in its conception, and leapt at once to that thought of ashes, which is its conclusion, but in re-composing it, I have spent more time than it is worth. . . . Above all, do not show it, not from mock modesty, but simply because I may wish to make another use of it. I have written it in haste, at twilight, and with various rhetorical slips, which pray excuse. . . .''   (245) 75.00

In April, 1859, a young minstrel performer composed a new song for Bryant's Minstrels, and called it ''Dixie.'' He had already achieved fame at sixteen years old, after running away from home to join a minstrel troop, when he composed ''Old Dan Tucker.'' Early in 1860, ''Dixie'' was published as ''I Wish I Was in Dixie's Land,'' and when it was played in New Orleans in a routine for forty roisterous female Zouaves, it was an overnight sensation.

Richard Harwell states: ''The first call to authors and composers of the South was for a national song — a song that would be a rallying cry for the patriots of the Confederacy, a battle song for her soldiers, and a hymn to the freedom they believed they were winning. None of the songs of the South completely filled the need. . . . The Southern people turned to a Northern minstrel tune, made it their own, and gave to it a degree of immortality rarely achieved. The tune is 'Dixie.' ''

The South adopted it with a fervor. It was played in 1861 at the inauguration of Jefferson Davis as President of the Confederacy. Henry Hotze, a Confederate trooper, wrote: ''It is marvellous with what wild-fire rapidity this tune of 'Dixie' has spread over the whole South. . . . It now bids fair to become the musical symbol of a new nationality.''

The North also needed a hymn for the conflict, a special song peculiar to their war. Julia Ward Howe, a fervent abolitionist, filled the need by using a hymn that had been making the rounds as ''John Brown's Body.'' M. S. Gerry writes: ''One night, while visiting a camp near Washington, too stirred by emotion to sleep, she composed 'The Battle Hymn of the Republic,' scribbling down in the dense darkness of her tent the lines she could not see.'' She sold it for four dollars. Published first as ''Glory Hallelujah,'' it quickly became the North's rallying song, and it brought upon the little lady honors ''seldom equalled in the career of any other American woman.''

1860   [Mr. Lincoln Goes to Washington]

POLITICAL DEBATES BETWEEN HON. ABRAHAM LINCOLN AND HON. STEPHEN A. DOUGLAS, IN THE CELEBRATED CAMPAIGN OF 1858, IN ILLINOIS . . . AS CAREFULLY REPORTED BY THE REPORTERS OF EACH PARTY.

Columbus: Follett, Foster and Company, 1860. 268pp. Original cloth. *First edition, first issue.* Bennett, p.125. Howes L338. Monaghan 69. Sabin 41156. Downs, Famous Books #81.   (246) 225.00

Lanham, Charles
BOHN'S HAND-BOOK OF WASHINGTON.
Wash.: Casimer Bohn, 1861. 134pp. Folding map. Original printed boards, gilt-edged. *Abraham Lincoln's copy, signed by him, from the library of Lincoln's Minister to England, Charles Francis Adams,* with his bookplate. With an interesting letter of authentication in which the history of the relationship between the new President and Lanham is traced. An extraordinary guidebook to the national capitol at the beginning of the Civil War, from the libraries of a President and of the son and grandson of a President. Laid in a full morocco slipcase.   (247) 2500.00

Lincoln, Abraham
INAUGURAL ADDRESS OF THE PRESIDENT OF THE UNITED STATES, ON THE FOURTH OF MARCH, 1861.
Wash., March 8, 1861. 10pp. Half morocco. *First printing.*   (248) 175.00

The publication of the Lincoln-Douglas debates, states R. B. Downs, was "an important element in Abraham Lincoln's election to the Presidency . . . [It was] the only book ever personally seen through the press by Lincoln. The Debates became a major campaign document and a best seller, read by innumerable voters" and many others ever since.

The great series of debates between Lincoln and Douglas in 1858 crystallized the major issue in the presidential campaign of 1860. Lincoln challenged Douglas "for you and myself to divide time and address the same audiences the present canvass." Douglas agreed to seven meetings in seven Illinois counties. Over 12,000 attended the first one on August 21, 1860.

Douglas made a frontal attack on Lincoln's "House Divided" theme, stating "I care more for the great principle of self-government, the right of the people to rule, than I do for all the Negroes in Christendom. I would not endanger the perpetuity of this Union." Lincoln hit hard against slavery, denouncing on the Dred Scott decision. Either Douglas must accept the Supreme Court's decision, which would permit slavery to spread, or he must stop urging the sanctity of the court's decisions. Lincoln charged that Douglas' policy would bring "no end to the institution of slavery."

The debates swiftly became the focal point of the slavery issue and on the two men personally. Douglas, well-dressed in ruffled shirt, shiny buttons, and broad-brimmed hat, contrasted with the gawky Lincoln in ill-fitting coat, baggy trousers, and old high-topped hat. In the election, Lincoln won the popular vote but because of gerrymandered districting, Douglas was reelected. Nevertheless, Lincoln's sincerity and ability in the debates, more than anything else, thrust him into the limelight that in 1860 won him the office of President of the United States.

On February 11, 1861, the new President left Springfield for Washington, which had changed greatly since he had been there in Congress twelve years earlier. He lived for a short time in a hotel before moving into the White House. On March 4, 1861, he delivered his Inaugural Address, ending with the memorable words: "I am loth to close. We are not enemies but friends. We must not be enemies. Though passion may have strained, it must not break our bonds of affection. The mystic chords of memory . . . all over this broad land, will yet swell the chorus of the Union, when again touched, as surely they will be, by the better angels of our nature."

One week later the Confederate Constitution was adopted by the South.

S. H. Galleher
Bowling Green

ARMY REGULATIONS,

ADOPTED FOR THE USE OF THE

Army of the Confederate States,

IN ACCORDANCE WITH LATE ACTS OF CONGRESS.

REVISED FROM THE ARMY REGULATIONS OF THE OLD UNITED STATES
ARMY, 1857; RETAINING ALL THAT IS ESSENTIAL
FOR OFFICERS OF THE LINE.

TO WHICH IS ADDED,

AN ACT FOR THE ESTABLISHMENT AND ORGANIZATION OF
THE ARMY OF THE CONFEDERATE STATES
OF AMERICA.

ALSO,

ARTICLES OF WAR,

FOR THE GOVERNMENT OF THE ARMY OF THE CONFED-
ERATE STATES OF AMERICA.

S. B. Buckner.
Bowling Green. Oct. 25, 1861.

RICHMOND, VA.:

WEST & JOHNSTON, PUBLISHERS,

NO. 145 MAIN STREET.

1861.

Genl. Buckner's copy.
Galleher was on my staff. He afterwards
became an Episcopal Preacher —

138

THE CONSTITUTION OF THE CONFEDERATE STATES OF AMERICA, ADOPTED MARCH 11, 1861.

15,[1]pp. Printed self-wrapers. Apparently unrecorded.   (249) 250.00

ACTS AND RESOLUTIONS OF THE FIRST SESSION OF THE PROVISIONAL CONGRESS OF THE CONFEDERATE STATES.

Montgomery, Ala.: Barrett, Wimbish & Co., 1861. 131pp. Gray printed wrappers. Very good copy. Crandall 15.   (250) 125.00

ARTICLES OF WAR FOR THE GOVERNMENT OF THE ARMIES OF THE CONFEDERATE STATES.

Charleston: Evans & Cogswell, 1861. 24pp. Green printed wrappers. Crandall 1214.

    (251) 450.00

ARMY REGULATIONS, ADOPTED FOR THE USE OF THE ARMY OF THE CONFEDERATE STATES . . .

Richmond: West & Johnston, 1861. 198,[2]pp. Original morocco-backed boards. Gen. S. B. Buckner's copy, signed by him and dated Oct. 25, 1861, with some notes on oats in his hand on blank endleaves.   (252) 450.00

Broadside, 12mo. *Election, Wednesday, November 6th, 1861, For President, Jefferson Davis, of Mississippi. For Vice-President, Alexander H. Stephens, of Georgia. . . .* Not in Crandall.   (253) 45.00

As soon as Lincoln was elected President, the South began to institute its plans for secession from the Union. By February of 1861, seven states had seceded and formed a provisional government of the Confederate States of America. They selected Jefferson Davis as President and Alexander Stephens as Vice President.

On April 13, 1861, Fort Sumter was attacked and surrendered to the Confederacy. Thus the sides were drawn and the war began. Lincoln called for 75,000 militia and the South began to arm and organize. On April 15, he ordered the armed forces to suppress the rebellion. On May 6 the Confederate Congress declared war on the United States. By the end of May, eleven states had seceded, and by the end of the year Confederate rump governments had been set up for Missouri and Kentucky.

By summer the two forces were ready for a major test of arms, and it came on July 21, 1861, at First Manassas, or Bull Run, an inglorious defeat for the United States. Some 40,000 men under Gen. McDowell were routed by 33,000 under Generals J. E. Johnston and P. G. T. Beauregard.

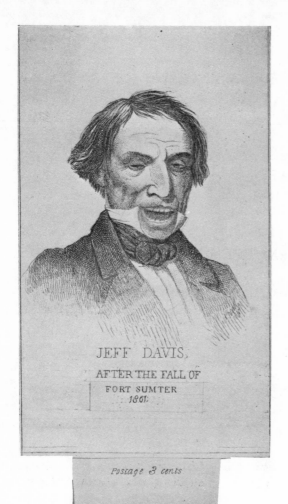
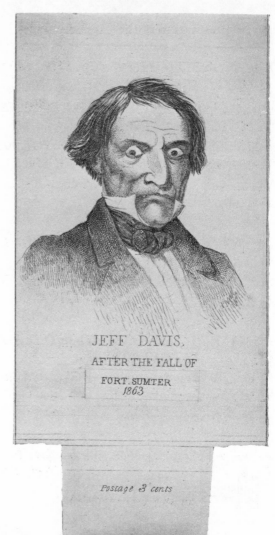

1862   [North and South at War]

Davis, Jefferson
POLITICAL CARTOON.
Interesting original pull-tab cartoon card depicting Jefferson Davis after the capture and after the loss of Fort Sumter. Boston: D. C. Johnston, ca. 1863.   (254) 45.00

OFFICIAL REPORTS OF BATTLES, PUBLISHED BY ORDER OF CONGRESS.
Richmond, Va.: Enquirer Book and Job Press, 1862. 571pp. Crandall 1376. A vital reference publication, containing a vast wealth of material not found in the Rebellion Records or elsewhere.   (255) 275.00

OFFICIAL REPORTS OF BATTLES, EMBRACING THE DEFENCE OF VICKS-BURG, BY MAJOR GENERAL EARL VAN DORN, AND THE ATTACK UPON BATON ROUGE, BY MAJOR GENERAL BRECKENRIDGE, TOGETHER WITH THE REPORTS OF THE BATTLE OF CORINTH . . . AND FORT DONELSON.
Richmond: Smith, Bailey & Co., 1863. 170pp. Sewn. Crandall 1379. Rare compilation with valuable reports.   (256) 375.00

Lincoln, Abraham

BY THE PRESIDENT OF THE UNITED STATES OF AMERICA: A PROCLAMATION.

Broadsheet, large 4to, printed on pp.[1] and [3], Wash., May 12, 1862, regarding the Federal blockade of Southern ports. Issued by the State Department. Rare, unrecorded Lincoln war proclamation.   (257) 125.00

Lincoln, Abraham. Original Autographed Letter Signed, March 18, 1862, as President, apparently to Secretary of War Edwin M. Stanton, regarding the appointment of Joseph N. Whittlesey as General in the 5th Cavalry.   (258) 1950.00

Moore, Mrs. M. B.

THE GEOGRAPHICAL READER, FOR THE DIXIE CHILDREN.

Raleigh: Branson, Farrar & Co., 1863. 48pp. Half morocco. Five, of six, hand-colored maps of States of the Confederacy. Exceedingly rare. Crandall 4070. Harwell, Cornerstones of Confederate Collecting #18. An absolutely astonishing volume, written for teaching Confederate propaganda to Southern children; not even the Third Reich could match it. Examples:

"The northern people began to preach . . . about the sin of slavery. The money for which they sold their slaves, was now partly spent in trying to persuade the Southern States to send theirs back to Africa. . . . In the year 1860 the Abolitionists became strong enough to elect one of their men for President. Abraham Lincoln was a weak man . . . so the Southern States seceded, and elected Jefferson Davis for their President. This so enraged Pres. Lincoln that he declared war. . . . The earth has been drenched with blood; but still Abraham Lincoln is unable to conquer . . . the South. The South only asks to be let alone. . . . The Northerners are refined, and intelligent on all subjects but that of Negro slavery, on this they are mad. . . . Then remember, little boys, when you are men, never to vote for a bad man to govern the country."

"Texas. The State was long noted for the refuge of bad men who ran away to prevent being punished; but of late years it has become a thriving State. . . . It has not suffered much from war."

"The African race . . . are slothful and vicious, but possess little cunning. . . . They sell their prisoners to white people for slaves. They know nothing of Jesus. . . . The slaves who are found in America are in much better condition. . . . We can not tell how they came to be black, and have wool on their heads."   (259) 1500.00

In 1862 and 1863 both sides began to fight in earnest, and some of the bloodiest battles in American history were fought, notably at Antietam, Vicksburg, and Gettysburg. Union command devolved on George B. McClellan and then Ulysses S. Grant, while Robert E. Lee led the Confederate forces.

Generally, the Confederates, who had better generals and more intense fighting traditions, were victorious in evenly matched contests, but gradually the industrial might of the North began to turn the tide against the South. Unable to arm and supply itself adequately or to replace lost troops, the war shifted from Confederate advantage in 1862 to distinct northern advantage by the end of 1863.

To-day, March 18. 1862, Major
Joseph H. Whittlesey, now com:
manding 5ᵗʰ Cavalry, calls &
wishes to be a Brig. Gen, of
Vols, or, what he prefers, a brevet-
Colonelcy in his own Regiment.
If made a General, he wishes
to go with Gen. Shields.

A. Lincoln

114

property equally. It would have been wise in the North to have said to her Southern sisters, "If you are not content to dwell with us longer, depart in peace. We will divide the inheritance with you, and may you be a great nation."

5. This country possesses many ships, has fine cities and towns, many railroads, steamboats, canals, manufactures, &c. The people are ingenious, and enterprising, and are noted for their tact in "driving a bargain." They are refined, and intelligent on all subjects but that of negro slavery, on this they are mad.

6. The large lakes, the long rivers, the tall mountains, with the beautiful farms and pretty towns and villages, make this a very interesting country to travelers.

SOUTHERN CONFEDERACY.

1. These states lie south of the United States, and possess a warmer climate.—The latter are mostly suited to raising grain and cattle, while the former grow more cotton, rice, tobacco, and sugar cane, with some cattle and much grain. A large portion of the country lies on the sea coast, and is level and sandy. The interior portions are hilly and mountainous.

2. This country is well watered by large rivers, and has many fine harbors. On some of these harbors, are large cities; but the Confederate States possess few ships and her cities do not grow so fast as if there was more commerce. But we have reason to hope that in a few years we shall not fall behind any nation in point of commerce, or ships to carry it on.

3. This is a great country! The Yankees thought to starve us out when they sent their ships to guard our seaport towns. But we have learned to make many things; to do without many others; and above all to trust in the smiles of the God of battles. We had few guns, little ammunition, and not much of anything but food, cotton and tobacco; but the people helped themselves and God helped the people. We were considered an indolent, weak people, but our enemies have found us strong, because we had justice on our side.

4. The Southern people are noted for being high minded and courteous. A stranger seldom lacks friends in this country. Much of the field work is done by slaves. These are generally well used and often have as much pocket money as their mistresses. They are contented and happy, and many of them are christians. The sin of the South lies not in holding slaves, but they are sometimes mistreated. Let all the little boys and girls remember that slaves are human, and that God will hold them to account for treating them with injustice.

5. The Southern Confederacy is at present a sad country; but President Davis is a good and wise man, and many of the generals and other officers in the army, are pious. Then there are many good praying people in the land; so we may hope that our cause will prosper. "When the righteous are in authority, the nation rejoiceth;

1863   [Emancipation Proclamation and Gettysburg Address]

Lincoln, Abraham

BY THE PRESIDENT OF THE UNITED STATES OF AMERICA: A PROCLAMA-
TION.

Wash., Gen. Orders No. 1, Jan. 2, 1863. 3pp. Slipcased. The Emancipation Proclamation.
Eberstadt 12. Grolier American Hundred #71.   (260) 135.00

THE EMANCIPATION PROCLAMATION.

Phila.: On Stone by L. Haugg, 1863. Published by F. W. Thomas. Tinted folio broadside,
with printed facsimile signature of Lincoln and border vignettes, the main one portraying
Liberty shielding slaves from masters and hounds. Text in double columns, enclosed in
elaborate illustrated border, with portrait of Lincoln in center medallion. Eberstadt 49,
locating only four known copies, of which this is one.   (261) 475.00

144

PROCLAMATION OF EMANCIPATION.

Davenport: W. H. Pratt, 1865. Folio broadside, with a striking portrait of Lincoln after Meserve 87. The text is calligraphic and prepared so as to produce a likeness of Lincoln. Eberstadt 40. (262) 250.00

PROCLAMATION OF EMANCIPATION.

Boston: A. J. Mayer & Co., 1865. Large folio broadside, 24x20 inches, with facsimile signature of Lincoln. One of the illustrated scenes depicts a slave auction. Eberstadt 44: ''One of the more artistic of the illustrated editions.'' Eberstadt locates only five other known copies. (263) 350.00

Group of 10 separately printed Congressional speeches, 1861-1863, by various Congressmen and Senators, relating to emancipation, 6 to 16 pages each. (264) 125.00

ADDRESS OF HON. EDWARD EVERETT, AT THE CONSECRATION OF THE NATIONAL CEMETERY AT GETTYSBURG, 19TH NOVEMBER, 1863, WITH THE DEDICATORY SPEECH OF PRESIDENT LINCOLN. . . .

Boston: Little, Brown and Company, 1864. [88]pp. Maps. Half morocco, gilt. *First authorized edition.* Monaghan 194. Olsen Collection #177. Howes E232. (265) 225.00

The central goal of the Lincoln administration, besides preserving the Union, was the ending of slavery, and the Emancipation Proclamation was one of the great milestones in the history of the United States.

Lincoln decided to issue it in 1862 and actually issued a preliminary proclamation on September 22, 1862, declaring that starting in 1863 all slaves would be free. On January 1, 1863, he issued the historic document, stating that ''all persons held as slaves . . . are, and henceforward shall be, free.''

On July 1-3, 1863, the battle that was heralded as the turning point in the Civil War was fought at Gettysburg, Pa. Lee's northern advance was stopped cold in the battle that resulted in some 50,000 casualties, and his army began a slow retreat. On November 19, 1863, Pres. Lincoln journeyed to the Gettysburg battleground to dedicate a national cemetery there. Edward Everett delivered a two-hour oration, and when Lincoln delivered his short two-minute address the crowd barely listened.

When Everett's address was published, the President's three paragraph speech was stuck in as an afterthought on page 84, opposite a musical Dirge by James G. Percival. Before long, however, it was recognized that Lincoln had presented an immortal summary of his conception of democracy, which he ended with: ''that the government of the people, by the people, and for the people, shall not perish from the earth.''

ADJUTANT AND INSPECTOR GENERAL'S OFFICE,
Richmond, February 6, 1865.

GENERAL ORDERS, }
No. 3. }

The following Act of Congress is published for the information of the army:

An Act to provide for the appointment of a General in Chief of the Armies of the Confederate States.

"SECTION 1. The Congress of the Confederate States of America do enact, That there shall be appointed by the President, by and with the advice and consent of the Senate, an officer, who shall be known and designated as 'General in Chief,' who shall be ranking officer of the army, and as such, shall have command of the military forces of the Confederate States.

SEC. 2. That the act providing a staff for the General who may be assigned to duty at the Seat of Government, is hereby repealed, and that the General in Chief, who may be appointed under the provisions of this act, shall have a staff not less than that now allowed a General in the field, to be assigned by the President, or to be appointed by him, by and with the advice and consent of the Senate." [Approved 23d January 1865.]

II. General ROBERT E. LEE having been duly appointed General in Chief of the Armies of the Confederate States, will assume the duties thereof, and will be obeyed and respected accordingly.

III. General Orders, No. 23, of 1864, is hereby revoked.

By order.

S. COOPER,
Adjutant and Inspector General.

HEAD-QUARTERS ARMIES OF THE UNITED STATES,
NASHVILLE, TENN. MARCH 17TH, 1864.

GENERAL ORDERS, }
No. 1. }

In pursuance of the following Order of the President:

"EXECUTIVE MANSION.

"Washington, D. C., March 10th, 1864.

"Under the authority of the Act of Congress, to revive the grade of Lieutenant General in the United States Army, approved February 29th, 1864, Lieutenant General ULYSSES S. GRANT, U. S. A., is assigned to the command of the Armies of the United States.

"ABRAHAM LINCOLN."

I assume command of the Armies of the United States.

Head-Quarters will be in the Field; and, until further orders, will be with the Army of the Potomac.

There will be an office Head-Quarters in Washington, D. C., to which all official communications will be sent, except those from the Army where Head-Quarters are at the time of their address.

U. S. GRANT,
Lieutenant General, U. S. A.

OFFICIAL:

Assistant Adjutant General.

GENERAL ORDERS NO. 1.

Broadside, 1p., small 4to, Nashville, Headquarters of the Armies of the United States, March 17, 1864, announcing the promotion by Lincoln of U. S. Grant to Lt. Gen. and to command of all U.S. forces in the field. "I assume command of the Armies of the United States. Head-Quarters will be in the Field, until further orders. . . . U. S. Grant." Very rare; printed by an army field press and hitherto unrecorded.   (266) 250.00

GENERAL ORDERS NO. 3.

Broadside, 1p., 8vo, Richmond, Feb. 6, 1865, announcing the appointment of Robert E. Lee as supreme commander of the Confederate Armies. "General Robert E. Lee having been duly appointed General in Chief of the Armies of the Confederate States, will hereby assume the duties thereof."   (267) 45.00

Lee, Robert E.

SIGNED PHOTOGRAPH.

Original carte-de-visite photograph of Gen. Lee, signed in ink on the front by him. By Boude & Miley, Lexington, Va. Stern, Lee: A Pictorial Biography, p.228; "Fortunately for posterity, a former Confederate soldier, young Michael Miley, set up a studio in Lexington in 1866. John C. Boude . . . provided the necessary capital. Since Miley was the only photographer in the area during the last years of Lee's life, he was able to make a vivid pictorial record of the former general."   (268) 450.00

Ulysses S. Grant entered the Civil War as an obscure employee in the adjutant general's office in Illinois; after awhile, he obtained a colonel's commission and began to participate in the fighting. It was not long before his abilities were recognized by Lincoln, who was beset by commanders almost as bad as those in Vietnam. In Grant, however, he found a fighting commander. After Grant captured Vicksburg and divided the Confederacy in half, Lincoln gave him command with the rank of lieutenant general.

Robert E. Lee, on the other hand, was recognized as a great commander from the beginning. Lincoln offered Lee command of the Union army at the beginning of the war, but Lee declined and resigned his commission. Lee commanded the Army of Northern Virginia throughout the war and was de facto commander of all Confederate forces, but did not receive his commission as supreme commander and general-in-chief until February of 1865.

Glory to God in the Highest: Peace on Earth, Good will amongst men.

EXTRA DISPATCH.

LEE'S SURRENDER i

FULL PARTICULARS.
Correspondence between Gens. Grant & Lee.

The Army of Northern Virginia Surrendered!!

The following correspondence concerning the most important event of the war, explains itself. It was dispatched to Gen. Pope from Washington this morning:

WASHINGTON, D. C., April 9, 1865.

To Maj. Gen DODGE:

This Department has just received the official report of the surrender this day of Gen. Lee and his army to Lieut. General Grant, on the terms proposed by General Grant. Details will be given as speedily as possible Signed

E. M STANTON,
Sec'y. of War.

HEADQ'RS ARMY OF UNITED STATES,
April 9, 1865, P M.

To Hon. E. M. Stanton, Sec'y of War:

General Lee surrendered the Army of Northern Virginia this afternoon upon terms proposed by myself. The accompanying and additional correspondence will show the conditions fully.

(Signed)   U. S. GRANT,
L'eut. General.

April 9, 1865.—General: I received your note of this morning on the picket line, whither I had come to meet you to ascertain definitely what terms were embraced in your propositions of yesterday with reference to the surrender of this army.

I now request an interview, in accordance with the offer contained in your letter of yesterday, for that purpose.

Very resp'y, Your ob't. s'vt.,

(Signed),   R. E. LEE, Gen.

To Lt. Gen. U. S. Grant, Com'dg U. S. A.

Your note of this date, is but this moment, 11:50 A. M. received. In consequence of my having passed from the Richmond and Lynchburg road, to the Fannville and Lynchburg I am thus writing about four miles of Walters Church and will push forward to the front for the purpose of meeting you. Notice sent to me on this road where you wish the interview to take place will meet me.

Very respectfully,
Your obedient servant,

U. S. GRANT, Lt. General.

APPOMATOX COURT HOUSE, April 9, '65.

GENERAL R. E. LEE, Com'dg C. S. A. :

In accordance with the substance of my letter to you of the 8th inst , I propose to receive the surrender of the Army of Northern Virginia on the following terms, to-wit : Rolls of all the officers and men to be made in duplicate, one copy to be given to an officer designated by me, and other to be retained by such officer or officers as you may designate.

The officers to give their individual paroles not to take up arms against the Government of the United States, until properly exchanged, and each company or regimental commander sign a like parole for the men of their commands, the arms, artillery and public property to be parked or stacked, and turned over to the officers appointed by me to receive them. This will not embrace the side arms of the officers.

This done, such officer and men will be allowed to return to their homes, not to be disturbed by U. S. authority so long as they observe their paroles and the laws in force where they may reside.

Very respectfully,

U. S. GRANT, Lt. Gen,

H'DQRS. ARMY OF NORTHERN VA.,
April 9, 1865.

Lt. Gen. U. S. Grant, Com'dg U. S. A.

General: I have received your letter of this date containing the terms of surrender of the Army of Northern Virginia, as proposed by you. As they are substantially the same as those expressed in your letter of the 8th inst., they are accepted.

I will proceed to designate the proper officers to carry the stipulations into effect.

Very Resp'y, Your Ob't. S'vt,

R. E. LEE, Gen.

Further particulars in first Edition Evening Dispatch.

LEE'S SURRENDER! THE ARMY OF NORTHERN VIRGINIA SURRENDERED!!

Broadside, 1p., long folio, n.p., April 9, 1865. Contains the official telegraphed dispatches from Appomatox, April 9, 1865, "of the surrender this day of Gen. Lee and his army to Lieut. General Grant," including the correspondence between Lee and Grant and the terms of the surrender. Unrecorded, and apparently unique.   (269) 485.00

HIGHLY IMPORTANT! THE PRESIDENT SHOT!

New York Daily Tribune, April 15, 1865. 8pp. Black-bordered. "The President was just shot at Ford's Theater. The ball entered his neck. It is not known whether the wound is mortal." Possibly the earliest printed announcement of the assassination.   (270) 150.00

GENERAL ORDERS NO. 67 . . . BY COMMAND OF LT. GEN. GRANT.

Broadside, 1p., 8vo, Wash., April 16, 1865. Announces the death of Lincoln and the accession of Johnson to the Presidency.   (271) 150.00

GENERAL ORDERS, HEAD-QUARTERS, DEPARTMENT OF NEW MEXICO.

Broadside, 1p., 8vo, Santa Fe, April 29, 1865. "A great and good man has fallen! Abraham Lincoln died on the morning of the 15th instant. He was assassinated!" First notification in the West. Issued by Gen. Carleton, and signed in ink by his aide.   (272) 300.00

Autograph Letter Signed by Boston Corbett, Wash., May 1, 1865, acknowledging thanks from a friend for his killing of John Wilkes Booth on April 26, five days earlier.

(273) 350.00

PROCLAMATION OF THE PRESIDENT [JOHNSON] OFFERING REWARDS FOR THE ARREST OF JEFFERSON DAVIS AND OTHERS.

Broadside, 1p., 8vo, Wash., May 2, 1865. Declares that there is evidence "that the atrocious murder of the late President was incited, concerted, and procured by and between Jefferson Davis . . . and other rebels and traitors." Offers $100,000 for the arrest of Davis.   (274) 150.00

OFFICIAL RECORDS OF THE WAR OF THE REBELLION, 1861–1865.

Wash., 1880-1895. 127 volumes plus Atlas. Complete set. This remarkable compilation is the essential basic source for any study of the Civil War. It includes hundreds of thousands of original letters, documents, battle reports, etc., from both the Union and the Confederacy.

(275) 1250.00

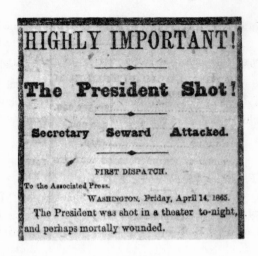

AN ACT TO ESTABLISH A BUREAU FOR THE RELIEF OF FREEDMEN AND REFUGEES.
Broadsheet, 2pp., small quarto, March 3, 1865. A historic document.   (276) 125.00

[THIRTEENTH, FOURTEENTH, AND FIFTEENTH AMENDMENTS]
Wash., 1866-1870. Three separate imprints, being the official government printings of the 13th, 14th, and 15th Amendments to the Constitution, and their ratification.   (277) 125.00

Throughout 1864 and early 1865 the Confederate forces suffered setbacks, and all peace proposals failed. Sherman made his devastating march through Georgia, and the end came on April 9, 1865, when Lee surrendered to Grant. On April 11, Lincoln made his last speech, speaking of his plans for reconstruction. On the evening of April 14, he was assassinated at Ford's Theatre by John Wilkes Booth, who was tracked down and shot on April 26 by Boston Corbett.

On May 2, 1865, amidst public paranoia, the new President, Andrew Johnson, offered a reward for the capture of Jefferson Davis and his cabinet, who were believed to have participated in the plot to kill Lincoln. On May 10, Davis was captured and put in irons in Fortress Monroe. He remained a prisoner there for two years without ever being brought to trial. On May 13, 1867, he was released, with Horace Greeley and Gerrit Smith standing bond.

On March 3, 1865, Congress passed the act creating the Freedmen's Bureau to deal with helping former slaves to adjust to their new freedom. It operated until 1872. On December 18, 1865, the 13th Amendment, making slavery constitutionally illegal, was ratified, and the 14th and 15th Amendments followed shortly thereafter, extending protection and suffrage to Negroes and expanding citizenship rights. Reconstruction of the Confederate States was to be slow and bitter, much more so because of the loss of Lincoln.

HEAD-QUARTERS, DEPARTMENT OF NEW MEXICO,
Santa Fé, N. M., April 29th, 1865.

GENERAL ORDERS,
  No. 13.

A great and good man has fallen! ABRAHAM LINCOLN died on the morning of the fifteenth instant. He was assassinated!

The following telegraphic despatch from the War Department has just been received, and is published for the information and guidance of all Commanders of posts and arsenals, in the Department of New Mexico.

WAR DEPARTMENT,
ADJUTANT GENERAL'S OFFICE,
Washington, D. C., April 17, 1865.

GENERAL ORDERS,
  No. 69.

By direction of the PRESIDENT OF THE UNITED STATES, the War Department will be closed Wednesday next, the day of the funeral of the late PRESIDENT OF THE UNITED STATES. Labor on that day will be suspended at military posts, on all public works under the direction of the War Department, the flags at all military posts, stations, forts, buildings and vessels will be kept at half-mast during the day, and, at 12 o'clock, meridian, twenty-one minute guns will be fired from all forts and all military posts, and at the Military Academy.

(Signed)   EDWIN M. STANTON,
                    Secretary of War.

By command of BRIGADIER GENERAL CARLETON:

Assistant Adjutant General.

151

Dimsdale, Thomas J.

THE VIGILANTES OF MONTANA; OR, POPULAR JUSTICE IN THE ROCKY MOUNTAINS. . . .

Virginia City, M.T.: D. W. Tilton & Co., 1866. 228pp. Half morocco. *First edition.* McMurtrie Montana #2. Adams Six Guns #308. Smith 2457. Graff 1086. *This is the first book printed in Montana.* "One of the best accounts of the Western vigilance committee, the institution that brought justice to the western frontier."—T. W. Streeter. Howes D345: "Not only the first, but textually the most important, book ever printed in Montana." Streeter, Americana Beginnings #72. (278) 1250.00

Same, second edition. Virginia City, 1882. 241pp. Original printed wrappers. Fine copy. (278A) 150.00

Fisk, James L.

CAPT. FISK'S FOURTH EXPEDITION, FROM ST. CLOUD, MINNESOTA, TO THE GREAT GOLD FIELDS OF MONTANA, IS NOW ORGANIZING AND WILL START ABOUT THE 22ND OF MAY, 1866: NEARLY A 1000 MILE TRAVEL SAVED BY THIS ROUTE! PASSAGE ONLY $100! MILITARY PROTECTION GUARANTEED BY THE GOVERNMENT.

St. Paul: Office of the Press Printing Co., 1866. 12pp. Sewn. In half morocco slipcase. Wagner-Camp 399 note: "Not seen." *This is the only known copy.* It begins with a description of Montana and proceeds with requirements for those desiring to join the overland expedition. Not in Graff or Howes. (278B) 1250.00

Armstrong, Moses Kimball

HISTORY AND RESOURCES OF DAKOTA, MONTANA, AND IDAHO, TO WHICH IS APPENDED A MAP OF THE NORTHWEST.

Yankton, Dakota Territory: Geo. W. Kingsbury, Printer, Union and Dakotaian Office, 1866. 72pp. Fine folding map. Original green printed wrappers. *First edition.* Slipcased. Fine copy. Allen, Dakota Imprints #35. Graff 90. Howes A322. *The first history of the Dakotas and Montana.* Only five other complete copies are known, this being the only one in private hands. Exceedingly rare and desirable copy. (279) 3500.00

The Civil War did not much interrupt activities in the Far West, where things went along pretty much as usual. In the period between 1862 and 1864, there was considerable excitement over the discovery of gold in Montana. In 1864 Congress established Montana Territory but actually "each locality had its own provisional government, and the law of the mining camps prevailed." Silver was discovered in 1866.

The first book printed in Montana is described by Thomas W. Streeter: "This is a contemporary account of an interesting phase of the beginnings of settlement in Montana.

... Henry Plummer, the leader of the road agents, was Sheriff ... and his chief associates were sworn in as deputies. [They instituted a] reign of terror and Plummer and twenty-one others were hanged by the Vigilantes. ... Dimsdale tells the story of these desperadoes and does it well. He was a versatile Englishman who had become editor of the *Virginia and Helena Post* and had finished his book only two weeks before his death, which occurred September 22, 1866, at the age of thirty-five.''

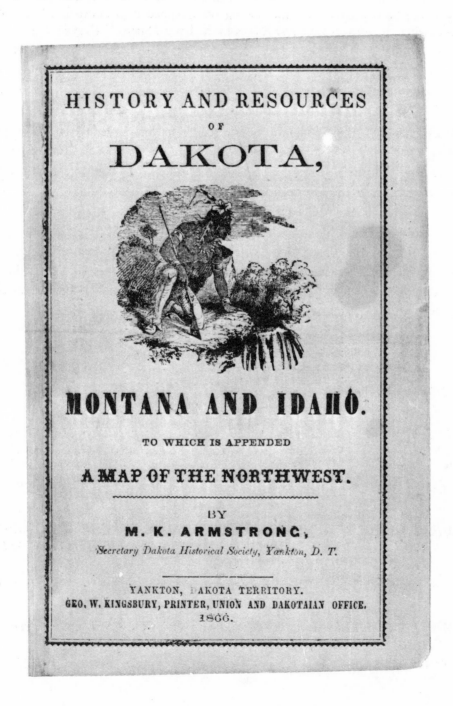

HISTORY AND RESOURCES
OF
DAKOTA,

MONTANA AND IDAHO.

TO WHICH IS APPENDED

A MAP OF THE NORTHWEST.

BY
M. K. ARMSTRONG,
Secretary Dakota Historical Society, Yankton, D. T.

YANKTON, DAKOTA TERRITORY.
GEO. W. KINGSBURY, PRINTER, UNION AND DAKOTAIAN OFFICE.
1866.

1867 [The Alaska Purchase]

Sumner, Charles
SPEECH ON THE CESSION OF RUSSIAN AMERICA TO THE UNITED STATES.
Wash.: Congressional Globe Office, 1867. 48pp. Large folding map. Original printed wrappers, *with signed presentation slip from William H. Seward to Mr. Robinson tipped in.* Howes S1134. Wickersham 4128. Lada-Mocarski 159: "Does not call for a map. However, occasionally one finds a copy with the folding lithographed map entitled: North Western America showing the territory ceded by Russia to the United States." *First edition.*

(280) 225.00

Same as above, without the map.

(281) 150.00

As early as 1857, the Russian minister to the United States made overtures that Russia might be willing to sell Alaska, but the Civil War delayed serious consideration of the matter. Secretary of State William H. Seward recognized the value of the land to the United States, and began in February of 1867 to negotiate its purchase. The treaty of purchase was quickly completed on March 30, at a price of $7,200,000.00.

The Senate balked at the price, but with the aid of Charles Sumner the treaty passed the Senate on April 9, and the appropriation after much debate was approved by Congress in July of 1868. Official transfer of control took place at Sitka on October 18, 1867, the United States gaining 586,400 square miles. Administration was placed under the war department and then the treasury department; Alaska was not made a territory until 1912.

1868 [Johnson Impeachment]

ARTICLES OF IMPEACHMENT, EXHIBITED BY THE HOUSE OF REPRESEN-TATIVES AGAINST ANDREW JOHNSON, PRESIDENT OF THE UNITED STATES.
Wash., March 4, 1868. 8pp.

(282) 50.00

ARGUMENT OF JOHN A. BINGHAM, CHAIRMAN OF THE MANAGERS ON THE PART OF THE HOUSE, BEFORE THE SENATE OF THE U.S. SITTING FOR THE TRIAL OF ANDREW JOHNSON.
Wash.: F. & J. Rives & Geo. A. Bailey, Reporters, 1868. 59pp.

(283) 150.00

ARGUMENT OF WILLIAM S. GROESBECK, OF COUNSEL FOR THE PRES-IDENT, IN THE SENATE OF THE U.S., APRIL 25, 1868.
Wash., 1868. 31pp. Sewn.

(284) 90.00

TRIAL OF ANDREW JOHNSON . . . BEFORE THE SENATE OF THE UNITED STATES, ON IMPEACHMENT . . . FOR HIGH CRIMES AND MISDEMEANORS. Wash., 1868. 3 volumes. Original cloth. *First edition.* Includes an original Autograph Letter Signed, 1p., small 4to, by William H. Evarts presenting the set to Isaac Markens. Evarts was Chief Counsel for President Johnson in the Impeachment proceedings and largely responsible for his acquittal. He served as Secretary of State, 1877-1881. (285) 250.00

Sumner, Charles. Original *Autograph Manuscript Signed,* 1p., 4to, being the original manuscript of his proposal delivered by him at the beginning of the famous Impeachment Trial that the legal rules of evidence be set aside for the Johnson trial. A masterful blow to the defense, it opened the trial to every possible charge and accusation against the President. The manuscript reads, in part:

"Considering the character of this proceeding; that it is a trial of impeachment before the Senate . . . & not a proceeding by indictment in an inferior court; considering that Senators are judges of law as well as fact, & that they are judges from whom there is no appeal; considering that the reasons for the exclusion of evidence on a trial by jury are not applicable to such a proceeding; therefore, it is deemed best that all evidence offered on either side not trivial or obviously irrelevant in character shall be received without objection, the same . . . to be carefully weighed by Senators in the final judgment. . . ." (286) 750.00

The impeachment and trial of President Andrew Johnson was the most important state trial in American history. Upon taking office after the assassination of Lincoln, Johnson continued Lincoln's plan of peaceful reconstruction of the South. He was thwarted at every turn by the Radical Republicans, who eventually maneuvered him into a position where he could be impeached. Johnson, bull-headed and without finesse, made the task easy for his opponents.

In February, 1868, Johnson fired Edwin M. Stanton as Secretary of State, in spite of an 1867 Tenure of Office Act, and the following day was impeached by the House on a vote of 126 to 47. On March 13, the trial by the Senate began, under Chief Justice Salmon P. Chase. John Bingham and Charles Sumner, for the Prosecution, led a savage and violent character attack, while William H. Evarts defended the President on the basis of the unconstitutionality of the Tenure Act. Sumner was particularly bitter: "In the movement for impeachment of Johnson, Sumner took a prominent part. He held . . . a settled conviction that the President was the chief menace to the country. Sumner regarded impeachment as a political rather than a judicial proceeding; hence neither in the Senate nor elsewhere did he put any curb upon his denunciations of Johnson's 'misdeeds,' and his opinion . . . was the longest and most bitter of all those who voted for conviction."—*D.A.B.* Sumner masterminded and introduced the procedure of not following the rules of evidence, and this more than any other act influenced the proceedings. "In this document Sumner is seen at his worst. Lurid and furious invective took the place of argument." It enabled the Senate to ruin Johnson politically, yet by its unfairness switched enough votes to ensure his acquittal.

On May 16, amidst supreme tension, the final vote was cast. Sen. Grimes, suffering from a paralyzing stroke, had himself borne on a cot into the Senate Chamber to cast the vote which made the vote for removal fail of two-thirds majority by one vote. But the Radicals had gained control of the country and their influence on Reconstruction is writ large in the nation's history.

TRANS-CONTINENTAL

"LET EVERY STEP BE AN ADVANCE."

Vol. 1.   Promontory Point, Utah, Monday, June 27, 1870.   No. 8.

The Trans-Continental.

Published Daily on the Pullman Hotel Express,
Between
Boston and San Francisco.

W. R. STEELE, *Editor.*

☞ *Communications and Exchanges for this paper should be addressed,* TRANS-CONTINENTAL, *46 State Street, Chicago.*

BOSTON TO SAN FRANCISCO.

The following salutatory verses from Boston to San Francisco, from the pen of our contemporary and fellow-excursionist, Curtis Guild, editor of the Boston *Commercial Bulletin*, which appeared in the San Francisco *Bulletin* of the 24th, are timely and appropriate as well as expressive:

How weak are mere words
  To the heart overflowing,
To tell its emotions or seek to convey
  Thoughts that thrill all its chords
    When with true warmth 'tis glowing,
And every base passion has faded away.

'Tis thus that we stand
  To respond to your greeting,
Fellow-countrymen, all 'neath our banner of stars;
  And we stretch forth each hand
    To clasp yours at meeting,
Our brothers in peace and our comrades in wars.

Where the granite shaft, gray,
  Of Bunker Hill rises
To tell where our fathers braved tyranny's shock,
  Where the sparkling spray
    Of the blue wave baptizes
The shore of our birthplace and old Plymouth Rock.

Where the rising sun's ray
  Lights the streets of old Concord,
And Lexington's plain lies in peaceful repose,
  There shines Plymouth Bay,
    Where the Mayflower was anchored,
'Tis old Massachusetts that every one knows.

But why need I tell
  Of these spots all so hallowed—
America's story on history's page?
  You know it full well,

And you mark what has followed—
The triumph of freedom the march of the age.

Scarce a century's flow
  Our country's veins filling,
In age 'mid the nations in infancy yet;
  But the beams on her brow
    To the old world is telling,
Our pole star is Progress—that never shall set.

Like the wonder of dreams,
  Or some old Eastern story,
These cities seem rising at magic's behest
  But learning's light gleams,
    Art shines in its glory,
The footprints of enterprise point to the West.

When treason awoke,
  And war's desolation
Wrote ruin and death with its fingers of flame;
  When we gazed through the smoke,
    There the flag of our nation,
Unfurled in the Golden State floated the same.

Ah! what loyal heart
  But then thrilled with emotion,
At the stars faintly seen in the fair sunset glow?
  What shall sever apart,
    Stretched from ocean to ocean.
The strong bonds of Union uniting us now?

War's thunders have ceased,
  Peaceful skies are o'erarching;
Section's hate and fierce feuds may we never recall;
  But North, South, West and East,
    'Neath our old flag still marching,
United we stand but divided we fall.

San Francisco, June 24, 1870.

THE MAIDEN'S GRAVE.

The *Trans-Continental Guide* in describing the early history of the country near the Palisades, about 435 miles from Sacramento, which we passed yesterday, narrates the following:

"In the early times spoken of, a party of emigrants from Missouri were encamped here, waiting for the water to subside. Among them were many families, women and children, who were accompanying their protectors to the land of gold. While here, the daughter of the train-master, an estimable young lady of 18 years, fell sick and despite the watchful care and loving tenderness of friends and kindred, her pure spirit floated into that unknown mist which enwraps the earth, dividing the real from the the ideal, the mortal from the immortal. Her friends reared an humble head-board to her memory, and in course of time—among the new life opening to them on the Pacific slope—the young girl's fate and grave were alike forgotten by all but her immediate relatives. When the advance guard of the Central railroad—the graders and culvert men—came to Gravelly Ford, they found the lone grave and the fast decaying head-board. The sight awoke the finer feelings of their nature and aroused their sympathies, for they were *men*, these brown, toil-stained laborers. The 'culvert men' (masons) concluded that it was not consistent with Christian usage to leave a grave exposed and undefended from the incursion of beasts of prey. With such men, to think was to act, and in a few days the lone grave was enclosed with a solid wall, and a cross—the sacred emblem of immortality—took the place of the old head-board. In the day when the final reckoning between these men and the recording angel is adjusted, we think that they will find a credit for that deed which will offset many little debits in the ledger of good and evil. Perhaps a fair spirit above may smile a blessing on their lives in recompense of the noble deed. Bare the head reverently in passing this grave—not alone in honor of her who is buried here, but also in honor of that higher spirit of humanity which recognizes in a stranger's grave an object too sacred to be passed lightly by, and pays to it the tribute of respect due the last resting place of the dead."

Ross, James, and George Gary
FROM WISCONSIN TO CALIFORNIA AND RETURN.
Madison: Atwood & Rublee, 1869. 132pp. Original printed wrappers. *First edition.* Howes R457. Very rare, being the first account of a transcontinental overland journey entirely by rail. (287) 450.00

THE TRANS-CONTINENTAL: PUBLISHED DAILY ON THE PULLMAN HOTEL EXPRESS BETWEEN BOSTON AND SAN FRANCISCO.
Niagara Falls, Omaha, Cheyenne, Ogden, Salt Lake City, Summit Sierra Nevadas, San Francisco, Promontory Point, Laramie, Grand Island Nebr., Burlington, Boston, May 24-July 4, 1870. 12 issues of 4pp. each, bound in contemporary cloth, gilt. W. R. Steele, Editor. Rare and interesting account of one of the first transcontinental round-trip journeys by rail, actually printed on the train. (288) 300.00

There was public agitation for a transcontinental railroad since the 1840's, and during the next decade the government sponsored numerous explorations for possible routes. On July 1, 1862, President Lincoln signed a bill authorizing construction.

Construction was undertaken by the Union Pacific building westward from Omaha and by the Central Pacific moving eastward from Sacramento. Thomas C. Cochran writes: "On May 10, 1869, the construction crews met and joined tracks at Promontory, Utah, in the mountains north of the Great Salt Lake. The junction was celebrated by the ceremony of driving the Golden Spike, as the telegraph instruments clicked out to the waiting and rejoicing United States the message: "The last rail is laid . . . the last spike is driven. . . . The Pacific Railroad is completed."

A few weeks later a group of excursionists under James Ross and George Gary left Chicago to make one of the first round-trip runs. Their fascinating account was written down in diary form and published immediately on their return. The trip between Omaha and Sacramento had been cut from many months to a few days.

The most entertaining account of the earliest transcontinental railway trips was that actually printed along the way on the plush Pullman Hotel Express. Leaving on May 24, 1870, a group of celebrities made the trip entirely across the continent from Boston to San Francisco in eight days. The sometimes hilarious and carefully informative account by printer-editor W. R. Steele was printed as they travelled along, and copies were bound up for the excursionists when they returned home, making a volume of extreme interest and rarity.

OFFICE OF *Pope's Hill*

Massachusetts Woman Suffrage Association,

3 PARK STREET,

Boston, Oct. 4 1888

Dear Dorchester League

I cannot meet with
you today. but am ready to
ratify anything you decide.
We can all rejoice in the 25,000
women who are getting ready to vote.
What a revolution!

Yours always for equal rights

Lucy Stone

1870   [Woman Suffrage]

THE JOINT SPECIAL COMMITTEE ON FEMALE SUFFRAGE . . . REPORT, RESOLVE PROVIDING FOR AN AMENDMENT OF THE CONSTITUTION TO SECURE THE ELECTIVE FRANCHISE, AND THE RIGHT TO HOLD OFFICE, TO WOMEN . . .

Boston, House. Rep. 268, March 31, 1870. 5pp. *One of the earliest attempts to enfranchise women.* Accompanied by a printed memorial by Lucy Stone recommending adoption, Boston, January, 1871, 8pp. With an original Autograph Letter Signed from Lucy Stone, 1p., 4to, a short letter declining a speaking engagement, and stating: "We can all rejoice in the 25,000 women who are getting ready to vote. What a revolution!"   (289) 175.00

Bushnell, Horace
WOMEN'S SUFFRAGE: THE REFORM AGAINST NATURE.
N.Y.: Charles Scribner and Company, 1869. 184pp. Original cloth. Fine copy. *First edition.* Indicates how women are by nature unfit for suffrage.   (290) 45.00

Anthony, Susan B., et al.
AN APPEAL TO THE WOMEN OF THE UNITED STATES, BY THE NATIONAL WOMAN SUFFRAGE AND EDUCATIONAL COMMITTEE.
Hartford: Case, Lockwood & Brainard, 1871. 4pp. Moving plea to work for women's rights. (291) 15.00

Seawall, Molly E.
THE LADIES' BATTLE.
N.Y.: The Macmillan Company, 1911. 119pp. *First edition.* (292) 35.00

Atkins, G. G.
THE RIGHT AND WRONG OF FEMINISM: A SERMON.
Providence, 1914. 16pp. Printed wrappers. Proves God is against woman suffrage.
(293) 15.00

Shurter, E. D.
WOMAN SUFFRAGE: BIBLIOGRAPHY AND SELECTED ARGUMENTS.
Austin, 1915. 86pp. Printed wrappers. Valuable reference work on women's rights.
(294) 15.00

Lucy Stone, Susan B. Anthony, and many others fought a long, tedious battle for woman suffrage. In 1870 Lucy Stone managed to get a woman suffrage amendment presented to the Massachusetts legislature and the same year Susan B. Anthony was able to get the Anthony Woman Suffrage Amendment before national Congressional hearings. But it was not until after World War I that women finally won the right to vote.

The campaign was incredibly bitter. Horace Bushnell, in his anti-woman book, points out that man should be in charge, to exercise ''what may be called his manly prerogative. That is, man is to govern; all government belongs to men.'' Women, of course, do not have man-sized brains, he said, and ''womanly nature, all over the world, is instinctively submitted to the manly nature.''

These ideas were still held by many men after the turn of the century. Rev. G. G. Atkins wrote a pamphlet-sermon proving beyond doubt that God meant for women to stay home where they belonged. The national suffrage amendment finally passed both houses of Congress in 1919, the Senate being won by a single vote. Fourteen months of debate in the states followed, and the last state was won in a dramatic battle in Tennessee that carried for ratification by a majority of one vote. Texas, by the way, was the only other southern state to ratify the amendment, which was proclaimed on August 26, 1920.

EVENING JOURNAL-EXTRA.

CHICAGO, MONDAY, OCTOBER 9, 1871.

THE GREAT CALAMITY OF THE AGE!

Chicago in Ashes!!

Hundreds of Millions of Dollars' Worth of Property Destroyed.

The South, the North and a Portion of the West Divisions of the City in Ruins.

All the Hotels, Banks, Public Buildings, Newspaper Offices and Great Business Blocks Swept Away.

The Conflagration Still in Progress.

Fury of the Flames.

Details, Etc., Etc.

Chicago is burning! Up to this hour of writing (1 o'clock p. m.) the best part of the city is already in ashes! An area of between six and seven miles in length and nearly a mile in width, embracing the great business part of the city, has been burned over and now lies a mass of smouldering ruins!

All the principal hotels, all the public buildings, all the banks, all the newspaper offices, all the places of amusement, nearly all the great business edifices, nearly all the railroad depots, the water works, the gas works, several churches, and thousands of private residences and stores have been consumed. The proud, noble magnificent Chicago of yesterday, is to-day a mere shadow of what it was; and, helpless before the still sweeping flames, the fear is that the entire city will be consumed before we shall see the end.

The entire South Division, from Harrison street north to the river, almost the entire North Division, from the river to Lincoln Park, and several blocks in the West Division are burned.

It is utterly impossible to estimate the losses. They must in the aggregate amount to hundreds of millions of dollars. Amid the confusion and general bewilderment, we can only give a few details.

The fire broke out on the corner of DeKoven and Twelfth streets, at about 9 o'clock on Sunday evening, being caused by a cow kicking over a lamp in a stable in which a woman was milking. An alarm was immediately given, but, owing to the high southwest wind, the building was speedily consumed, and thence the fire spread rapidly. The firemen could not, with all their efforts, get the mastery of the flames. Building after building was fired by the flying cinders, which, landing on the roofs, which were as dry as tinder, owing to the protracted dry weather, instantly took fire. Northwardly and northeastwardly the flames took their course, lapping up house after house, block after block, street after street, all night long.

The scene of ruin and devastation is beyond the power of words to describe. Never, in the history of the world, has such a scene of extended, terrible and complete destruction, by conflagration, been recorded; and never has a more frightful scene of panic, distress and horror been witnessed among a helpless, sorrowing, suffering population.

It is utterly impossible, at he first thougnt, for he mind to take in any conception of he fearful ravages of the fire-fiend, al hough the as ounding facts stated above, is enough to appal the most heroic. The awful ru h of the si ua ion will be more fully comprehended by a glance at he follow ing very imperfec lis of he ci y's loss. It is, however, proper to state that, at his writing, the confusion in the police and fire departments is so complete as to render it impossible to give anything like a detailed accoun of he terrible conflagra ion.

PARTIAL DETAILS OF THE LOSSES.

The first to be mentioned, and possibly the most startling feature of this carnival of flame, is the total destruction of the City Water Works, by which calamity the firemen are rendered helpless to make the least endeavor to arrest the onward march of the devouring element. Should any other fires oc cur in parts of the city not burning, they most certainly have their way. At about 1? o'clock last night the sheet of flames licked across the river in the neighborhood of Jackson street, first igniting a small wooden building, which communicated the fire to the Armory, and soon to the South Side Gas Works, the immense gasometer exploding with a fearful detonation, heard all over the city. Then commenced the fearful ravages, which in a few hours laid the the entire South side in ashes, north of Harrison. The Post Office and Custom House, the Chamber of Commerce, the Court House and the rest soon went down in the ocean of fire and smoke. In brief, the following prominent buildings have perished with, in almost every case, their entire contents: the New Jerusalem Church, on Adams street, and the Catholic Church, on Desplaines street.

THE JOURNAL office, the Tribune, the Times, the Republican, the Post, the Mail, the Staats Zeitung, the Union, and many other publications.

Crosby's Opera House, McVicker's Theater, Hooley's Opera House, Dearborn Theater, and Wood's Museum.

First, Second, Third, Fourth, Fifth, Union-Northwestern, Manufacturers' Cook County, and Illinois National Banks.

The Second Presbyterian Church, St. Paul's Universalist Church, Trinity (Episcopal) Church.

The magnificent depot of the Chicago, Rock Island and Pacific and Lake Shore and Michigan Southern Railroads, on Van Buren street, at the head of La Salle street. The Great Central Union depot, and the Wells street depots of the Chicago and Northwestern Railroad.

The National Elevator, corner of Adams and the river, Armour, Dole & Co's Elevator, corner Market and the river. Hiram Wheeler's Elevator, on same corner as the above, the Galena Elevator, corner Rush street bridge and river, and "A" of the Illinois Central, near the Illinois Depot at the basin.

Tremont House, Sherman House, Briggs House, Metropolitan, Palmer, Adams, Bigelow, European, (Burke), Garden City and the new Pacific, in process of erection, on Clark and La Salle streets.

The following prominent business houses are in ashes: Field, Leither and Co. J. V. Farwell's block, and all the magnificent blocks in that locality. The Lake Side Publishing Company's new build ing, on Clark street, Terrace Row, on Michigan Av. and adjacent residences.

Farwell Hall burned at about four o'clock this morning.

The great breweries, on the North Side, are gone.

In fact, as stated above, the entire South and North sides, from Harrison street, northwardly, with a few isolated buildings left standing in some remark able manner, are in hopeless ruins.

HELP COMING.

During the night, telegrams were sent to St. Louis, Cleveland, Milwaukee and nearer cities for aid, and at the time of going to press several trains are on the way to the city, bringing free engines and men to assist us in this dire calamity.

BOARD OF TRADE

The Board of Trade has leased for present use the northwest cor. of Washington and Canal streets. We call attention to the card announcing a meet ing of the Directors of the Chicago Board of Trade, to-morrow morning, at 10 o'clock, at 51 and 53 Canal Street.

COUNCIL MEETING—A PROCLAMATION.

The Common Council and a number of of promi nent citizens are holding a meeting this afternoon in the First Congregational Church, to make such arrangements as may be possible for the safety of the city.

The Mayor has issued a proclamation that all fires in stoves in the city shall be extinguished.

THE EVENING JOURNAL.

We are under great obligations to the Interior Printing Company, 15 and 18 Canal street, for ac commodations by which we are enabled to issue this Extra. We hope before many days, to be able to announce permanent arrangements for issuing THE EVENING JOURNAL regularly. We have saved a portion of our sub scription books, and hope to be able to resume publication without great delay.

160

RARE GROUP OF NINE ORIGINAL CHICAGO NEWSPAPERS DESCRIBING THE FIRE AS IT OCCURRED:

(1) *Chicago Post-Extra!* Oct. 9, 1871. "Chicago on Fire!."

(2) *Chicago Journal-Extra!* Oct. 9, 1871. "Chicago in Ashes! The Conflagration Still in Progress."

(3) *Chicago Evening Post-Extra!* Oct. 10, 1871. "A Night of Horror!"

(4) *Chicago Sun-Extra!* Oct. 10, 1871. "Fires Still Raging But Nearly Subdued."

(5) *Chicago Evening Journal.* Oct. 10, 1871. "Destruction of Chicago!"

(6) *Chicago Evening Mail.* Oct. 11, 1871. "Chicago Destroyed!"

(7) *Chicago Tribune.* Oct. 11, 1871. "Fire! Eighteen Thousand Buildings Destroyed."

(8) *Chicago Evening Journal.* Oct. 12, 1871. "Our Calamity! The Smoke Begins to Clear Away. List of Persons Missing."

(9) *Chicago Evening Journal.* Oct. 14, 1871. "Proclamation by the Mayor." Map of the fire area.   (295) 350.00

FULL ACCOUNT OF THE GREAT FIRE IN CHICAGO.

Racine: Utley & Son, 1871. 20pp. Printed wrappers. Includes a "Business Directory of Firms That Were Burned Out."   (296) 75.00

THE BURNING OF CHICAGO, BY LIEUT. VESEY OF GADS HILL.

Broadside, narrow folio, Chicago, 1871. Includes the quatrain about Mrs. O'Leary's barn, ending: "The old cow shook her angry head, and lashed her flowing tail, / She raised her foot and kicked the lamp that stood their [sic] on the pail. . . ."   (297) 125.00

CHICAGO, THE GREAT FIRE . . . REPORT OF THE JOINT COMMITTEE OF THE RELIEF FUND . . .

Newark: Daily Journal Office, 1872. 31pp. Original printed wrappers.   (298) 30.00

In 1871 Chicago had a population of 300,000, with buildings by the thousand stretching in every direction — almost all built of wood. Even the sidewalks were constructed of resinous pine, and the single pumping station which supplied the mains with water had a wooden roof.

The inevitable occurred. After an exceptionally dry summer, on the night of October 8-9, a fire broke out. The traditional story is that a cow belonging to a Mrs. O'Leary upset a lamp in her in-town barn, but no one really knows how it began.

Over 18,000 buildings were destroyed, over 100,000 people were rendered homeless, over $200,000,000.00 in property damaged was suffered, and the city was in ruins. The townspeople, with help from all over the country, rebuilt the great city anew. By 1890 it had over a million inhabitants and was America's second-largest metropolis.

National . Park Langford

The Author

PACKING A RECALCITRANT MULE.

1872   [Yellowstone National Park]

Barlow, J. W., and D. P. Heap
REPORT OF A RECONNAISSANCE OF THE YELLOWSTONE RIVER IN 1871.
Wash., SED66, 1872. 43pp. Large folding map. In cloth case. Howes B145. *First edition.*

(299) 85.00

162

Langford, N. P.

REPORT OF THE SUPERINTENDENT OF THE YELLOWSTONE NATIONAL PARK FOR THE YEAR 1872.

Wash., 1873. 9pp. Blue printed wrappers. Large folding map. "Congress, by an act approved March 1, 1875, has set apart a tract . . . to be known as Yellowstone National Park." *This is the first official report.* (300) 150.00

Doane, Gustavus C.

REPORT UPON THE SO-CALLED YELLOWSTONE EXPEDITION OF 1870.

Wash., 1873. 40pp. Blue printed wrappers. *First edition.* Howes D371. Graff 1097. (301) 85.00

Ludlow, William

REPORT OF A RECONNAISSANCE . . . TO THE YELLOWSTONE NATIONAL PARK.

Wash., 1876. 145pp. Folio. Original cloth. Folding maps. Plates. *First edition. Inscribed and signed by Maj. George H. Elliot, U.S. Engineers.* Howes L588. (302) 50.00

Langford, N.P.

DIARY OF THE WASHBURN EXPEDITION TO THE YELLOWSTONE . . . IN 1870.

N.p., 1905. 122pp. Original cloth. *Inscribed and signed by Langford.* Jones 1704. Graff 2389. *First edition of the first publication of Langford's account of the discovery of Yellowstone Park.* (303) 75.00

The first recorded visit to Yellowstone Park was made by John Colter in 1810 when he took refuge there from hostile Indians. No one believed his story of what he saw there, nor did they believe that of the next visitor, Joseph Meek, in 1829. Finally, in the 1850's the region was described in considerable detail in the writings of Father DeSmet, the famous Jesuit missionary, who had obtained most of his information from the mountain man, Jim Bridger. In 1859 Capt. W. F. Reynolds led a government expedition to the area, but it brought back little information and was discredited by a public dead set on not believing what was there.

Finally, in 1870, N. P. Langford and H. D. Washburn led a well-equipped, thorough expedition that not only established the facts about the region but also led directly to the creation of Yellowstone National Park on March 1, 1872. Langford was appointed the first Superintendent of the Park, which was the Federal government's first program for preserving any extensive area of the national lands for public use. The magnificent park included over two million acres in Wyoming, Montana, and Idaho, and included some of the most beautiful and breathtaking area in the country.

Ames, Oakes

DEFENCE OF OAKES AMES AGAINST THE CHARGE OF SELLING TO MEMBERS OF CONGRESS SHARES OF THE CAPITAL STOCK OF THE CREDIT MOBILIER OF AMERICA, WITH INTENT TO BRIBE SAID MEMBERS OF CONGRESS.

N.p., 1873. 20pp. Sewn. Eloquent defence, read by Ames on the floor of Congress.

(304) 60.00

Patterson, J. W.

OBSERVATIONS ON THE REPORT OF THE COMMITTEE OF THE SENATE RESPECTING THE CREDIT MOBILIER OF AMERICA.

Wash.: M'Gill & Witherow, 1873. 45pp. Original color printed wrappers. Defence by Sen. Patterson in answer to his condemnation by a Senate Committee.   (305) 45.00

Group of eight pamphlets relating to the Credit Mobilier Case, in the case of Jim Fisk vs. Union Pacific Railroad and others. Original printed wrappers, 1868-1870. Includes Summons, Complaint, and Order to the Court; Opinion of the Court; Deposition of Oliver Ames, et al; Argument of James Emott for the Defendants; etc. In half morocco slipcase.

(306) 450.00

Original Autograph Letter Signed, 1p., 4to, Executive Mansion, Wash., Sept. 16, 1872, from Gen. F. T. Dent, Grant's aid, to Gen. H. H. Bingham of Phila. An intriguing (in two senses of the word) letter written during the Presidential campaign, stating: ''Do you get the last cash? You know what I mean. There is treachery in the camp somewhere and the President says he thinks Pennsylvania is lost. Work, man, work. Money you can have all you want only work. . . .''   (307) 125.00

Garfield, James A.

REVIEW OF THE TRANSACTIONS OF THE CREDIT MOBILIER COMPANY AND AN EXAMINATION OF THAT PORTION OF THE TESTIMONY TAKEN BY THE COMMITTEE OF INVESTIGATION . . . WHICH RELATES TO MR. GARFIELD.

Wash., 1873. 28pp. Sewn. *First edition* of Garfield's defence of his actions.   (308) 125.00

Credit Mobilier of America was a company used by leaders of the Union Pacific Railroad to enable them to pocket illegal profits from the construction of the Pacific Railroad. Oakes Ames and others managed to strip the Union Pacific of 23 million dollars by feeding the funds provided for construction through the railroad company to Credit Mobilier. When Congress got wind of the activities, Ames distributed 343 shares of Credit Mobilier stock to congressmen and officials of the executive department.

Late in Grant's 1872 presidential campaign charges were levelled in the press. Grant's race for re-election was tougher than expected as many of his officials were involved. In 1873 Ames and others were censured, Sen. James Patterson was recommended for expulsion, and Vice President Colfax and James A. Garfield were implicated. This and other scandals severely damaged Grant's own reputation and the country was plunged into the Panic of 1873 and a severe three-year depression.

1874 [The Modoc War]

Grover, Lafayette
THE REPORT OF GOVERNOR GROVER TO GENERAL SCHOFIELD, ON THE MODOC WAR, AND REPORTS OF GENERAL J. E. ROSS TO THE GOVERNOR, WITH ACCOMPANYING DOCUMENTS.
Salem, Oregon: Mart. V. Brown, 1874. 68pp. Half morocco. *First edition.* Howes G448. Graff 3119.   (309) 250.00

Sherman, William T.
GENERAL ORDERS NO. 3.
Original black-bordered announcement of the murder of Gen. E. R. S. Canby by the Modocs, Wash., April 14, 1873, 2pp., 8vo. Printed just 72 hours after his death.   (310) 25.00

The Modoc War started in 1872 when the Modoc chief Captain Jack went on the warpath in Oregon and northern California to resist efforts to force him and his followers to live on a reservation. Although Captain Jack had only about four dozen warriors, his stomping grounds were in the near-impenetrable lava beds of the Tule Lake region.

Gen. E. R. S. Canby was sent with Oregon and U.S. troops to capture him. Sherman, in General Order No. 3 on April 14, 1873, announced that Canby "was, on Friday last, April 11, shot dead by the chief 'Jack' while he was endeavoring to mediate for the removal of the Modocs from their present rocky fastness on the northern border of California to a reservation where the tribe could be maintained and protected by the proper civil agents of the Government. . . . Alas! the end is different from that which he and his best friends had hoped for, and he now lies a corpse in the wild mountains of California, while the lightning [telegraph] flashes his requiem to the furthermost corners of the civilized world."

The Modocs finally gave themselves up and Captain Jack was tried by a military court and hanged on October 3, 1873, and in the winter of 1873-1874 the surviving tribesmen were removed to a distant reservation.

Eddy, Mary Baker
SCIENCE AND HEALTH.
Boston: Christian Scientist Pub. Co., 1875. 458pp. plus errata. Original black cloth, gilt. Fine copy. *First edition.* Streeter 4281. Grolier American Hundred #78. Downs, Famous American Books #21: "Cheaply bound, crudely printed, and full of typographical errors. Today it is one of the rarest books in the world, for only a handful of copies survive; the remainder have been systematically destroyed."   (311) 1250.00

Eddy, Mary Baker
DEFENCE OF CHRISTIAN SCIENCE.
Boston: Published by the Author, 1885. 19pp. Original printed wrappers.   (312) 75.00

Eddy, Mary Baker
MIND-HEALING: HISTORICAL SKETCH.
Boston: Published by the Author, 1886. 24pp. Original printed wrappers.   (313) 90.00

Same, second issue, revised. 1888.   (314) 75.00

Same, second edition, revised. 1889.   (315) 75.00

Same, third edition, revised. 1890.   (316) 75.00

"America has given the world two major religions," writes R. B. Downs, "the Church of Jesus Christ of Latter-day Saints, or Mormonism, and the Church of Christ, Scientist, or Christian Science. The latter has the distinction of being the *only* religion founded by a woman."

Mrs. Eddy's theories, particularly as refined by later editors of her work, were in accord with much of the premises of modern psychiatry. Of her original 1875 volume, Stefan Zweig writes: "This almost unobtainable version, the only one that was exclusively Mary Baker's work and was untouched by any editorial hand, is essential to the psychological understanding of the book and its author, for none of the very numerous subsequent editions have more than a trace of the . . . charm of the original."

Starting from a single book in 1875, the religion grew to a membership of perhaps a million by the turn of the century and in 1971 was estimated to have 3200 churches in some 45 countries. The Grolier American Hundred Exhibit states: "This book has influenced the lives of more people than any other book written by a woman."

DRAFT OF A CONSTITUTION PUBLISHED UNDER THE DIRECTION OF A COMMITTEE OF CITIZENS OF COLORADO, FOR CONSIDERATION AND DISCUSSION BY THE CITIZENS OF THE CENTENNIAL STATE.

Denver: Chain & Hardy, 1875. 54,[4]pp. plus errata leaf. Original printed wrappers. Fine copy. Kuhlman, p.8. McMurtrie and Allen #245. Working draft of proposed constitution, with numerous annotations and notes.   (317) 300.00

THE CONSTITUTION OF THE STATE OF COLORADO, ADOPTED IN CONVENTION, MARCH 14, 1876; ALSO THE ADDRESS OF THE CONVENTION TO THE PEOPLE OF COLORADO.

Denver: Tribune Book and Job Printing House, 1876. 65pp. Original printed wrappers, wanting plain back wrapper. Kuhlman, p.8. Harvard Exhib. #7. McMurtrie and Allen #289. Library of Congress Exhib. 96. Shearer 45.   (318) 400.00

Mathews, A. E.
PENCIL SKETCHES OF COLORADO, ITS CITIES, PRINCIPAL TOWNS AND MOUNTAIN SCENERY.

N.Y.: Lithography by J. Bier, 1866. Elephant folio. Original cloth. 23 superb lithographic plates in full color. Howes M413. Graff 2709. Peters, America on Stone, p.273. Stokes and Haskell, American Historical Prints, p.208. "These views are celebrated for their Documentary accuracy — apparently contemporary viewers could identify in the street views the rigs of various townspeople."—T. W. Streeter.   (319) 5000.00

On March 3, 1875, President Grant signed an act enabling Colorado Territory to elect a constitutional convention, which assembled in Denver on December 20, 1875. On March 14, 1876, the convention completed its task and published its work. H. H. Bancroft wrote: "The constitution-makers of Colorado were skilled artificers. It was a noble document, with those errors only which the course of events develops." The address to the voters at the end is a long one, concluding with the query: "Who is there among you that would not rather be a citizen of an independent State, than a mere settler upon the public lands of the Territory, governed by satraps appointed and removed at pleasure?"

On July 1, 1876, three days before the Centennial of the United States, the people of Colorado went to the polls and overwhelmingly voted for statehood, and one month later, President Grant proclaimed the admission of the Centennial State into the Union.

THE

CONSTITUTION

OF THE

STATE OF COLORADO,

ADOPTED IN

CONVENTION, MARCH 14, 1876;

ALSO THE

Address of the Convention

TO THE

PEOPLE OF COLORADO.

ELECTION, SATURDAY, JULY 1, 1876.

DENVER, COL.
TRIBUNE BOOK AND JOB PRINTING HOUSE.
1876.

THE
CENTENNIAL

1776. JULY 4. 1876.

GOOD-BYE TO THE OLD CENTURY.

Miles of Men, Carriages and Torches Ushering in the Second Century of the Republic—The Greatest Pageant that America Has Yet Seen.

THE NEW BIRTH OF THE NATION.

Emperors, Princes, Statesmen and Patriotic Americans Joining Hands to Celebrate the Centennial Anniversary of the Nation's Independence.

Trusses.

Undertakers.

REMEMBER that there is no necessity to-day for throwing lighted squibs into hay-lofts or carpenters' shops, nor for firing pistols into large crowds of citizens. Be careful, over-careful, with your combustibles. A spark might lay half the city in ashes and a stray shot might kill a patriot.

1776. 1876.
UNITED STATES CENTENNIAL COMMISSION.
INTERNATIONAL EXHIBITION, 1876.
PHILADELPHIA.
THE NATIONAL COMMEMORATION, JULY 4, 1876.

The ceremonies to be observed, under the direction of the United States Centennial Commission, in commemoration of the one hundredth anniversary of the Declaration of Independence of the United States, will take place in Independence Square, Philadelphia, July 4, beginning at 10 A. M., or soon thereafter, upon the conclusion of the military review.

The following order will be observed:

1. Grand Overture, "The Great Republic," founded on the national air "Hail Columbia," and arranged for the occasion by the composer, George F. Bristow, of New York. Orchestra, P. S. Gilmore, director.
2. The President of the Commission will call the assembly to order, and announce the President of the United States, or, in his absence, the Vice President, as the presiding officer of the day.
3. Prayer, by the Rt. Rev. Wm. B. Stevens, D. D., Bishop of Pennsylvania.
4. Hymn, "Welcome to All Nations." Words by Oliver Wendell Holmes, of Massachusetts. Music, "Keller's Hymn." Orchestra and Chorus.
5. Reading of the Declaration of Independence, by Richard Henry Lee, of Virginia. The original manuscript will be brought forward for the purpose by his Honor the Mayor of Philadelphia, to whose care it has been entrusted by the President of the United States.
6. "Greeting from Brazil," a Hymn for the First Centennial of American Independence, composed by A. Carlos Gomes, of Brazil, at the request of his Majesty Dom Pedro II, Emperor of Brazil. Orchestra.
7. Poem, "The National Ode," by Bayard Taylor, of Pennsylvania. Introduced by the President of the Centennial Board of Finance.
8. Grand Triumphal March, with Chorus, "Our National Banner," Words by Dexter Smith, of Massachusetts; Music by Sir Julius Benedict, of England.
9. Oration by William M. Evarts, of New York.
10. Hallelujah Chorus from Handel's "Messiah." Orchestra and Chorus.
11. Doxology, "The Old Hundredth Psalm," in which all present will be requested to join.

By order of the Commission.
JOSEPH R. HAWLEY, President.
JOHN L. CAMPBELL, Secretary.

CENTENNIAL NOTES.

There were only three drunken men at the Centennial yesterday, and of these two were politicians.

Miss Rosa D'Erina played and sang in the Main Building yesterday afternoon before a large audience. Her songs of all nations were cordially greeted, but when she soared into opera her success was not so marked.

THE parade of the Grand Army of the Republic yesterday was in every way worthy that order and the historic times which it celebrated. As the column of scarred veterans passed down Chestnut street it was greeted with huzzas that spoke the admiration and gratitude with which our people must ever regard the remnant of their victorious armies. The tattered battle-flags, the empty sleeves, the wooden limbs were so many reminders of the sacrifices which the young men of America have made for American liberty and union. In our commemoration of the heroic deeds of the founders of the Republic, we do not forget the services of its saviors, and Philadelphia, which was foremost in hospitalities to the soldiers of 1861, is now proud to welcome and entertain the veterans.

THE PHILADELPHIA TIMES: 1776—JULY 4—1876.

Philadelphia, July 4, 1876. Complete original newspaper from the birthplace of American Independence, 4pp., elephant folio, containing news of "To-Day's Pageant" and much on the centennial celebration.   (320) 45.00

THE CENTENNIAL CELEBRATION OF AMERICAN INDEPENDENCE AT CANTON, CHINA, ON THE 4TH JULY, 1876.

Canton: Office of the Daily Advertiser, 1876. 60pp. Original wrappers, in later paper boards. Inscribed and signed by the author, Gideon Nye.   (321) 125.00

Grobe, Charles

CENTENNIAL MEMORIAL MARCH, 1776-1876.

Phila., 1876. 8pp. Pictorial sheet music, large folio, dedicated "to Alfred T. Goshorn, Esq., Director–General of the Centennial Exhibition."   (322) 15.00

"GLORIA IN EXCELSIS DEO. She is a hundred years old to-day." Thus the *Philadelphia Times* began its issue for July 4, 1876. "You can't all get into Independence Hall, but by coming down town at an early hour you may have a look at the exterior decorations." They were expecting rain "before midnight. Keep cool. . . .

"Last night, the city of Philadelphia was recording the propriety of John Adams' sanguine prediction, that the work done early in July, 1776, would be celebrated. He mentioned bonfires. But bonfires are not permissible under the changed conditions of cities, since Mr. Adams lived. Gas has been introduced since that day. Almost everything possible of safety, comfort and luxury has been introduced since the celebrated few voted for the Declaration. Omnibusses, street cars, envelopes, free postal delivery, telegraph, ocean cables, steamboats . . . waterworks, baths, five crackers, breech-loaders, percussion caps, cartridges, coal have been presented to the world since Adams lived."

In China, in a flower garden house in Canton, the 4th of July centennial celebration began with a prayer, the singing of "My Country 'tis of Thee," the reading of the Declaration of Independence, the singing of the "Star Spangled Banner" and "Columbia, the Gem of the Ocean," and toasts and patriotic addresses. Afterwards, the people so far away from home in such strange surroundings, held an American-style picnic.

The high spot of the centennial year was the Centennial Exposition in Philadelphia. Fifty nations sent exhibits that were housed in 180 buildings covering 236 acres of land. Almost ten million people visited the mammoth exhibition, which included a prototype of Bell's telephone, a web printing press, a self-binding reaper, a typewriter, a refrigerator, and hundreds of technological exhibits.

Continuing its report of the 4th of July celebration, the *Philadelphia Times* concluded: "We celebrated the act of our forefathers in our own way last night. . . . We illuminated, we arched, we entertained . . . in short, we blazed."

Alfred T. Goshorn, Esq.

Director-General of the Centennial Exhibition,

PHILADELPHIA.

1776 # CENTENNIAL 1876

Memorial March.

— BY —

CHARLES GROBE.

PHILADELPHIA, **Mirsalis & Hamel,** 610 ARCH STEEET.

(OPPOSITE ARCH STREET THEATRE.)

AMERICAN CELEBRATION

The Second Hundred Years

PROCEEDINGS OF THE ELECTORAL COMMISSION . . . TO REGULATE THE COUNTING OF VOTES FOR PRESIDENT AND VICE-PRESIDENT, AND THE DECISIONS OF QUESTIONS ARISING THEREON.
Wash., 1877. 309pp. Folio. Original half morocco, marbled boards.   (323)   100.00

PROCEEDINGS OF THE ELECTORAL COMMISSION AND OF THE TWO HOUSES OF CONGRESS IN JOINT MEETING RELATIVE TO THE COUNT OF ELECTORAL VOTES . . . FOR THE PRESIDENTIAL TERM COMMENCING MARCH 4, 1877.
Wash., 1877. 1087pp. Original full morocco, gilt.   (324)   100.00

Samuel J. Tilden was elected President of the United States but never served, due to the outcome of the extraordinary electoral commission that convened after the election. Tilden had risen to prominence as a leader in reorganizing the Democratic Party after the Civil War, particularly in overthrowing the Tweed Ring and as reform governor of New York. He became the Democratic nominee in 1876 on the first ballot.

His opponent was Rutherford B. Hayes, who was nominated only after a deadlocked Republican convention, which went six ballots for James G. Blaine. The ensuing campaign was filled with bitterness, Republicans throwing up the war (giving us the phrase ''waving the bloody shirt'') and Democrats denouncing the scandals of the Grant administrations.

Tilden was elected by popular vote, but when the electoral college met he received 184 votes to 165 for Hayes, with 20 votes contested by two sets of returns. The Constitution made no provision for such an unprecedented event, so both houses of Congress created an extra-constitutional body, the ''Electoral Commission,'' composed of five Senators, five Representatives, and five Supreme Court Justices, supposedly consisting of seven Democrats, seven Republicans, and one independent. Ultimately, the commission voted party lines and gave every vote to Hayes by 8 to 7. Although the House refused to accept the results, provision had been made for the Commission's results to stand, and Hayes was declared elected.

Tilden put the nation first and counselled his followers to abide by the result. ''I can retire to private life,'' he said, ''with the consciousness that I shall receive from posterity the credit of having been elected to the highest position in the gift of the people, without any of the cares and responsibilities of the office.''

1878 [The Silver Question]

Weston, George M.
THE SILVER QUESTION.
N.Y.: I. S. Homans, 293pp. Original cloth. *First edition.*   (325) 45.00

Jones, John P., of Nevada
COINAGE OF SILVER . . . SPEECH IN THE SENATE OF THE UNITED STATES.
Wash., 1878. 32pp. Sewn.   (326) 20.00

Jones, John P.
THE MONEY QUESTION: REMONETIZATION OF SILVER.
Wash., 1894. 463pp. Original printed wrappers. Extensive reports and data on the whole history of the silver question.   (327) 35.00

Group of eight reports and speeches on the silver question, 1878-1896.   (328) 85.00

The depression following the Panic of 1873 brought about a national debate over the nation's monetary system. In 1873 the market value of silver had dropped in its ratio to gold, making silver worth less just at the time when western mining states were beginning to find it in large quantities and just as a protracted depression was setting in. Moreover, in the same year the government removed its authorization of the minting of silver dollars, further hurting the silver market.

The result was that silver interests pressured the government to promote higher silver prices, which it was felt would help the mining areas and the country in general pull out of the depression. If a man's silver certificates and easy-to-get silver would buy more gold, and most of the world was on a gold standard, then his earnings would buy more for him.

On February 28, 1878, Congress passed the compromise Bland-Allison Act over President Hayes' veto. Silver interests had urged bimettalism — going off the gold standard and on a dual silver-gold standard at a value ratio of 16 to 1. The compromise act did not go this far, but did require the government to purchase 24 to 48 million dollars worth of silver a year at that ratio to be minted into silver dollars and used to back up silver certificates.

The result was to put the problem before the public as a political issue, which affected every presidential campaign for the next two decades and, since much demagoguery and capitalist-labor relationships were involved, to thrust a confusing cloud over political activities for the rest of the century.

13

Why did you take up the line of rubber
experimentation, rather than another? What
interested you in the idea?

I got tired of Mechanics
~~and~~ always wanted
to experiment on plant
breeding — bought land
at Ft Myers Fla
43 years ago but
never had time to do
anything until lately
when I started the
rubber experiments —
I have collected up to date
nearly 1600 wild plants
The seeds of ~~1500~~ 1400
wild plants are being
sowed in my garden of
9 acres

McClure, J. B.
EDISON AND HIS INVENTIONS . . . THE PHONOGRAPH, TASIMETER, ELECTRIC LIGHT, AND ALL HIS PRINCIPAL DISCOVERIES.
Chicago: Rhodes & McClure, 1879. 171,36,[2]pp. Illus. Original red decorated cloth, gilt. Fine copy. *First edition, with original check signed by Edison inserted.*   (329) 185.00

Edison, Thomas Alva
[SCIENTIFIC MANUSCRIPT]
Original Autograph Manuscript on 18 leaves, 4to, comprising Edison's handwritten answers to a series of questions designed to elicit his thoughts on the future of science and agriculture to the United States. Accompanied by a telegram from Edison to writer Wheeler McMillen granting the interview, and by a Typed Manuscript Signed, 6pp., folio, by Miller about the interview and incorporating many of Edison's responses. Edison makes statements covering a broad range of predictions, suggestions, and criticisms, and the manuscript is thereby choice for research.   (330) 875.00

In 1879, Thomas A. Edison arranged for special trains to bring several thousand people to his laboratories in Menlo Park, where he displayed the incandescent light bulb — just one of many of the products of his brain factory that changed the nature of civilization. Two years earlier he had produced the phonograph, which has been called his ''greatest single achievement from the standpoint of daring imagination.''

By 1882 Edison had his electric light system working in New York City, from where it spread to everywhere in the world. Thereafter, he worked on other practical developments and advances, both by new inventions and by improvements on other inventions — the motion picture, radio-telephony, cement manufacture, iron mining, dictation machines, mimeographs, batteries, submarine periscopes, and scores of others.

In 1928 he was cited by Congress as ''the man with the fifteen billion dollar brain'' — a reference to the reputed value of his inventions — and ''for development and application of inventions that have revolutionized civilization in the last century.'' In 1929, while attending a 50th anniversary celebration of his 1879 display of the light bulb, Edison suffered a stroke from which he never recovered, dying in 1931 as the most famous of all American inventors.

Hayes, Rutherford B.
ANNUAL MESSAGE OF THE PRESIDENT . . . AT THE COMMENCEMENT OF THE THIRD SESSION OF THE 46TH CONGRESS.
Wash., Dec. 6, 1880. 34pp. Printed wrappers.   (331) 20.00

LETTERS AND MESSAGES OF RUTHERFORD B. HAYES . . . WITH LETTER OF ACCEPTANCE AND INAUGURAL ADDRESS.
Wash., 1881. 368pp. Original half morocco. With card autographed by Pres. Hayes tipped in.   (332) 85.00

THE REPUBLICAN CAMPAIGN TEXT BOOK FOR 1880.
Wash., 1880. 215pp. Original printed wrappers.   (333) 25.00

[ASSASSINATION OF GARFIELD]
Original telegram, written out in ink on printed form, White House, [Wash.], 9:20 A.M., July 5, 1881, reading in part: "President very much better. Had poor night. Pulse reduced 12 beats. Temperature over 3 less. No nausea. Eats & digests. Good spirits. No more swelling of stomach or bad sensation in feet. Physicians think more favorable than ever. Steadily improving, but danger, of course, always imminent. All in house very much encouraged. . . ."
                                                                               (334) 125.00

[DEATH OF GARFIELD]
Utica Morning Herald, Sept. 20, 1881, containing black-bordered announcement of Garfield's death. Chipped.   (335) 35.00

Group of seven memorial addresses on Garfield's death, 1881-1882, all in original printed wrappers, including addresses by James G. Blaine and Horace Greeley.   (336) 60.00

One result of the contested election of Hayes was a deal with Democrats to remove Federal troops occupying the South, and in 1877 Hayes honored the deal, ending Reconstruction. A strong President, he stood firm against his party in insisting on patronage reform and fighting the spoils system. He also honored his pledge not to run for re-election in 1880. His lame-duck State of the Union message of Dec. 6, 1880, is a notable address, interesting for its summary of the results of Reconstruction and of the state of national affairs at the beginning of the long era of port-Reconstruction peace and prosperity, and for its prophetic condemnation of "the pernicious competition of influence and official favoritism in the bestowal of office."

Without Hayes in the race, the Republican Party held a rip-roaring convention that took 36 ballots before a dark horse, James A. Garfield, was nominated. For his running mate they chose Chester A. Arthur, who had been removed from a Federal office by Hayes for his support of the spoils system. The two men won the election by a narrow margin.

Four months after taking office, on July 2, 1881, Garfield was shot by a disappointed office seeker while standing in a train station. For 90 days he lingered barely conscious, and the country was without a functioning President. On September 19, Garfield died and Arthur was sworn in the next day. To the amazement of most, Arthur shucked his pro-patronage stance and served admirably, although he was not re-nominated.

No. 16—Form 1.

THE AMERICAN RAPID TELEGRAPH COMPANY.

EXPRESS MESSAGE.

☞ Delivered by Special Messengers. ☜

EXPRESS MESSAGES TAKEN BY THIS COMPANY SUBJECT TO THE FOLLOWING TERMS

To guard against mistakes or delays, the sender of a message should order it REPEATED; that is, telegraphed back to the originating office for comparison. For this, one-half the regular rate is charged in addition. It is agreed between the sender of the following message and this Company, that said Company shall not be liable for mistakes or delays in the transmission of delivery, or for non-delivery, of any REPEATED message, whether happening by negligence of its servants or otherwise, beyond the amount received for sending the same, nor for mistakes or delays in the transmission or delivery, or for non-delivery, of any REPEATED message beyond fifty times the sum received for sending the same, unless specially insured; nor in any case for delays arising from unavoidable interruption in the working of its lines, or for errors in cipher or obscure messages.

And this Company is hereby made the agent of the sender, without liability, to forward any message over the lines of any other Company when necessary to reach its destination.

Correctness in the transmission of messages to any point on the lines of this Company can be insured by contract in writing, stating agreed amount of risk, and payment of premium thereon at the following rates, in addition to writing, stating agreed amount of risk, and payment of premium thereon at the following rates, in addition to the usual charge for repeated messages, viz.: One per cent. for any distance not exceeding 1,000 miles, and one per cent. for any greater distance. No employee of the Company is authorized to vary the foregoing.

No responsibility regarding messages attaches to this Company until the same are presented and accepted at one of its transmitting offices; and if a message is sent to such office by one of the Company's messengers, he acts for that purpose as the agent of the sender.

Express messages will be delivered free within the established free delivery limits of the terminal office; for delivery at a greater distance, a special charge will be made to cover the cost of such delivery.

This Company will not be liable for damages in any case where the claim is not presented in writing, within sixty days after sending the message.

GERRITT SMITH, Engineer-in-Chief.   I. A. SHERMAN, Gen'l Sup't.   EDWIN REED, President.

CHECK	NUMBER	TIME.
	White House, —	9-20 a m

Send the following Express Message subject to the above terms which are agreed to. Sep 5 — 1881

To Dear Girls

President very much better. Had good night. Pulse reduced 12 beats. Temperature over 3 less. No nausea. Eats & digests. Good spirits. No more swelling of stomach, or bad sensation in feet. Physicians think more favorable than ever. Steadily improving, but danger, of course, always imminent. All in house very much encouraged. Tell the Greens. Aff.
W. P.

☞ Read the Notice and Agreement at the Top.

UPON THE

Production of Sound by Radiant Energy.

By ALEXANDER GRAHAM BELL.

PAPER READ BEFORE THE NATIONAL ACADEMY OF SCIENCES, APRIL 21, 1881.

WASHINGTON, D. C.
GIBSON BROTHERS, PRINTERS.
1881.

Bell, Alexander Graham

UPON THE PRODUCTION OF SOUND BY RADIANT ENERGY.

Wash.: Gibson Brothers, Printers, 1881. 45pp. Illus. Printed wrappers, stamped ''With the Author's compliments.'' *First edition.* Paper read before the National Academy of Sciences, April 21, 1881.   (337) 175.00

Bell, Alexander Graham

THE TELEPHONE, A LECTURE ENTITLED RESEARCHES IN ELECTRIC TELEPHONY . . . DELIVERED BEFORE THE SOCIETY OF TELEGRAPH ENGINEERS.

London: E. and F. N. Spon, 1878. 32pp. Original printed wrappers. *First edition, inscribed ''with the author's compliments.''*   (338) 175.00

Dickerson, E. N.

U.S. CIRCUIT COURT: AMERICAN BELL TELEPHONE, ET AL. V. THE PEOPLE'S TELEPHONE COMPANY ET AL.

Boston: Alfred Mudge, 1884. 165pp. Illus. Original printed wrappers. Fascinating testimony encompassing Bell's defence and proof of having invented the telephone. ''The cause which has been committed to my care by Mr. Bell is the most important ever heard in this or any other court in the United States involving private interests. . . . Actually, it is a controversy between 100,000 people on the one side . . . and piracy, in which 100 millions of dollars are involved. There is no village in the United States having a population of 5,000 and upwards, in which there is not established a telephone plant, put there by the capital of tens of thousands of people . . . who have their eyes fixed upon this court room to ascertain whether this decision shall ruin them. . . . It is a subject of national interest.''   (339) 125.00

    In 1881 the first commercial long-distance telephone service in the country opened for business, with wires running 45 miles between Boston and Providence. Alexander Graham Bell, an immigrant, had invented the telephone some years before, his famous first message (''Mr. Watson, come here; I want you'') being spoken on March 10, 1876. In the meantime, important practical improvements had been made by Edison, Bell, and Emile Berliner.

    From this point on, the telephone, like the telegraph and electric light, began making America a network of wires. Bell was beset by lawsuits and patent cases, but was entirely vindicated as inventor by the courts. By 1884 there were telephone companies throughout the country. In 1915, telephone long-distance service was initiated, when Bell himself transmitted from New York to Watson in San Francisco the same message that he had spoken forty years earlier.

ROBBERY OF THE AUSTIN AND SAN ANTONIO STAGE.

TREACHEROUS DEATH OF JESSE JAMES BY ROBERT AND CHARLES FORD

182

Triplett, Frank

THE LIFE, TIMES AND TREACHEROUS DEATH OF JESSE JAMES . . . DICTATED . . . BY MRS. JESSE JAMES, WIFE OF THE BANDIT, AND MRS. ZERELDA SAMUEL, HIS MOTHER.

St. Louis: J. H. Chambers & Co., 1882. 416pp. Original pictorial cloth. Fine copy. *First edition, first issue.* Howes T355: Adams One Fifty #138. Adams Six Guns #2243: ''Exceedingly rare. The few copies in existence are usually in poor condition.'' (340) 450.00

Wallace, William H.

CLOSING SPEECH FOR THE STATE MADE BY WM. H. WALLACE, ESQ., PROSECUTING ATTORNEY OF JACKSON COUNTY, MO., IN THE TRIAL OF FRANK JAMES FOR MURDER.

Kansas City, Mo.: Published by the Citizens of Gallatin, Missouri, 1883. 65pp. Printed wrappers. *Signed in ink by T. B. Yates, the county official who headed the movement for the work,* ''paid for by money raised by the proud citizens for a watch and chain, which Wallace declined.'' Adams Six Guns #2294. Howes W56. (341) 250.00

Frank and Jesse James grew up in a pro-Southern family in Missouri, and during the Civil War their home was twice raided by Northern militia. They joined Quantrill's Raiders while still teenagers, participating in some bloodcurdling escapades. After the war, with the Younger brothers and others, they formed their notorious gang of bank and train robbers.

In an abortive raid on a bank in Northfield, Minn., in 1876, all of the gang except Frank and Jesse were killed or captured. Jesse moved to St. Joseph, Mo., under the name of Thomas Howard. When a large dead or alive reward was offered for him, one of the members of the gang, Robert Ford, shot Jesse in the back of the head on April 3, 1882. Frank James surrendered later in the year and lived until 1915. Both men became folk heroes, while Governor T. T. Crittenden, who issued the reward for Jesse, and W. H. Wallace, who prosecuted Frank, were so maligned by the pro-James public that neither was re-elected or ever held office again.

The Triplett volume had an interesting history. Jesse's mother and wife sued the publisher, claiming they had not given permission for their names to be used, but signed contracts and cancelled checks were provided proving that they had. Ramon Adams writes: ''The author devotes a long chapter to an accusation that Governor Crittenden conspired [in the murder of] Jesse, and he uses strong language. Apparently Crittenden did not become aware of the book for several months after its publication, but when he did, he caused all copies he could lay his hand on to be destroyed. To make matters worse, the publisher was sued by Mrs. James, and on top of it all, Frank James objected to the book because it accused him of moral misconduct. All things considered, there is no wonder it is an exceedingly rare volume.''

AN ACT

GRANTING LANDS TO AID IN THE CONSTRUCTION
OF A RAILROAD AND TELEGRAPH LINE FROM
LAKE SUPERIOR TO PUGET'S SOUND
ON THE PACIFIC COAST BY THE
NORTHERN ROUTE,

BY THE NAME AND TITLE OF THE

NORTHERN PACIFIC RAILROAD

COMPANY.

APPROVED JULY 2, 1864.

BOSTON:
PRINTED BY ALFRED MUDGE & SON, 34 SCHOOL STREET.
1864.

REPORT IN RELATION TO AN AGREEMENT

MADE BETWEEN

JOSEPH KAY McCAMMON,

Assistant Attorney General,

ON BEHALF OF THE UNITED STATES, AND THE

CONFEDERATED TRIBES OF THE FLATHEAD, KOOTENAY, AND
UPPER PEND D'OREILLES INDIANS

FOR THE SALE OF

A PORTION OF THEIR RESERVATION IN MONTANA

FOR THE USE OF THE

NORTHERN PACIFIC RAILROAD.

WASHINGTON:
GOVERNMENT PRINTING OFFICE.
1883.

1883

Smalley, Eugene V.
HISTORY OF THE NORTHERN PACIFIC RAILROAD.
N.Y.: G. P. Putnam's Sons, 1883. 437pp. Folding map in pocket. Original cloth, gilt. Very fine copy. *First edition.* Howes S561.   (342) 100.00

REPORT IN RELATION TO AN AGREEMENT MADE BETWEEN JOSEPH KAY McCAMMON, ASST. ATT. GEN., ON BEHALF OF THE U.S., AND THE CONFEDERATED TRIBES OF THE FLATHEAD, KOOTENAY, AND UPPER PEND D'OREILLES INDIANS FOR THE SALE OF A PORTION OF THEIR RESERVATION FOR THE USE OF THE NORTHERN PACIFIC RAILROAD.
Wash., 1883. 28pp. Nine folding maps. Original cloth, gilt.   (343) 85.00

Stevens, Gov. Isaac I., Supt., and James Buchanan
TREATY BETWEEN THE UNITED STATES AND THE FLATHEAD, KOOTENAY, AND UPPER PEND D'OREILLES INDIANS.
Wash., 1859. 8pp. Tied. Long folio. The treaty referred to above, made by Gov. Stevens of Washington Territory on July 16, 1855, and ratified by the Senate and President on April 18, 1859. *First printing.* Rare.   (344) 125.00

Lincoln, Abraham

AN ACT GRANTING LANDS TO AID IN THE CONSTRUCTION OF A RAILROAD AND TELEGRAPH LINE FROM LAKE SUPERIOR TO PUGET'S SOUND ON THE PACIFIC COAST BY THE NORTHERN ROUTE, BY THE NAME AND TITLE OF THE NORTHERN PACIFIC RAILROAD COMPANY.
Boston: Alfred Mudge, 1864. 18pp. Approved by Pres. Lincoln, July 2, 1864. (345) 150.00

The completion in 1883 of the Northern Pacific Railroad was another milestone in American transportation history, as stated by *Encyc. Brit.:* ''It was constructed under an act of Congress approved by President Lincoln on July 2, 1864. With its completion in 1883 the vast territory adjacent to it was first made accessible to settlers, and the government's long-cherished aim of opening to the north Pacific coast a route following, roughly, that taken by the explorers Lewis and Clark, was at length realized.'' It connected a fine harbor at Tacoma with Lake Superior: ''Thus would the navigation of the Great Lakes be connected overland with navigation of the Pacific.''

Unfortunately, it also marked another low spot of the many dismal chapters in American-Indian relations. In 1859 the Flatheads and other tribes had been forced into a treaty buying much of their land and granting them title to a reservation. The boundaries of the reservation were largely ignored during ensuing years by gold hunters who drove off the game the Indians depended upon. In late 1882, the U.S. sent J. K. McCammon with orders to insist on a revision of the treaty to allow the Northern Pacific to build the railroad through the middle of the reservation. The verbatim report of his meeting includes a fascinating insight into the plight of the tribes involved. One chief said: ''I am crowded on both sides . . . I want you to keep the whites off the land at the head of Flathead Lake. . . . It may be true that the railroad would help the Indians, but I [don't believe it.]''

Another said: ''There are things that the government promised in that treaty [of 1859] that I have never seen. . . . We did not get one-half of the [money and land we were promised]. It was divided among yourselves. You told us that after a while we would be intelligent and rich and like white men. We are poor now. We try to have whites to assist us, and they won't because we are Indians. That is the reason we want to have the whites kept out of the Flathead Lake country. . . . You had better go the other way. . . . Ours is a small country; it is valuable to us; we support ourselves by it; there is no end to these lands supporting us; they will do it for generations. If you say you will give us money for our lands, I doubt if we get it, because we didn't before.''

McCammon replied: ''The Great Father is not treated with respect when I am told you will not get the money. The matter will be submitted to the Great Council, and the Indians will get the money. . . . You can rely upon the good faith of the government.'' The Indians were forced to sign, and one can imagine what the railroad did to their hunting grounds and just how reliable the government was about paying for it.

what it would take three days to fix it. If I'd a called it a bolt-head it would a done just as well.

Now I was feeling pretty comfortable all down one side, and pretty uncomfortable all up the other. Being Tom Sawyer was easy and comfortable; and it stayed easy and comfortable till by-and-by I hear a steamboat coughing along down the river— then I says to myself, spose Tom Sawyer come down on that boat? —and spose he steps in here, any minute, and sings out my name before I can throw him a wink to keep quiet? Well, I couldn't *have* it that way—it wouldn't do at all. I must go up the road and waylay him. So I told the folks I reckoned I would go up to the town and fetch down my

"WHO DO YOU RECKON IT IS?"

baggage. The old gentleman was for going along with me, but I said no, I could drive the horse myself, and I druther he wouldn't take no trouble about me.

Suppressed Plate
from
Huckleberry Finn
100 Proofs

Clemens, Samuel L.
THE ADVENTURES OF HUCKLEBERRY FINN.
London: Chatto & Windus, 1884. 438,[32]pp. Original red cloth. Some wear, but a very good copy. *First edition, first issue,* preceding the American first edition by nearly five months. B.A.L. 3414. Grolier American Hundred #87. Johnson, High Spots of American Literature, p.23.   (346) 300.00

ADVENTURES OF HUCKLEBERRY FINN.
N.Y.: Charles Webster and Company, 1885. 366pp. Original dark green pictorial cloth, gilt. *First edition,* with most first issue points. *Card signed by Clemens inside front cover:* "Very Truly Yours, Mark Twain." Grolier American Hundred #87. BAL 3415. Peter Parley to Penrod, p.75.   (347) 485.00

SUPPRESSED PLATE FROM HUCKLEBERRY FINN.
One of 100 proofs drawn from the infamous suppressed plate 283. "The engraving is in the original state but defaced; whether by accident or design is not known although Mark Twain was convinced that the defacement was deliberate. The blemish is such that the engraving is ribald [decidedly so]. No examined copy of the published book has the defaced plate."   (348) 125.00

The publication of this book, writes Burton Rascoe, was "the most important single event in American literature." No other American book has received such overwhelming and universal praise. Ernest Hemingway said "all American literature comes from one book by Mark Twain called *Huckleberry Finn*. . . . All American writing comes from that. There was nothing before. There has been nothing as good since." H. L. Mencken called it "one of the great masterpieces of the world. [Twain] was the true father of our rational literature." William Lyon Phelps called it America's greatest novel; Herman Wouk said it is the crown of our literature; W. L. Alden claimed it is "the best book ever written."

The work is much more than a juvenile adventure tale, although it is a cracking good one. Sculley Bradley states: "On the adult level, this is a complex work of art, sometimes approaching profundity in its psychological perceptions, its moral judgments, and its social criticism." T. S. Eliot calls Huck Finn "one of the permanent symbolic figures of fiction, not unworthy to take a place with Ulysses, Faust, Don Quixote, Don Juan, Hamlet, and other great discoveries that man has made about himself." William Dean Howells wrote: "Emerson, Longfellow, Lowell, Holmes — I knew them all, and all the rest of our sages, poets, seers, critics, humorists; they were like one another and like other literary men; but Clemens was sole, incomparable, the Lincoln of our literature."

APPENDIX No. 15.

LETTER FROM GEORGE B. LOVING, ESQ., OF FORT WORTH, TEX., IN REGARD TO THE LOSSES OF CATTLE DURING THE WINTER OF 1884– '85, THE DECLINE IN THE VALUE OF STOCK, AND THE FUTURE OF THE STOCK-GROWING INTERESTS OF TEXAS.

[Daily and Weekly Gazette, George B. Loving, proprietor.]

FORT WORTH, TEX., *April 15, 1885.*

DEAR SIR: Absence from the city and pressure of business has prevented me from answering your several letters sooner. The loss of cattle in this State during the past winter has been very heavy in some localities, while in others it has been much less. The loss in that part of the State known as the Panhandle will probably not exceed 5 per cent., and the same may be said of the extreme western part of the State in what is known as the Pecos River country. In some localities in the central part of the State the loss is estimated as high as 30 to 40 per cent. Taking the entire State, it will probably average between 15 and 20 per cent. The loss during the past winter has been the heaviest ever known in Texas for some length of time and will probably not occur again for many years; although, from present appearances, there is a strong probability that the entire grazing country in Texas will be largely overstocked within the next few years, caused by the outlets for surplus cattle being cut off by the recent enactment of quarantine laws in Kansas and other States and Territories. These laws, if enforced, will very materially injure the stock business in this State, from the fact that in order to carry it on successfully, an outlet must be found for our surplus stock cattle each year. Stock cattle in Texas have declined in value fully one-third in the last six or eight months. This decline was first caused by the stringency in money matters, but has been greatly increased within the last few months by the quarantine laws referred to above.

Nearly the entire drive from Texas, heretofore by trail, has been made between the 1st of March and the 1st of July. It will be impossible to drive Texas cattle to Kansas, if they must enter that State between the 1st of December and 1st of March, as the latter date is too early to handle cattle from this State, while December is too late, the cold weather making it impossible to handle them at that time. Heretofore thousands of cattle have been contracted for earlier than this for the spring drive, while this spring comparatively nothing has been done in that respect. The depression in the cattle business here, now that winter is over, is almost entirely due to the rigid quarantine laws enacted by Kansas and other Northern and Western Territories. In reference to Mr. Atwater's suggestion as to the days of free grazing in Texas being over, will say that there will doubtless be for many years to come still much free grazing in this State, although there is a very considerable disposition among the cattlemen to buy or lease their ranges where it can be done. The grazing section of Texas being unsuited for agricultural purposes, it will be impossible for ranchmen to ever grow feed to fatten their cattle on during the winter. They may, however, by buying or leasing and inclosing their ranges be able to protect the grass to a considerable extent; as by this arrangement their range would not be subjected to the drifts of neighboring herds, and would enable them to regulate the number of cattle grazed on any given quantity of land in such a way as not to permanently injure the range.

Instead of cattlemen being hopeful of better times my observation has led me to believe quite the reverse. The majority of cattle ranches now in Texas are now for sale at fully 25 per cent. less than they could have been bought for twelve months ago, and, generally speaking, it may safely be said that a large majority of the ranchmen of Texas would willingly retire from the business if they could dispose of their holdings at anything like a reasonable price. There is considerable talk of trying to establish a trail through the neutral strip and the eastern part of Colorado, thus avoiding Kansas, but I am of the opinion that this route is not feasible, first on account of the scarcity of water in Eastern Colorado, and, secondly, for the reason that in all probability the ranchmen and citizens of eastern Colorado would soon raise the same objection to the establishment of a trail through the eastern part of their State

226

1885 [Cattle Industry]

Nimmo, Joseph, Jr.
THE RANGE AND RANCH CATTLE BUSINESS OF THE UNITED STATES.
Wash., 1885. 562pp. Full morocco. *First edition, first issue.* Five large folding maps. Treasury Dept. Report on Internal Commerce of the United States. Reese Six Score #81: "One of the 'big four' cattle books; an indispensable source for research in the field. This issue, the 'Treasury' issue, is the most desirable because of its maps and apparent priority of issue. . . . Nimmo's report is a unique collection, and should be the first point of reference for anyone interested in this period. It contains more solid facts than any other primary source of the time." Adams Herd #1674. Merrill Aristocrats of the Cow Country: "Excessively rare." Howes N158. Dobie, p.112. (349) 1850.00

Richthofen, Walter Baron von
CATTLE-RAISING ON THE PLAINS OF NORTH AMERICA.

N.Y.: D. Appleton and Company, 1885. 102,[6]pp. Original cloth. Very fine copy. *First edition.* Merrill, Aristocrats of the Cow Country. Rader 2786. Graff 3499. Howes R273: "The Baron was a leading cattleman of Colorado and father of Germany's famous flyer." Adams Herd #1892: "Helped to create the cattle boom of the eighties." Reese Six Score #90.   (350) 165.00

Roosevelt, Theodore
HUNTING TRIPS OF A RANCHMAN: SKETCHES OF SPORT ON THE NORTHERN CATTLE PLAINS.

N.Y.: G. P. Putnam's Sons, 1885. [18],318pp. Folio. 20 plates, 4 India-proof etchings by R. S. Gifford. 7 Japan-proof illus. by J. C. Beard. *First edition, first issue, the handsome Medora Edition,* limited to 500 numbered copies, issued a year prior to the first trade edition.   (351) 135.00

PROCEEDINGS OF A NATIONAL CONVENTION OF CATTLE BREEDERS AND OTHERS, CALLED IN CHICAGO, ILLINOIS . . .

Wash., [1883]. 85pp. Printed wrappers. Included George B. Loving from Texas and cattle-men from most western states. Similar to Adams Herd #1598 "Rare," which relates a convention held in St. Louis.   (352) 200.00

The Civil War reduced the number of cattle east of the Mississippi by half, but Texas was overflowing with literally millions of cattle by 1866. In that year Texas cattlemen began driving herds north up the Chisholm and other trails to railheads in Kansas and Nebraska. From there some were used to start new herds in the newly opened areas on the western plains but most were shipped to eastern markets for slaughter.

The year 1885 was a turning point in the cattle industry. By 1885, over five million cattle had gone up the trails from Texas. The western plains had been covered with huge ranches, many owned by foreign capitalists, like that of Baron von Richthofen of Colorado. The corn states were well supplied with cattle to fatten for market, and great packing plants and stockyards had altered the economies of centers like Chicago, Kansas City, and Ft. Worth.

But also by 1885, the ranges had become overstocked — at the very time when settlers were beginning to fill up the land and to demand the dreaded fences. The over-supply caused beef prices to crash, and this was compounded by severe drought and cold in the next two winters. The industry never fully recovered, and from this time on the great ranches declined.

Headquarters Department of Arizona,
PRESCOTT, DECEMBER 27, 1871.

GENERAL ORDERS,
No. 35.

In accordance with the terms of the orders of the Division Commander, the time within the limits of which all roving bands of Apache Indians are required to go upon their Reservations, is announced and fixed as February 15th, 1872, on, and after which date all Apache Indians found outside of their Reservations, will be considered and treated as hostile.

The bands temporarily provided for at Camps Beale's Springs, Date Creek and McDowell, will, so long as they can be regularly mustered and accounted for by the post commanders, in accordance with existing regulations and orders, be protected and fed at those posts as heretofore.

Commanding officers of posts will communicate the contents of this order, without delay, and by every available means, to the Indians concerned.

GEORGE CROOK,
Lieut.-Col., 23d Infantry.
Brevet Major General.
Commanding.

OFFICIAL:

John G. Bourke,
Aide-de-Camp.

1886   [The Apaches and Geronimo]

Bourke, Capt. John G.
NOTES UPON THE GENTILE ORGANIZATION OF THE APACHES OF ARIZONA.
N.p., ca. 1886. 15pp. Original printed wrappers, complimentary copy with printed presentation slip from Bourke inside front cover. *Very rare, small private printing.* "Gentile" used in the sense of "pagan."   (353) 200.00

GERONIMO.
Original cabinet photograph of the Apache chief, c.1886.   (354) 125.00

190

Bourke, John G.

ON THE BORDER WITH CROOK.

N.Y.: Charles Scribner's Sons, 1891. 491pp. plus adv. Original pictorial cloth. Extremely fine, near mint copy. *First edition,* with a loosely inserted original octavo broadside, Headquarters Dept. of Arizona, issued by Gen. George Crook and *signed in ink by Bourke* as aide-de-camp, about the "roving bands of Apache Indians." Howes B654. Jennewein 61. Graff 367. Dobie, p.32. Rader 426. "A truly great book, on both Apaches and Arizona frontier."—J. Frank Dobie.   (355) 450.00

Mazzanovich, Anton

TRAILING GERONIMO: SOME HITHERTO UNRECORDED INCIDENTS BEARING UPON THE OUTBREAK OF . . . GERONIMO'S BAND IN ARIZONA AND NEW MEXICO.

Hollywood, 1931. 322pp. Original cloth, in dustjacket. Best edition, revised. Adams Guns 1470. Adams Herd 1464. Excellent especially for the 112 original photographs of the campaign.   (356) 45.00

The most famous of all Apaches was named Geronimo (Spanish for Jerome) by the Mexicans, but his Indian name was Goyathlay, which means "the one who yawns." There was little time for yawning, however, during the many years he led the Apaches on the warpath. He started as a young warrior under such chiefs as Cochise, Victorio, and Mangas Coloradas, until he became the leader of the incredibly vicious and determined band who were captured and put on reservations in 1876, 1880, 1882, 1883, and 1885, each time escaping to go on the warpath. In 1886 he broke out for the final time until he surrendered his band on Sept. 4, 1886, at Camp Bowie, Arizona.

Gen. George Crook spent the better part of his career chasing Geronimo, for 14 years accompanied by scholar-soldier John G. Bourke, whose works on Apache customs and on his Indian campaign experiences are classics even today. Bourke had an appreciation and understanding of the Plains Indian that place his works beyond comparison among others of his time. Walter Hough states: "Bourke's historical writings are unusually vivid, as he was a good story teller and had a generous fund of wit and humor, while his scientific writings, compiled from his notes and unmarred by immature generalizations, will always be storehouses upon which workers may draw with profit. [He possessed] a lively, kind, shrewd, and attractive spirit."

The incorrigible Geronimo was sent to prison in Florida, then to Alabama, and finally to Oklahoma. After a number of attempts to escape, he finally settled down somewhat and became a farmer. In 1905 he was a conspicuous figure in Teddy Roosevelt's inaugural procession, and in 1909 he died at the age of 80.

account of that state which
I believe comes in Chapter
II.

I am sorry that I could
not have given the M.S.
to the messenger but I
has taken me all the
afternoon to place the
illustrations. They are
not evenly distributed but
the text requires them
to be placed as they are
I am sure that I can
do better regarding the
subjects for illustrating the
next time in next book —
Very truly Yours
Elizabeth B Custer

192

Custer, Elizabeth B.

TENTING ON THE PLAINS; OR, GENERAL CUSTER IN KANSAS AND TEXAS.

N.Y.: Charles L. Webster & Company, 1887. 702pp. Original pictorial cloth. Very fine, bright copy. *First edition, with an extraordinary Autograph Letter Signed by Mrs. Custer,* 2 leaves, small 4to, Nov. 30, [1886], to her editor about Chapter Eight of the book, and discussing in detail the map of Texas which appears on page 26 of the volume, and discussing the imminent delivery of the manuscript of the book: "I am sorry that I could not have given the ms. to the messenger but it has taken me all the afternoon to place the illustrations. . . ." Luther #5. Raines, p.69. (357) 300.00

GEN. GEORGE A. CUSTER

Original carte-de-visite photograph, by Matthew Brady, of Custer in uniform, apparently at the end of the Civil War. The picture appears on page 265 of the above book. (358) 65.00

Custer, George A.

MY LIFE ON THE PLAINS; OR, PERSONAL EXPERIENCES WITH INDIANS.

N.Y.: Sheldon and Company, 1874. 256pp. Illus. Pictorial cloth. *First edition.* Fine copy. Dustin 81. Howes C981. Graff 961. Luther #7. Jones 1566. Smith 2188. (359) 65.00

Whittaker, F. A.

A COMPLETE LIFE OF GEN. GEORGE A. CUSTER.

N.Y., 1876. 648pp. Pictorial cloth. *First edition.* Luther #1. Dustin 275. Jennewein 51. The first biography of Custer, and first account in a book of Custer's Last Stand. (360) 65.00

OFFICIAL ARMY REGISTER.

Wash., Jan. 1, 1877. 262pp. plus addenda leaf. Sewn. On pages 239-40 are the official announcements of Custer's death and names of all officers killed, wounded, and missing in the battle. (361) 85.00

Hyde, George

BRAVE BEAR'S STATEMENT OF CUSTER'S FIGHT ON LITTLE BIG HORN.

Autograph Manuscript Signed, March 8, 1906, 9pp., in pencil. Taken down by Hyde from Brave Bear's lips: ". . . I understand whites don't like hear that Custer did not act brave in this battle, but Indians all think he act cowardly here. . . ." (362) 600.00

While America was gearing up for the 1876 Centennial celebration, Gen. George A. Custer was leading the 7th Cavalry up the Little Big Horn River against the Sioux Indians under Sitting Bull. On June 25, 1876, he was surrounded and he and his men massacred in the most famous of all Indian battles.

A writer of no mean talent, he had earlier written a classic on his Indian campaigns, *My Life on the Plains,* and his wife followed this with several works of her own, one of the best being *Tenting on the Plains.*

Bryce, James
THE AMERICAN COMMONWEALTH.
London, 1888. 3 volumes. Extremely handsome three-quarter morocco, gilt. *First edition.*
Howes B906: "Remains the most authoritative study of American political and social insti-
tutions." Downs, Famous American Books #25.   (363) 200.00

Bellamy, Edward
LOOKING BACKWARD, 2000-1887.
Boston: Ticknor and Company, 1888. 470pp. Original green cloth. Very good copy. *First
edition, first issue.* BAL 956. Grolier American Hundred #90. Johnson High Spots p.16.
Adams, Radical Amer. Lit., 57. Downs, Books That Changed America #10. Jenkins, Works
of Genius #35. Bleiler, p.46.   (364) 185.00

James Bryce, an Englishman, came to America to study its social and political past and
the nature of its institutions. The result was his monumental analysis of our system of society,
immediately recognized for its profound contribution "in its deep understanding of American
political philosophy . . . second to none as a systematic analysis and interpretation of American government." For decades, the book has served as a basic text for the study of political
science as applied in America.

Bryce was the first to closely examine the nature of local government in America,
coming to the conclusion that "there is no denying that the government of cities is the one
conspicuous failure of the United States." He criticized other aspects of our system and made
suggestions for improvement, but found American social democracy basically sound.

Edward Bellamy also closely studied American social structure. His masterpiece,
Looking Backward, is a utopian novel with the specific goal of social reform. John Dewey
and Charles Beard, in 1935, ranked it as the single most influential American book of the
previous fifty years. *Encyc. Brit.* records that it has continued to be a living force in times
"when many of the inventions he prophesied have become realities." As Heywood Broun
said, Bellamy was "one of the most authentic prophets of our age."

CONSTITUTION OF SOUTH DAKOTA.

[Pierre], 1889. 100pp. Not in Kuhlman or Allen.   (365) 250.00

CONSTITUTION OF THE STATE OF MONTANA, AS ADOPTED BY THE CONSTITUTIONAL CONVENTION.

Helena, 1889. 76pp. Original pink printed wrappers. Kuhlman p.43. Shearer 269.

(366) 30.00

CONSTITUTION OF THE STATE OF WASHINGTON.

Seattle, 1889. 74pp. Original printed wrappers. Not in Kuhlman.   (367) 350.00

Turner, Frederick Jackson

THE SIGNIFICANCE OF THE FRONTIER IN AMERICAN HISTORY.

Wash., [1895]. [30]pp. From the Report of the Amer. Hist. Assn. Later cloth, leather label. First national printing. ''Without warning he set forth a new hypothesis, and then and there opened a new period in the interpretation of the history of the United States.''—F. L. Paxson. Howes T422. Downs, Famous Books #99. Cowley, Books That Changed Our Minds #3. Printing and the Mind of Man 379.   (368) 65.00

Turner, Frederick Jackson

THE FRONTIER IN AMERICAN HISTORY.

N.Y., 1920. [8],375pp. Original cloth. *First edition.* Howes T421. An amplification of his thesis after thirty years of research and reflection.   (368A) 85.00

Making states out of the territories of Dakota, Montana, and Washington marked the close of most of the American frontier. North and South Dakota were admitted on November 2, 1889; Montana on November 8, 1889; and Washington on November 11, 1889. By this time the country had 42 states and over 60 million people, double the populace at the beginning of the Civil War. The fight for the West was virtually won.

Reflecting on this watershed in the country's history, a young Wisconsin professor, Frederick Jackson Turner, introduced his brilliant Frontier Thesis, a conception of American history that has exerted immense influence on American historians and philosophers. Turner recognized that the American people, derived from diverse European cultures, had developed their particular American culture basically from the availability in America of a land frontier. For each generation, there had always been available cheap, arable land in virtually unlimited quantity. This constant nearness of cheap land had done much to develop the spirit of freedom and independence of the people and shaped the nature of American institutions and government. As the frontier was beginning to close, he asked the pertinent question of what effect the future lack of it would have.

1890   Mahan, Alfred T.

THE INFLUENCE OF SEA POWER UPON HISTORY.
Boston: Little, Brown, and Company, 1890. 557pp. Original cloth. *First edition, with an original 2-page Autograph Letter Signed by Mahan tipped in.* Downs, Famous Books #97. Grolier American Hundred #93. Books That Changed America #11.   (369) 250.00

Alfred T. Mahan was a graduate of Annapolis, son of a Dean of West Point, and an active captain in the American navy, giving him unique qualifications to write ''the first philosophy of sea power.'' He did so with gusto, and his stunning formulation of the theory that ''whoever rules the waves rules the world'' had immediate and far-reaching impact.

Mahan pointed out that major wars have almost invariably been won by the nations who controlled the seas, and by those who have most effectively advocated the use of sea power. The sea power of a nation was defined as much more than its naval might, comprising as well its merchant shipping, natural harbors, naval bases, and attitude towards use of the seas.

Kaiser Wilhelm ordered a copy put on every German warship. Every Japanese naval officer was ordered to read and study the book. The British Cabinet held numerous meetings to discuss it. It was quickly translated into Russian, French, Italian, Spanish, German, and Japanese. In America, Theodore Roosevelt stated: ''Captain Mahan has written distinctively the best and most important — and by far the most interesting — book on naval history which has ever been produced. . . . I am greatly in error if it does not become a classic.''

A recent critic wrote that no other single writer has ever so directly influenced the doctrines and national policies of so many nations, and another stated the Mahan ''profoundly modified in his own lifetime the history of the age in which he lived.''

REPORT

OF

COMMISSIONER ROOSEVELT

1891   [Roosevelt and Civil Service]

Roosevelt, Theodore
*REPORT OF COMMISSIONER ROOSEVELT CONCERNING POLITICAL
ASSESSMENTS AND THE USE OF OFFICIAL INFLUENCE TO CONTROL
ELECTIONS. . . .*
Wash., U.S. Civil Service Commission, 1891. 146pp. Original printed wrappers. (370) 60.00

Roosevelt, Theodore
SEVENTH REPORT OF THE UNITED STATES CIVIL SERVICE COMMISSION.
Wash., 1890. 28pp. Printed wrappers.   (371) 45.00

In 1886 young Theodore Roosevelt ran for mayor of New York and finished a dismal
third. Two years later he was an aggressive supporter of Harrison and the winning Republican
ticket for President. Frederic L. Paxson states: "Harrison made him a civil-service commissioner in May, 1889, and Roosevelt was soon convinced that the spoilsmen were alarmed
at his arrival in Washington. There was some reason to fear that civil-service reform had died
aborning, for politicians tried to evade the specific requirements. . . . The commissioners were
inconspicuous until Roosevelt brought a glare of happy publicity into his petty office. . . .
Already set to the notion that in ethics lay the cure of politics, Roosevelt wrote and spoke as a
lay evangelist, and applied great energy to the task of keeping out the crooks and protecting
the competent. This philosophy remained with him for life."

He was aggressive and vociferous in his attacks on abuses of the civil service act. "The
personal conflicts," states Paxson, "that were its consequence made made good news stories
in which he was generally as right as he always looked." His success led in 1894 to his being
appointed police commissioner of New York in William L. Strong's reform administration,
where Roosevelt was able to gain more extremely valuable experience, and where "he
penetrated the lowest levels of slum life, observed an unholy alliance of graft, politics, and
crime, and again by his ability to turn his daily routine into pungent news brought public
attention to a focus on the cesspool." And to his own abilities.

197

A BILL TO ENABLE THE PEOPLE OF UTAH TO FORM A CONSTITUTION AND STATE GOVERNMENT, AND TO BE ADMITTED INTO THE UNION ON AN EQUAL FOOTING WITH THE ORIGINAL STATES.

Wash., H.R. 9689, July 30, 1892. Original folio bill, 15pp., lines numbered along left side of each sheet. In half morocco slipcase.   (372) 375.00

Mercer, A.S.

THE BANDITTI OF THE PLAINS; OR, THE CATTLEMEN'S INVASION OF WYOMING IN 1892.

Cheyenne, 1894. 139pp. Illus. Original cloth. Very fine copy. *First edition.* Adams Guns 1478. Adams Herd 1474. Howes M522. Jones 1573. Smith 6735. Graff 2750. Streeter 2385. Adams One-Fifty #103: "One of the rarities of Western Americana. It had a tempestuous history. Immediately after its printing, the Wyoming cattlemen objected to having their activities thus expressed and in the course of a libel suit the entire issue was impounded by a local court and ordered destroyed. While the books were in the custody of the court, a number of copies were stolen and smuggled to Denver, which lay outside the court's jurisdiction." Only a few survived.   (373) 1250.00

CONSTITUTION OF THE STATE OF WYOMING.

[Cheyenne, 1890]. 60pp. Original cloth. Shearer 614? Not in Kuhlman.   (374) 385.00

As long as they were practicing polygamy, which was abhorrent to Victorian era Americans, the Mormons were unable to succeed in their quest for statehood. In 1878 the Supreme Court decided against them on the issue and in 1887 Congress ordered Mormon property seized and held it until polygamy was renounced. In 1892 bills were introduced for statehood, and in 1896, after 46 years of being a territory, Utah was admitted as a state.

Wyoming came to the United States piecemeal. The first portion came as part of Louisiana, the second as part of the Republic of Texas, the third as part of Oregon, and the remainder as the part of Mexico ceded in 1848. Parts of Wyoming were included in Oregon Territory, Utah Territory, Washington Territory, Nebraska Territory, Dakota Territory, and Idaho Territory, and finally in 1868, Wyoming Territory. Wyoming's most remarkable political feature was that woman suffrage was granted in 1869 and in 18870 a woman served as justice of the peace. Between 1870 and 1890 the population increased tenfold, and statehood was granted in 1890.

The Wyoming country was wild and for the most part untamed, run by cattle barons and plagued with rustlers and outlaws. One of the great rarities among Western books was on this subject, written by the editor of a Wyoming stock journal, Asa Shinn Mercer. He exposed the way the cattle ranchers were importing hired killers to exterminate their competitors and other citizens of the region. The cattlemen sued him and a rigged court ordered all copies destroyed. Mercer smuggled a few to Denver and a handful have survived. Ramon Adams writes: "The rarity of the book is due not only to the impounding and destruction of most copies but also to the fact that for many years members of the Wyoming Stock Growers Assn. and their descendants destroyed every copy they came across." Mercer's printing house was burned to the ground and he was run out of Wyoming.

PROCLAMATION.

In its earlier history Hawaii possessed a Constitutional Government honestly and economically administered in the public interest.

The Crown called to its assistance as advisers able, honest and conservative men whose integrity was unquestioned even by their political opponents.

The stability of the Government was assured; armed resistance and revolution unthought of, popular rights were respected and the privileges of the subject from time to time increased and the prerogatives of the Sovereign diminished by the voluntary acts of the successive Kings.

With very few exceptions this state of affairs continued until the expiration of the first few years of the reign of His late Majesty Kalakaua. At this time a change was discernable in the spirit animating the chief executive and in the influences surrounding the Throne. A steadily increasing disposition was manifested on the part of the King, to extend the Royal prerogatives; to favour adventurers and persons of no character or standing in the community; to encroach upon the rights and privileges of the people by steadily increasing corruption of electors, and by means of the power and influence of office holders and other corrupt means to illegitimately influence the elections, resulting in the final absolute control of not only the executive and legislative; but to a certain extent the judicial departments of the government, in the interest of absolutism.

This finally resulted in the revulsion of feeling and popular uprising of 1887 which wrested from the King a large portion of his ill-gotten powers.

The leaders of this movement were not seeking personal aggrandisement, political power or the suppression of the native government. If this had been their object it could easily have been accomplished, for they had the absolute control of the situation.

Their object was to secure responsible government through a representative Cabinet, supported by and responsible to the people's elected representatives. A clause to this effect was inserted in the Constitution and subsequently enacted by law by the Legislature, specifically covering the ground that, in all matters concerning the State the Sovereign was to act by and with the advice of the Cabinet and only by and with such advice.

The King willingly agreed to such proposition, expressed regret for the past, and volunteered promises for the future.

Almost from the date of such agreement and promises, up to the time of his death, the history of the Government has been a continual struggle between the King on the one hand and the Cabinet and the Legislature on the other, the former constantly endeavoring by every available form of influence and evasion to ignore his promises and agreements and regain his lost powers.

This conflict upon several occasions came to a crisis, followed each time by submission on the part of His Majesty by renewed expressions of regret and promises to abide by the constitutional and legal restrictions in the future. In each instance such promise was kept until a further opportunity presented itself, when the conflict was renewed in defiance and regardless of all previous pledges.

Upon the accession of Her Majesty Liliuokalani, for a brief period the hope prevailed that a new policy would be adopted. This hope was soon blasted by her immediately entering into conflict with the existing Cabinet, who held office with the approval of a large majority of the Legislature, resulting in the triumph of the Queen and the removal of the Cabinet. The appointment of a new Cabinet subservient to her wishes and their continuance in office until a recent date gave no opportunity for further indication of the policy which would be pursued by Her Majesty until the opening of the Legislature in May of 1892.

The recent history of that session has shown a stubborn determination on the part of Her Majesty to follow the tactics of her late brother, and in all possible ways to secure an extension of the royal prerogatives and an abridgment of popular rights.

During the latter part of the session, the Legislature was replete with corruption; bribery and other illegitimate influences were openly utilized to secure the desired end, resulting in the final complete overthrow of all opposition and the inauguration of a Cabinet arbitrarily selected by Her Majesty in complete defiance of constitutional principles and popular representation.

Notwithstanding such result the defeated party peacefully submitted to the situation.

Not content with her victory, Her Majesty proceeded on the last day of the session to arbitrarily arrogate to herself the right to promulgate a new Constitution, which proposed among other things to disfranchise over one-fourth of the voters and the owners of nine-

EX-QUEEN LILIUOKALANI.

S. B. DOLE, ,
PRESIDENT OF THE REPUBLIC OF HAWAII.

1893 [The Republic of Hawaii]

Dole, Sanford B., et al.
PROCLAMATION.

Large broadside, elephant folio, [Honolulu], January 17, 1893, *the original proclamation overthrowing the monarchy in Hawaii.* ''The Hawaiian Monarchial system of government is hereby abrogated.'' Exceedingly rare; perhaps the most important event in Hawaiian history.   (375) 1250.00

TWO WEEKS OF HAWAIIAN HISTORY, JANUARY 14-28: A BRIEF SKETCH OF THE REVOLUTION OF 1893.

Honolulu: Hawaiian Gazette, 1893. 44pp. Illus. Original printed wrappers. Carter, p.177. *First edition.*   (376) 175.00

Harrison, Benjamin
MESSAGE TRANSMITTING A TREATY OF ANNEXATION CONCLUDED ON THE 14TH DAY OF FEBRUARY, 1893, BETWEEN THE UNITED STATES AND THE PROVISIONAL GOVERNMENT OF THE HAWAIIAN ISLANDS.

Wash., SED76, 1893. 69pp. Includes the first U.S. printing, Proclamation of Jan. 17, 1893, overthrowing the monarchy, the treaty for annexation, the Hawaiian Constitution of 1887, and many other keystone documents and letters.   (377) 125.00

PROCLAMATION OF THE REPUBLIC.

CONSTITUTION OF THE REPUBLIC OF HAWAII.

[Honolulu, 1894]. 55pp. Half morocco. *First edition, first issue,* of the Constitution creating the Republic of Hawaii. Exceedingly rare.   (378) 550.00

Dole, Sanford B. [?]

THE REBELLION OF 1895: A COMPLETE AND CONCISE ACCOUNT OF THE INSURRECTION IN THE REPUBLIC OF HAWAII . . . ALL THE INTERESTING EVENTS AND A CHAPTER OF GOSSIP.

Honolulu: The Hawaiian Star, March 15, 1895. 84pp. Illus. Pink printed wrappers, repaired.   (379) 275.00

Alexander, W. D.

HISTORY OF THE LATER YEARS OF THE HAWAIIAN MONARCHY, AND THE REVOLUTION OF 1893.

Honolulu: Hawaiian Gazette, 1896. 239pp. Original cloth. Oblong quarto. Illus. Fine copy. *First edition.*   (380) 185.00

Sanford B. Dole, son of missionaries, was born in Hawaii in 1844, and became a leading citizen and judge in the monarchy. In 1877 he was a leader in a movement which reduced the autocratic powers of the throne in Hawaii, and when these reforms were ignored, he led a revolution which began on January 17, 1893, and overthrew the monarchy. Pres. Harrison immediately submitted the Hawaiian offer of annexation to Congress, but incoming Pres. Cleveland prevented its acceptance. The next year a convention was held in Hawaii. which set up the Republic of Hawaii under a republican constitution, one article of which made Sanford Dole the President of Hawaii for a six-year term.

In January, 1895, a counter-revolution was attempted and put down. After difficult negotiations, Hawaii was annexed to the United States in 1898. Sanford Dole was appointed first governor of the Territory of Hawaii at its creation in 1900. Hawaii became the 50th state in August, 1959.

Ford, Paul Leicester
THE HONORABLE PETER STIRLING, AND WHAT PEOPLE THOUGHT OF HIM.
N.Y.: Henry Holt and Company, 1894. 417,[2]pp. *First edition, first issue,* with "Sterling" on spine and cover. Bennett, p.173: "Superlatively rare in first issue." Extremely fine, bright copy. BAL 6206. Wright III-1964. Johnson High Spots p.33. Streeter 4213. *An important copy, with an original Typewritten Letter Signed from Grover Cleveland inserted,* regarding whether "the leading events in the career of the hero in the book entitled, 'Peter Sterling' [sic], had any connection or were inspired by incidents in my life. . . . I am only able to state that I have received information quite authoritative that certain incidents in my life were in the mind of the author when he wrote the book." (381) 275.00

Great-grandson of Noah Webster, Paul Leicester Ford was educated in the extensive family library and printed a Webster genealogy on a hand press at the age of eleven. His later literary fame derived primarily from his novel, *The Honorable Peter Stirling.* A. P. Hackett records that it "had an interesting publishing history. Its publisher, Henry Holt & Company, was chiefly known for scholarly volumes and textbooks, although in 1895 it had taken a successful fling in trade publishing with *The Prisoner of Zenda.* Issued in a small first printing, *Peter Stirling* did not reach large sales until one San Francisco bookseller announced that the chief character was modeled upon President Cleveland. Word-of-mouth advertising brought the sales of the book eventually to 228,000 copies."

William Rose Benet writes: "A portrait of an honest and fearless politician, it enjoyed a great vogue in its time, partly because readers believed that Stirling was modeled on Grover Cleveland. This was denied by Ford." As evidenced by the original hitherto unpublished letter in the copy above, Cleveland himself believed that he was the model.

The book enjoyed great fame, and a successful dramatization was done. Unfortunately, this rankled Ford's brother, who murdered him and then committed suicide.

Yours very sincerely,

1895   [Psychology of War]

Crane, Stephen
THE RED BADGE OF COURAGE.
N.Y.: D. Appleton and Company, 1895. [4],233,[4]pp. Original cloth, some binding wear, but a good copy. *First edition.* BAL 4071. Grolier American Hundred #98. Johnson High Spots p.25. Jenkins, Works of Genius #98.   (382) 750.00

Same, *first English edition,* published simultaneously with the American. London: William Heinemann, 1896 [but actually issued Nov. 2, 1895]. Very good copy, with colored vignette title page.   (383) 200.00

Stephen Crane was the herald of the literature of the 20th century. D. W. Heiney says of *Red Badge of Courage,* which Crane wrote before he was 23 and before he ever got near a war, that it was "the first book to be written about the Civil War which did not treat the subject romantically . . . the first modern treatment of war in American literature."

It is a psychological work with few equals even today, proving Crane to be, says Carl Van Doren, "one of the clearest cases of genius in American fiction." It provides such an astounding insight into the Civil War, and into war itself, that in spite of being fiction it should be at the top of any list of books for gaining an understanding of that great conflict and its meaning for those who experienced it. Ernest Hemingway called it "one of the finest books in our literature. It is all as much as one piece as a great poem is."

Bryan, William J.
THE FIRST BATTLE: A STORY OF THE CAMPAIGN OF 1896.
Chicago: W. B. Conkey Company, 1896. 629pp. Illus. Original cloth, stamped in silver. *First edition, with an original Autograph Letter Signed by Bryan tipped in,* to the owner of the book, who was born on the same day and was married on the same day as Bryan. Contains the first book printing of his "Cross of Gold" speech.   (384) 50.00

OFFICIAL PROCEEDINGS OF THE ELEVENTH REPUBLICAN NATIONAL CONVENTION, HELD IN THE CITY OF ST. LOUIS, MO., JUNE 16, 17 AND 18, 1896, RESULTING IN THE NOMINATION OF WILLIAM McKINLEY, OF OHIO, FOR PRESIDENT....
N.p.: Reported by James Francis Burke of Pittsburg, Pa., Official Stenographer, 1896. 170,[1]pp. Adv. slip tipped in front. Original cloth, gilt.   (385) 45.00

REMINISCENCES OF THE PRESIDENTIAL CAMPAIGN OF MAJ. WILLIAM McKINLEY.
Chicago: Magnus A. Hess, 1896. c.50pp. Folio. Original pictorial wrappers. Sample copy of the proposed book.   (386) 35.00

William Jennings Bryan served two terms in Congress and was never again elected to a public office. But he was three times Democratic nominee for President and a major force in politics for thirty years. A rather simple-minded demagogue, his power base came from middle Americans who loved him for his eloquence and fundamentalist religious beliefs.

His entry into national prominence came in the 1896 Democratic Convention when he spoke in favor of free silver, ending a ringing oration with: "We will answer their demand for a gold standard by saying to them: You shall not press down upon the brow of labor this crown of thorns, you shall not crucify mankind upon a cross of gold." The awe-struck delegates, after five ballots, nominated Bryan, who barnstormed the country from coast to coast.

The Republicans nominated William McKinley, who was ably advised — and managed — by Mark Hanna. McKinley stayed at home and maintained a low profile while Hanna marketed him through the media like a commodity. McKinley won the election and the Republicans took uninterruped control of the government for sixteen years. The Bryan–controlled Democrats were led into political stances that splintered the party until 1912.

1897   [Alaska Gold Rush]

*THE OFFICIAL GUIDE TO THE KLONDIKE COUNTRY AND THE GOLD
FIELDS OF ALASKA, WITH THE OFFICIAL MAPS.*

Chicago: W. B. Conkey Company, 1897. 296pp. Illus. Maps. Original pictorial wrapers.
First edition. ''The most complete and thoroughly exhaustive collection of every known
information necessary to a full realization of the immense resources of the gold fields of
Alaska, with instructions regarding how to get there, when to go, and what to do. . . .''
Wickersham 3906. Tourville #1001.   (387) 85.00

Harris, A. C.

*ALASKA AND THE KLONDIKE GOLD FIELDS, CONTAINING A FULL
ACCOUNT OF THE DISCOVERY OF GOLD . . . ROUTES TRAVERSED BY
MINERS, HOW TO FIND GOLD, CAMP LIFE AT KLONDIKE. . . .*

N.p., 1897. 528pp. Full contemporary blind-stamped morocco, spine and front cover gilt.
Color folding map. Illus. Fine copy. *First edition.* Includes material by Joaquin Miller.
Wickersham 3927. Tourville #1958.   (388) 85.00

During the latter decades of the century, gold was discovered several times in various
parts of Alaska, without arousing great interest. But on August 17, 1896, a new discovery
was made on Rabbit Creek (renamed Bonanza Creek), a tributary of the Klondike River.
Because of the extremely difficult means of travel, word did not reach the United States until
July of 1897. The message was accompanied by over a million dollars in bullion.

The news brought on the clamorous Klondike Gold Rush, which for two years filled
Alaska and the Yukon with mining camps and thousands of prospectors, filling Alaska's
major towns and creating many other villages that soon became ghost towns. By 1950, over
535 million dollars in gold had been removed from Alaska.

REPORT OF THE NAVAL COURT OF INQUIRY UPON THE DESTRUCTION OF THE U.S. BATTLE SHIP MAINE IN HAVANA HARBOR, FEB. 15, 1898, TOGETHER WITH THE TESTIMONY TAKEN BEFORE THE COURT.

Wash., 1898. 291pp. Folding maps. Illus. The official report. (389) 85.00

AFFAIRS IN CUBA: RELATIONS OF THE UNITED STATES TO SPAIN BY REASON OF WARFARE IN THE ISLAND OF CUBA.

Wash., 1898. 636pp. Folding maps. Illus. Numerous excellent official reports and documents; a mine of information. (390) 100.00

Roosevelt, Theodore
THE ROUGH RIDERS.

N.Y.: Charles Scribner's Sons, 1899. 298pp. Original cloth. Fine copy. *First edition, autographed by Roosevelt.* This copy belonged to and is signed and dated 1899 by Trooper Edgar A. Knapp, a Rough Rider, who is listed in the text on p.250. Also contains an original 4x7 cabinet photograph of Roosevelt loosely inserted. (391) 250.00

SECRET PROCEEDINGS OF THE PEACE COMMISSION: OFFICIAL VERBATIM REPORT . . . AND THE PROTOCOLS AND TREATY IN FULL BETWEEN THE UNITED STATES AND SPAIN.

N.Y., 1898. 210pp. Stapled. Preliminary sheets, not published, but "Issued for the information of U.S. Senators and Representatives, etc." *First printing of the Treaty with Spain,* the document by which Puerto Rico and Guam became part of the United States and Cuba was freed from Spain. (392) 300.00

The Spanish-American War was an outgrowth of the Cuban revolt against Spain in 1895. During the three years of savage fighting, trade was brought to a stop and the fifty million dollars of investments by American businessmen in Cuba were threatened. The sensationalist American press played up Spanish cruelties and brought public indignation to a fever pitch. On February 15, 1898, the Battleship Maine was destroyed by a mysterious explosion and the public demanded revenge. The explosion, it later turned out, was probably not caused by Spanish sabotage but by a faulty boiler.

War was declared in April and Cuban independence recognized. American troops invaded the island and on July 1, 1898, Col. Teddy Roosevelt led his Texas-trained Rough Riders up San Juan Hill to victory and the Presidency.

On August 12, Spain sued for peace, and a treaty of peace was signed in December that ended the war, made Cuba independent, and ceded Puerto Rico and Guam to the United States.

Young, L. S. [ed.]
THE BOUNDING BILLOW, PUBLISHED IN THE INTERESTS OF AMERICAN MEN-O-WARSMEN.
Manila: U.S.S. Olympia, June, 1898. 16pp. Color pictorial wrappers. Map. Entirely devoted to the Battle of Manila Bay, with eyewitness accounts and sidelights of the decisive victory of the U.S. Fleet. The battle map was etched out with sail needles while in progress, said to be the first thing of its kind ever done. The issue is printed entirely on captured Spanish paper.
(393) 275.00

Harden, Edward W.
REPORT ON THE FINANCIAL AND INDUSTRIAL CONDITIONS OF THE PHILIPPINE ISLANDS.
Wash., 1898. 34pp. Printed wrappers. Mint.   (394) 40.00

Dewey, George, and Jacob G. Schurman
PROCLAMATION TO THE PEOPLE OF THE PHILIPPINE ISLANDS.
Broadside, elephant folio, Manila, April 4, 1899, signed in type by Schurman as President of the Commission, Dewey as commanding admiral, and E. S. Otis as commanding general. *Keystone Document, announcing the takeover of the Philippines by the United States and the transfer of sovereignty from Spain:* "The cession to the United States . . . of the sovereignty which Spain possessed and exercised over the Philippine Islands has now . . . received a complete and indefeasible consummation." Also sets up initial regulations, such as: "The supremacy of the United States must and will be enforced throughout every part of the Archipelago, and those who resist it can accomplish no end other than their own ruin."
(395) 750.00

        In February, 1899, the U.S. Senate approved the Treaty with Spain but added a supplement by which the U.S. acquired the Philippine Islands. In return for twenty million dollars, Spain agreed.
        On May 1, 1898, George Dewey had sailed into Manila Bay and completely destroyed the Spanish fleet defending it. Marines and troops had occupied Manila. In September the Filipinos declared themselves independent and in January, 1899, set up a constitution and government. On April 4, 1899, Dewey and Schurman proclaimed the sovereignty of the United States. After a protracted guerrilla war, peace was restored and in 1900 William Howard Taft was put in charge of the civil government.

THE BOUNDING BILLOW.

PUBLISHED IN THE INTERESTS OF AMERICAN MEN-O'-WARSMEN.

Published at intervals on U. S. F. S. Olympia. | MANILA, PHILIPPINE ISLANDS, JUNE, 1898. | VOL. I. NO. 5.

THE BATTLE OF MANILA BAY.

"We Came! We Saw! We Conquered!"

"'Twas for Cuba and our honor, to avenge our heroes slain,
That victory wreathed our banner when we fought the ships of Spain."

PROCLAMATION.

TO THE PEOPLE OF THE PHILIPPINE ISLANDS:

The Treaty of Peace between the United States and Spain, ratified several weeks ago by the former, having on March 20th been ratified by the latter, the cession to the United States, as stipulated by the Treaty, of the sovereignty which Spain possessed and exercised over the Philippine Islands has now, in accordance with the laws of nations, incurred a complete and indisputable consummation.

In order that the high responsibilities and obligations with which the United States has thus become definitely charged may be fulfilled in a way calculated to promote the best interests of the inhabitants of the Philippine Islands, His Excellency, the President of the United States, has appointed the undersigned a Civil Commission on Philippine affairs, clothing them with all the powers necessary for the exercise of that office.

The Commission desire to assure the people of the Philippine Islands of the cordial good will and fraternal feeling which is entertained for them by His Excellency, the President of the United States, and by the American people. The aim and object of the American Government, apart from the fulfilment of the solemn obligations it has assumed toward the family of nations by the acceptance of sovereignty over the Philippine Islands, is the well being, the prosperity and the happiness of the Philippine people, and their elevation and advancement to a position among the most civilized peoples of the world.

His Excellency, the President of the United States, believes that this felicity and perfection of the Philippine people is to be brought about by the assurance of peace and order; by the guarantee of civil and religious liberty; by the establishment of justice; by the cultivation of letters, science and the liberal and practical arts; by the enlargement of intercourse with foreign nations, by the expansion of industrial pursuits, trade and commerce; by the multiplication and improvement of the means of internal communication; by the development—with the aid of modern mechanical invention—of the great natural resources of the Archipelago; and, in a word, by the uninterrupted devotion of the people to the pursuit of those useful objects and the realization of those noble ideals which constitute the higher civilization of mankind.

Unfortunately, the pure aims and purposes of the American Government and people have been misinterpreted to some of the inhabitants of certain of the Islands. As a consequence, the friendly American forces have without provocation or cause been openly attacked.

And, why these hostilities? What do the best Filipinos desire? Can it be more than the United States is ready to give? They are patriots and want liberty, it is said. The Commission emphatically asserts that the United States is not only willing, but anxious, to establish in the Philippine Islands an enlightened system of government under which the Philippine people may enjoy the largest measure of home rule and the amplest liberty consonant with the supreme ends of government and compatible with those obligations which the United States has assumed toward the civilized nations of the world.

The United States striving earnestly for the welfare and advancement of the inhabitants of the Philippine Islands, there can be no real conflict between American sovereignty and the rights and liberties of the Philippine people. For, just as the United States stands ready to furnish armies, navies and all the infinite resources of a great and powerful nation to maintain and support its rightful supremacy over the Philippine Islands, so it is even more solicitous to spread peace and happiness among the Philippine people; to guarantee them a rightful freedom; to protect them in their just privileges and immunities; to accustom them to free self-government in an ever-increasing measure; and to encourage them in those democratic aspirations, sentiments and ideals which are the promise and potency of a fruitful national development.

It is the expectation of the Commission to visit the Philippine peoples in their respective provinces, both for the purpose of cultivating a more intimate mutual acquaintance, and also with a view to ascertaining, from enlightened native opinion what form or forms of government seem best adapted to the Philippine peoples, most apt to conduce to their highest welfare, and most conformable to their customs, traditions, sentiments and cherished ideals. Both in the establishment and maintenance of government in the Philippine Islands it will be the policy of the United States to consult the views and wishes, and to secure the advice, co-operation and aid of the Philippine people themselves.

In the meantime the attention of the Philippine people is invited to certain regulative principles by which the United States will be guided in its relations with them. The following are deemed of cardinal importance:—

1. The supremacy of the United States must and will be enforced throughout every part of the Archipelago, and those who resist it can accomplish no end other than their own ruin.

2. The most ample liberty of self-government will be granted to the Philippine people which is reconcilable with the maintenance of a wise, just, stable, effective and economical administration of public affairs and compatible with the sovereign and international rights and obligations of the United States.

3. The civil rights of the Philippine people will be guaranteed and protected to the fullest extent; religious freedom assured, and all persons shall have an equal standing before the law.

4. Honor, justice and friendship forbid the use of the Philippine people or Islands as an object or means of exploitation. The purpose of the American government is the welfare and advancement of the Philippine people.

5. There shall be granted to the Philippine people an honest and effective civil service in which, to the fullest extent practicable, natives shall be employed.

6. The collection and application of taxes and revenues will be put upon a sound, honest and economical basis. Public funds, raised justly and collected honestly, will be applied only in defraying the regular and proper expenses incurred by and for the establishment and maintenance of the Philippine government and for such general improvements as public interests may demand. Local funds, collected by local persons, shall not be diverted to other ends. With such a prudent and honest fiscal administration, it is believed that the needs of the government will in a short time become compatible with a considerable reduction in taxation.

7. A pure, speedy and effective administration of justice will be established whereby the evils of delay, corruption and exploitation will be effectually eradicated.

8. The construction of roads, railroads and other means of communication and transportation, as well as other public works of manifest advantage to the Philippine people, will be promoted.

9. Domestic and foreign trade and commerce, agriculture and other industrial pursuits, and the general development of the country in the interest of its inhabitants will be constant objects of solicitude and fostering care.

10. Effective provision will be made for the establishment of elementary schools in which the children of the people shall be educated. Appropriate facilities will also be provided for higher education.

11. Reforms in all departments of the government, in all branches of the public service, and in all corporations closely touching the common life of the people must be undertaken without delay and effected, conformably to right and justice, in a way that will satisfy the well-founded demands and the highest sentiments and aspirations of the Philippine people.

Such is the spirit in which the United States comes to the people of the Philippine Islands. His Excellency, the President, has instructed the Commission to make it publicly known. And in obeying this behest, the Commission desire to join with his Excellency, the President, in expressing their own good will toward the Philippine people, and to extend to their leading and representative men a cordial invitation to meet them for personal acquaintance and for the exchanging of views and opinions.

Manila, April 4th, 1899.

JACOB GOULD SCHURMAN,
President of Commission.
GEORGE DEWEY,
Admiral U. S. N.
ELWELL S. OTIS,
Major General U. S. Vols.
CHARLES DENBY.
DEAN C. WORCESTER.

JOHN R. MacARTHUR,
Secretary of Commission.

1900 [The Motor Car]

Woods, C. E.
THE ELECTRIC AUTOMOBILE: ITS CONSTRUCTION, CARE, AND OPERATION.
Chicago & New York: Herbert S. Stone & Company, 1900. 177,[2]pp. 21 plates. Original cloth. Fine copy. *First edition.* Kramer 246.   (396) 125.00

Homans, James E.
SELF-PROPELLED VEHICLES: A PRACTICAL TREATISE ON THE THEORY, CONSTRUCTION, OPERATION, CARE AND MANAGEMENT OF ALL FORMS OF AUTOMOBILES . . . WITH UPWARDS OF 500 ILLUSTRATIONS AND DIAGRAMS, GIVING THE ESSENTIAL DETAILS OF CONSTRUCTION . . . OF THE VARIOUS TYPES OF MOTOR CARRIAGES DRIVEN BY STEAM, GASOLINE, AND ELECTRICITY.
N.Y., 1902. 632pp. Illus. *First edition.*   (397) 65.00

Although self-propelled vehicles had been operated in one form or other for a hundred years, little progress was made in practical automobiles until the turn of the 20th century. This was primarily due to the atrocious roads of the early period, on which modern automobiles would fall to pieces, and to the concentration on railroad development. "After 1890, however, American pioneers began working in homes and workshops . . . and by 1900 they had laid the basis for a new industry." — Cochran, *Dict. Amer. Hist.* Twelve firms working in 1900 produced 4192 vehicles.

C. E. Woods, advocates the electric vehicle as best, but predicts gasoline and electric vehicles will both sweep the country. His famous pioneer book contains a history of automobiles, detailed construction techniques, operation and maintenance instructions, descriptions of various types, and proposed regulations for automobile clubs. Some of his comments are fascinating, such as his farsighted preference for electric over gasoline vehicles — but he states: "Will not a battery some time be made to run a vehicle 100 or more miles on one charge? While this may be possible, the writer hardly thinks it probable." "It is very hard to refrain from drawing the conclusion that the horse must go," he concludes, stating that "mechanically propelled vehicles are here to stay."

James E. Homans' work, published in 1902, has an interesting comment: "Scarcely three years ago it was a comparatively rare occurrence in this country to see a self-propelled vehicle, or 'automobile' of any description. To-day they are among the most familiar sights — hundreds of firms are engaged in their manufacture. . . ."

sketches. Occasionally. I wish you and dear
Cecil would run out to Stone Mountain and
see the work develop.

Some how I feel that the work this year
of my darling boys is going to be the
happiest and most telling that you have
had. To be sure some of it will be
very hard, but I believe you will rejoice
more keenly at the victories.

I have to go again to inspect the diseases
in the peanut fields, how I would love
to have my darling boys with me.
I wish all three of us could go rather 4.
"Dana, Cecil, Rossmond" & myself.

Yes its going to take hard work but you are
abundant able to do it.

I am positively happy over my boys.
Very sincerely,
G. W. Carver.

Washington, Booker T.
UP FROM SLAVERY, AN AUTOBIOGRAPHY.
N.Y.: Doubleday, Page & Co., 1901. 330pp. Original cloth, gilt. Fine copy. *First edition, with an original Letter Signed by Washington,* from Tuskegee, April 5, 1901, about the school: "Our students pay their own board partly in cash and partly in labor, but are wholly unable to pay their tuition in addition. . . . Any sum, however small, will help us. . . ." Porter 301. Miller, p.74. Kaplan 5980. Downs, Famous American Books #29.   (398) 175.00

Another copy, without letter.   (399) 85.00

Washington, Booker T.
THE FUTURE OF THE AMERICAN NEGRO.
Boston: Small, Maynard & Company, 1899. 244pp. Original cloth, gilt. *First edition.*
                                                                               (400) 45.00

Hughes, Mary Lou
LIFE AND WORK OF DR. GEORGE WASHINGTON CARVER.
Typed Manuscript Signed, 103pp., clothbound, Master's Thesis for S.M.U., 1941. An unusually fine biography, unpublished, and better than any published biography to date. Includes a copy of a letter to the author from Carver, Sept. 3, 1941, stating that the work is the "most monumental piece of work" done on his life and attesting to its accuracy. Includes unpublished photographs of Carver and sections on his contributions to education and on his influence on chemurgy.   (401) 125.00

Carver, George W.
[COLLECTION OF UNPUBLISHED LETTERS]
Exceptionally fine collection of 12 Autograph Letters Signed, 48 full pages, 4to, 1930-1931, to a young man who is either a close relative or friend, as the letters are written as though to a favorite nephew. An intensely personal correspondence going into great detail about his experiments with peanuts, his work at Tuskegee, his accomplishments and plans, etc. Of the highest possible autobiographical content, with literally dozens of reports of the progress of his scientific experiments.   (402) 2000.00

    Booker T. Washington was born a slave on a Virginia plantation in 1856. He was reared in a floorless cabin and remembered never "having slept in a bed until after our family was declared free by the Emancipation Proclamation." Determined to get an education, he entered school in 1872, working as a janitor to pay his way. He knew himself only as Booker, and when asked his name at the time of his first enrollment, he added Washington, hoping such a name would make him "equal to the situation." Only later did he learn that his mother had named him Booker Taliaferro, so he added his real last name in the middle.

At school he encountered for the first time "meals at regular hours, eating on a table-cloth, using a napkin, the use of the bathtub and of the toothbrush, as well as the use of sheets upon the bed." He did well in his studies, became a teacher, and in 1881 became the first president of the new Alabama Negro college, Tuskegee Institute. He worked gamely to improve the lot of blacks in America, which by the 1890's "brought him national recognition as the leader of the negro people." In 1901, he dined at the White House with President Roosevelt. His autobiography, published the same year, has become an American classic and has been translated into scores of languages. Upon his death from overwork in 1915, Henry Watterson said, "No man, since the war of sections, has exercised such beneficient influence and done such real good for the country."

George Washington Carver was also born a slave, about 1864. His father died and a short time later he and his mother were stolen and carried into Arkansas. He was traded off for a race horse and never saw his mother again. After many struggles he was able to attend and graduate from college and in 1896 accepted Booker T. Washington's offer to settle at Tuskegee as director of the school's agricultural experiment station.

There he performed his life's work, developing and creating agricultural innovations that have profoundly affected farming in America. His work on the peanut and its multiplicity of uses brought him worldwide recognition. Through him the previously uncommercial peanut and sweet potato became leading crops in the South. He expanded our knowledge of soil revitalization, unlocked the secrets of the soybean, and invented many derivative products such as milk and coffee substitutes, dyes, shaving cream, plastics, synthetic rubber, linoleum, and synthetic marble.

As early as 1916 he was elected a Fellow of the Royal Society of Arts in London, but the U.S. Agriculture Dept. seemed deliberately reluctant to acknowledge his accomplishments, and government officials "seldom mentioned them in their publications." One searches in vain to find reprints of his now-famous treatises such as "How To Grow The Peanut and 105 Ways of Preparing It" and "How To Maintain The Virgin Fertility of Our Soils." As late as the 1930's, in the peak of his international fame, he was still being subjected to intense prejudice in the South for which he had done so much. He died in 1943 and was buried beside Booker T. Washington, leaving his entire estate to Tuskegee for research.

Wister, Owen

THE VIRGINIAN, A HORSEMAN OF THE PLAINS.

N.Y.: The Macmillan Company, 1902. 504,[6]pp. Illus. by A. I. Keller. *First edition, one of only a handful of advance trial copies,* with no illustrations on the title page, bound in slate-blue cloth, gilt top; red, black, and gold stamped vertically-ribbed cloth, considerably different from the first trade edition. Apparently only five copies were made thus, for friends, each containing a printed presentation on the verso of the front free endpaper, "This volume has been especially made for . . . May, 1902." Slipcased. Included is a letter from W. J. Campbell to David Randall detailing the circumstances of the edition (one copy went to Teddy Roosevelt, one to H. O. Esling who had convinced Wister to let the Virginian live rather than killing him off as he had done, this copy to Henry Grassie of Chicago, and two others to unknown recipients. Also included is an article from Publisher's Weekly about this rare edition. Bennett, p.194. Johnson, High Spots of American Literature, p.81. Newton, 100 Good Novels #96. Mumey, Rare Books, 426. Downs, Famous American Books #30.

(403) 1250.00

Same, *first edition.* Fine copy.   (404) 90.00

Same, *first English edition,* London, 1902.   (405) 60.00

Harry Sinclair Drago, in listing his choice of the 20 best Western novels, says: "Wister was the first to make the Western story respectable, and *The Virginian* . . . remains the best picture of ranch life on the high plains of the 80's that we have." The novel is dedicated to his close friend and school-mate Teddy Roosevelt, with whom Wister explored the West as a young man.

Wister's daughter recounts that one evening at the Philadelphia Club Wister was describing his five trips to the West, when the question was raised why no novelist had ever tried to report the West faithfully as Roosevelt had done in his articles and Remington in his illustrations. Wister, who had planned to be a musician, was impressed with the thought and began that very night writing his first western story.

The Virginian, states Wallace Stegner, "became a model and a high-water mark in cowboy fiction. . . . *The Virginian* is notable less as realism than as a triumphant definition of the cowboy as folk hero. . . . His humor, chivalry, and courage — plus his ultimate reliance on direct action — set a model that many have imitated but few have matched."

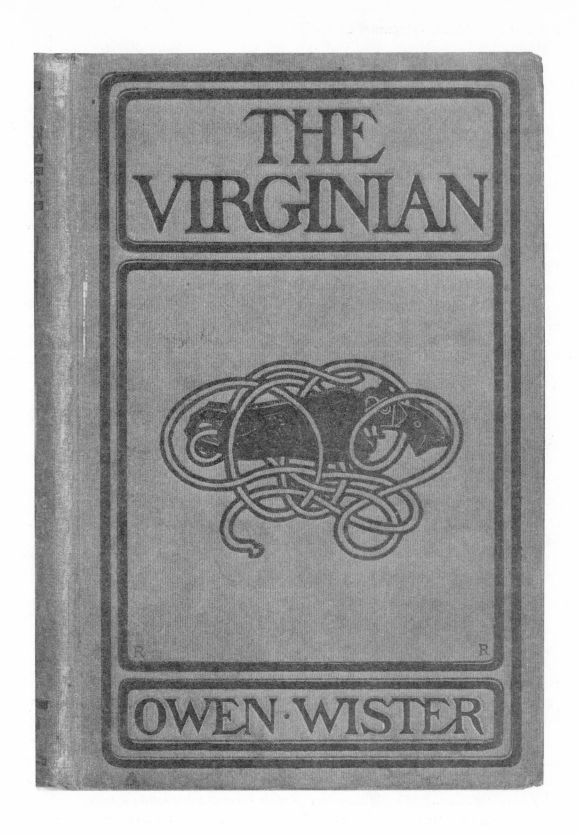

1903 [The Wildlife Adventure Classic]

London, Jack
THE CALL OF THE WILD.
N.Y.: The Macmillan Company, 1903. 231,[2]pp. Illus. Original vertically-ribbed dark green decorated cloth, top edges gilt. Extremely fine, bright near-mint copy. *First edition, first state.* B.A.L. 11876. Woodbridge 19. Walker 6. Johnson, High Spots of American Literature, p.51. Peter Parley to Penrod, p.119. (406) 160.00

Same, fine copy. (407) 110.00

This wildlife story, at once sentimental and poetic, has become one of the favorite American adventure stories. Translated many times, it had sold over six million copies by 1964. The story is something of an allegory on Darwinism, with overtones from Spencer and Nietzsche, but it is his poetic telling of the tale that makes it outstanding.

W. F. Taylor writes: "London's vision of beauty and of brutal adventure forms itself into a strong rhythmical, semi-poetic style which more than anything else lifts *The Call of the Wild* from the level of mere entertainment to that of true literature." Dale Walker calls it "London's supreme achievement as a story-teller, and it remains one of the very great short novels in American literature."

1904 [O. Henry]

Porter, William S.
CABBAGES AND KINGS.
N.Y.: McClure, Phillips & Co., 1904. 344pp. Original pictorial cloth. *First edition, first issue, of O. Henry's first book, autographed:* "O. Henry, New York, Mch 4th, 1905." Clarkson, #1. Bennett, p.196, calling it his rarest volume. (408) 425.00

Same, not signed. (409) 125.00

William S. Porter was born in 1862 and moved to Austin, Texas, in 1882 to make his fortune. After living and working on a ranch, he became a teller in a bank, and in 1896 was arrested on embezzlement charges. He fled to Honduras, but returned and in 1898 went to prison in Ohio. Released in 1901, he moved to New York City and began writing short stories under the name O. Henry.

Under this pseudonym he found his forte. His first volume of stories, *Cabbages and Kings,* made him famous and led to half a dozen more in the next few years. In 1907 he married and lived in Asheville, N.C. (where Thomas Wolfe was a child of 7-10 years old) until 1910. He died that year, the most famous of all American short story writers.

J. Donald Adams states: "Like F. Scott Fitzgerald, but with an even defter touch, O. Henry could strike off a phrase that lingers in the memory, as when he wrote of the 'thistledown moods' of a girl." Bennett writes that "it is certain that no other story writer in English — or, perhaps, any other language — ever created such a gallery of literary vignettes within such a space of time."

Roosevelt, Theodore

MESSAGE OF THE PRESIDENT OF THE UNITED STATES AT THE BEGIN-NING OF THE FIRST SESSION OF THE 59TH CONGRESS.

Wash., 1905. 56pp. Blue printed wrappers. Much on labor problems, big business, and anti-trust laws. Roosevelt's first State of the Union address as an elected President.

(410) 25.00

Roosevelt, Theodore

LETTER OF THEODORE ROOSEVELT, ACCEPTING THE REPUBLICAN NOMINATION FOR PRESIDENT OF THE UNITED STATES.

N.Y., Sept. 12, 1904. 32pp. Original printed wrappers.   (411) 35.00

Roosevelt, Theodore. *Typewritten Manuscript Signed,* 9 pages, large 4to, heavily corrected throughout in pencil in Roosevelt's hand, with one page entirely in his hand, ca.1910, concerning labor injustices and inequities among the working men and women, especially in New York's garment industry, where women and children worked under intolerable conditions. It constitutes a passionate, eloquent plea for redress, directed to the New York legislature.   (412) 550.00

The exploits of the Rough Riders in Cuba helped gain Roosevelt the Vice Presidential nomination and election in 1900. When President McKinley was assassinated in 1901, the 42-year-old Roosevelt became President. In 1904 he was able to obtain the Republican nomination and win the election on his own. In his acceptance speech in 1904 and his first State of the Union address as an elected President, he explained the Roosevelt progressive and reform policies that would mark his administration.

He called for labor reform, anti-trust action, aggressive Big Stick foreign policy, conservation of resources, and an end to isolationism. He especially called for trust busting and began to utilize the anti-trust and interstate commerce laws to that end.

Roosevelt was America's most aggressive President. "No President," he said, "has ever enjoyed himself as much as I." He loved being the center of attention; a relative said "when Theodore attends a wedding he wants to be the bride and when he attends a funeral he wants to be the corpse."

 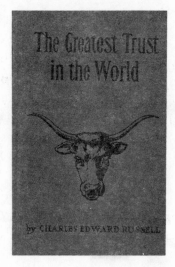 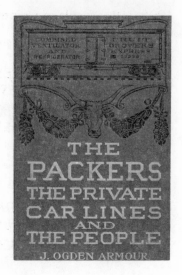

1906   [Stockyards Scandal]

Sinclair, Upton
THE JUNGLE.
N.Y.: The Jungle Publishing Co., 1906. 413pp. Original pictorial cloth. Fine copy. *First edition.* Reese Six Score #98. Downs, Books That Changed America #14. Johnson, High Spots of American Literature, p.68.   (413) 90.00

Same, with Doubleday, Page & Co. imprint. With original Typewritten Letter Signed, 1p., by Sinclair loosely inserted. Reese, Six Score #98: "An identical edition. . . . No priority has been determined."   (414) 135.00

Sinclair, Upton. Original Typewritten Letter Signed, 1p., 4to, Los Angeles, Jan. 9, 1934, outlining his major works, beginning with *The Jungle:* ". . . I will indeed to have the Grafico translate and publish these works. These are my best and principal novels. . . ." Much on translation and contractual rights.   (415) 85.00

Russell, Charles Edward
THE GREATEST TRUST IN THE WORLD.
N.Y.: Ridgway-Thayer Co., 1905. 252pp. Original cloth. *First edition.* Reese Six Score #6n: "An attack on the packers and the Beef Trust's control of the shipping lines and illegal rebates." Adams Herd 1966.   (415A) 85.00

Armour, J. Ogden

THE PACKERS, THE PRIVATE CAR LINES, AND THE PEOPLE.

Phila.: Henry Altemus Company, 1906. 380pp. Original cloth. *First edition.* Reese Six Score #7: "Armour, who was generally accepted as the spokesman of the Beef Trust, replied [to criticisms of the meat packers] in this book, a defense of the packing interests against 'hostile and mistaken agitators.'" Adams Herd 167.   (415B) 125.00

When it finally appeared in print, after five publishers had rejected it, this shocking account of the Chicago stockyards exploded on the public as few books have ever done. "Rarely has a book had such direct influence upon peoples lives," states Max Herzberg. "The book became the *Uncle Tom's Cabin* of its generation." Stewart Holbrook said that "Sinclair was adept at revolting descriptions, and in *The Jungle* he wallowed in them. They were so effective that a goodly portion of the United States became, for a period, vegetarian."

Teddy Roosevelt summoned Sinclair to the White House for a conference; a congressional investigation was initiated; the Pure Food and Drug Act of 1906 was the result. "I aimed it at the public's heart," commented Sinclair, "and by accident I hit it in the stomach."

Arthur Koestler wrote: "I can think of no contemporary writer whose non-existence would leave such a gaping hole in the face of the 20th century than Upton Sinclair's." Writing years later, Sinclair said, "Anyone who reads *The Jungle* will have his imagination stimulated, his sympathies widened, and his understanding of the world he lives in increased. At least, that is why the book was written, and if it doesn't happen there is something wrong with either you or with the author."

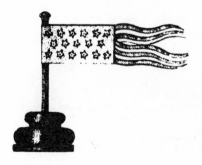

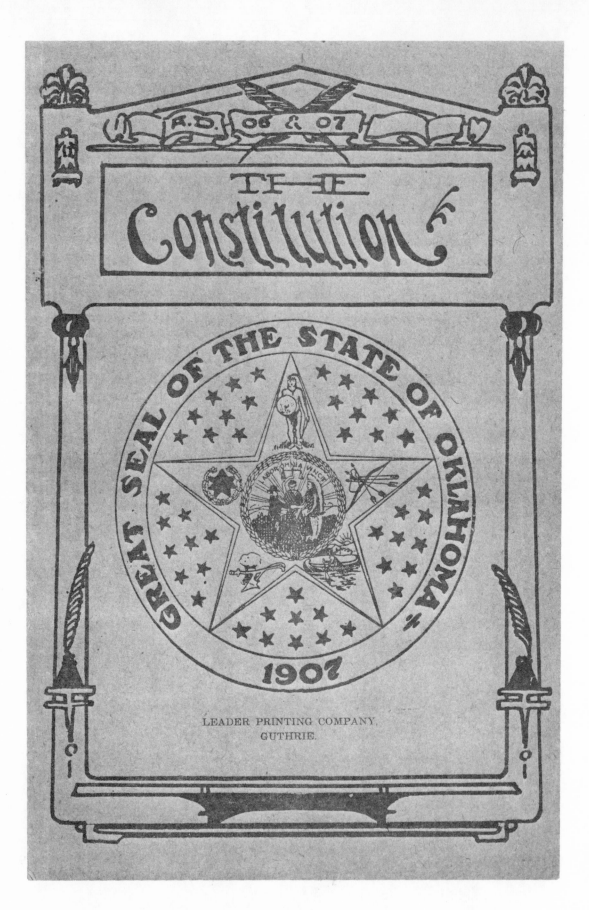

A. D. 06 & 07

THE Constitution

GREAT SEAL OF THE STATE OF OKLAHOMA

1907

LEADER PRINTING COMPANY,
GUTHRIE.

CONSTITUTION OF THE STATE OF OKLAHOMA.
Guthrie, Okla.: Leader Printing Company, 1907. 64pp. Printed wrappers. *First edition.* Not in Kuhlmann. Foreman, p.256.   (416) 400.00

CONSTITUTION AND ENABLING ACT OF THE STATE OF OKLAHOMA . . .
Ardmore: Bunn Brothers, 1907. 195pp. Half calf. First complete edition. Not in Kuhlmann. Foreman, p.257.   (417) 300.00

TREATY BETWEEN THE UNITED STATES OF AMERICAN AND THE CHICKASAW INDIANS.
Wash., 1834. 9pp. Folio. Approved by Andrew Jackson. ''The Chickasaws are about to abandon their homes, which they have long cherished and loved, and . . . hope to find a country adequate to the wants and support of their people, somewhere west of the Mississippi . . . the United States hereby consent to protect and defend them against the inroads of any other tribe of Indians. . . .''   (418) 200.00

TREATY BETWEEN THE UNITED STATED OF AMERICA AND THE CREEK AND SEMINOLE TRIBES OF INDIANS.
Wash., 1845. 6pp. Folio. Approved by James K. Polk.   (419) 200.00

TREATY BETWEEN THE UNITED STATES OF AMERICA AND THE CHERO-KEE NATION OF INDIANS.
Wash., 1866. 15pp. Folio. Approved by Andrew Johnson.   (420) 200.00

CONSTITUTION AND LAWS OF THE CHEROKEE NATION.
St. Louis: R. & T. A. Ennis, 1875. 284,[7]pp. Calf. Signed by Joshua Ross, Muskogee, May 13, 1891.   (421) 185.00

ORGANIZATION OF THE TERRITORY OF OKLAHOMA.
Wash., HR1684, 1886. 26pp. Large folding map.   (422) 55.00

CONSTITUTION AND LAWS OF THE CHEROKEE NATION.
Parsons, Kansas, 1892. 426,[7]pp. Later cloth. Chipped. Rader 714.   (423) 250.00

FIRST ADMINISTRATION OF OKLAHOMA.
Oklahoma City, 1908. 230pp. Full morocco. Story ''of the making of the Constitution,'' with mug book of the members and officers.   (424) 50.00

Gittinger, Roy
THE FORMATION OF THE STATE OF OKLAHOMA, 1803-1906.
Berkeley, 1917. 256pp. *First edition.*   (425) 45.00

Oklahoma was ceded to the United States in 1803 as part of the Louisiana Purchase. In the period 1820 to 1840 the American government utilized it as a giant reservation for "the Five Civilized Tribes" of Cherokee, Creek, Choctaw, Chickasaw, and Seminole Indians. The land was deeded to the tribes, each of which formed its own republic, with written constitutions and laws. The Indian nations held slaves and even joined the Confederacy during the Civil War.

Ignoring previous treaties, as usual, the Federal government took the western half of Oklahoma away from the tribes after the war and dumped some twenty more tribes into the area. On April 22, 1889, all the remaining unassigned lands were opened to white settlement and in May, 1890, Oklahoma Territory was formally created. After much hassle over white vs. Indian ownership, the Dawes Commission was created to solve various claims, leading to an Enabling Act in 1906, permitting a convention to meet at Guthrie and form a constitution. On November 16, 1907, Oklahoma became the 46th state.

1908   [Labor Organizes]

IN THE SUPREME COURT OF THE DISTRICT OF COLUMBIA: BUCK'S STOVE & RANGE CO. VS. AMERICAN FEDERATION OF LABOR: PETITION TO HAVE SAMUEL GOMPERS . . . ADJUDGED GUILTY OF CONTEMPT.
Wash., 1908. 38pp. Printed wrappers.   (426) 45.00

Gompers, Samuel
Original Typewritten Letter Signed, 1page, quarto, Wash., A.F.ofL. Headquarters, Jan. 23, 1920, to The Officers of The League for Political Education, declining an engagement at Hotel Astor.   (427) 35.00

In 1864, a fourteen-year-old immigrant named Samuel Gompers joined the New York Cigarmakers' Union. "All my life," he later wrote, "I had been accustomed to the labor movement and accepted as a matter of course that every wage-earner should belong to the union of his trade. I did not yet have a conscious appreciation of the labor movement." That consciousness came to fruition in 1886 when he helped organize the American Federation of Labor. He became its first president, holding the office for 37 of the next 38 years.

Under his guidance, the A.F.ofL. slowly became the largest labor organization in the country. By the first decade of the 20th century it had two million members. More reasonable in its demands than the I.W.W., it made immense headway towards raising working standards and recognition of labor rights. Gompers was frequently at odds, as might be expected, with big business interests, and was often in litigation. For example, in March, 1908, he was ordered by a court to cease an A.F.ofL. boycott of Buck's Stove and Range Co. When he refused, he was held in contempt of court. But Gompers worked better with business than previous labor leaders, because they recognized the prime fact of his life — that he did not seek to replace management with labor but rather to obtain better working conditions and a better standard of living for the laboring people.

IN THE SUPREME COURT OF THE UNITED STATES: STANDARD OIL COMPANY . . . V. UNITED STATES OF AMERICA. BRIEF FOR THE UNITED STATES, DETAILED STATEMENT OF FACTS.

[Wash.], October Term, 1909. vii,641pp. Original stiff printed wrappers. Signed by William Allen Butler on front cover. (428) 65.00

FROM THE DIRECTORS OF THE STANDARD OIL COMPANY TO ITS EMPLOYEES AND STOCKHOLDERS.

N.p., 1907. 32pp. Printed wrappers. Stamped on cover: "Received Sep 28, 1907 Bureau of Corporations, Dept. of Commerce and labor." A statement from the company alleging its "absolute innocence of wrongdoing in any of the prosecutions lately instituted against it in the Federal Courts." The statement is issued to give the "true facts" of the case and "rescue it from the field of public clamor and from the domain of vindictive politics." (429) 45.00

Taft, William H.
MESSAGE ON THE ANTI-TRUST STATUTE.

Wash., Dec. 5, 1911. 43pp. Printed wrappers. Contains a list of 55 "Suits Brought and Prosecutions Instituted by the U.S. under the Sherman Antitrust Law" with seven or eight lines of description on each, making this a valuable reference tool as well as a fine, historic summation of the anti-trust question by Pres. Taft. (430) 35.00

Standard Oil Company was incorporated by John D. Rockefeller in 1870 and began spreading its tenacles throughout the oil industry. By 1879 it controlled 95% of the refining capacity of the United States, and had become "the nucleus of an almost nation-wide industrial organization, the richest and most powerful in the country." In 1882 the Standard Oil Trust was set up, creating the first trust in the sense of a monopoly in American history. In 1892 this was successfully contested, whereupon twenty constituent companies were organized, with unity of action and control maintained by informal agreement.

Public antipathy to monopolies had crystallized finally in 1890 with the Sherman Antitrust Act. Its use against industrial monopolies was rare at first, unions being the principal defendants during the first years. Under Roosevelt, however, the era of trust-busting began, the major target being Standard Oil. Anti-trust suits were filed against the company in late 1906 and made their way up through the courts. After hearing the arguments in 1910, the Supreme Court ordered its dissolution into 33 independent subsidiaries on May 15, 1911.

TWENTY YEARS
AT HULL-HOUSE

JANE ADDAMS

[handwritten inscription]

1910 [Hull House]

Addams, Jane

TWENTY YEARS AND HULL HOUSE, WITH AUTOBIOGRAPHICAL NOTES. THE SECOND TWENTY YEARS AT HULL HOUSE.

N.Y.: The Macmillan Company, 1910 and 1930. 2 volumes. Original cloth. Fine copies. *First edition of each*, the second inscribed and signed by Addams to Mary Dunlop, "with appreciation for her work at H. H." Downs, Books That Changed America #16. Kaplan #44-45.   (431) 175.00

Jane Addams, daughter of a wealthy Illinois entrepreneur, spent much of her early life travelling the world and might well have spent the rest of it in idleness. Instead, just before turning thirty, she and her friend Ellen Starr bought Hull House in the roughest and "most needy neighborhood in Chicago." There, for over forty years, she waged an incessant campaign in behalf of the poor, women's rights, and world peace. She won the Nobel Peace Prize in 1931.

A. J. Kennedy wrote of her: "Her richly feminine nature, appealing charm, and high purpose were the loadstone that attracted and held the people who were the settlement. Her tact in handling people and social situations, her affection for children, her revulsion against all forms of injustice and cruelty, and her swift impulse to help disarmed criticism and attracted love. . . . Her feminism was nearly as marked an aspect of her personality as her moral interest. She was convinced by her experience that the health, happiness, and sanity of her sex depended upon women's active participation in the work and ordering of the world, and the supreme practical achievement was to have recruited and held a large group of able women of widely different gifts and interests. . . . *Twenty Years at Hull-House* was her masterpiece. The book was recognized at once as the best handbook available to potential settlement workers, and it remains a document for the study of American civilization."

Taylor, Frederick Winslow
THE PRINCIPLES OF SCIENTIFIC MANAGEMENT.
N.Y.: Harper & Brothers, 1911. 144pp. Original and cloth, gilt. Fine copy. First published edition. Downs, Famous Books #104. Printing and the Mind of Man #403.   (432) 150.00

Since the beginning of the Industrial Revolution, American industry had grown from small one-house units to consolidated, nationwide concerns. In spite of improvements in machines, the laborer's lot was little improved and his work style was much the same as always. Turner was the first to scientifically study the problem, the world's first efficiency expert.

As foreman of the giant Bethlehem Steel plant, he introduced time, distance, and motion studies, they advised changes in tools and work styles. Achieving spectacular results, both in increased production and in improved work standards for the laborers, he began to formulate general theories which he introduced in his now-famous book.

Taylor was quickly maligned both by conservative management and especially by labor organizations. Yet, as Justice Brandeis said, it was the working man ''for whom he labored most.'' His system of determining what a fair day's work and of improving the style of labor (raising table levels, improving shovel handles) shortening distances traversed, etc.) when not carried too inane lengths was of immeasurable practical benefit to the working man — and called attention to his needs and rights. The chain assembly line replaced back-breaking, wasteful, slower methods, and his emphasis on constant study (''question everything . . . prove everything'') are now a part of production systems everywhere. Taylor's system, ''now spread throughout the world, has profoundly influenced 20th century industrial development.''

THE AMENITIES OF THE CAMPAIGN

GREAT LEADERS AND NATIONAL ISSUES OF 1912.

N.p., 1912. 320pp. Original half morocco, gilt. *First edition.* Contains "My Administration" by Taft, "My Political Creed" by Roosevelt, and "The Gospel of the Progressive" by Wilson, as well as chapters by Champ Clark, Henry Cabot Lodge, Elihu Root, and Robert M. La Follette.   (433) 30.00

THE DEMOCRATIC TEXT-BOOK FOR 1912.

Wash., 1912. 432pp. Congressman James L. Slayden's copy.   (434) 20.00

SPEECH OF WILLIAM HOWARD TAFT, ACCEPTING THE REPUBLICAN NOMINATION FOR PRESIDENT OF THE UNITED STATES.

Wash., 1912. 21pp. Printed wrappers.   (435) 20.00

A CHARTER OF DEMOCRACY: ADDRESS OF HON. THEODORE ROOSEVELT.

Wash., 1912. 16pp. Printed wrappers.   (436) 20.00

In 1912 the Democrats won the Presidency for the first time in twenty years, following one of the most interesting of all American political campaigns. In June the Republican Party met and renominated President Taft after turning away hundreds of pro-Roosevelt delegates. Taft had split with Roosevelt following a speech in which he referred to Progressives as "extremists, not progressives; they are political emotionaries or neurotics." Roosevelt swiftly organized the Progressive "Bull Moose" Party and ran as its nominee. He later said of Taft: "He meant well, but he meant well feebly."

The Democrats also met in June in a wild and stormy convention. For 29 straight ballots, Champ Clark held the lead without gaining a majority. Then William Jennings Bryan, President-maker if not President, threw his support to Woodrow Wilson, who was finally nominated on the 46th ballot.

The campaign was heated and exciting. On October 14, Roosevelt was shot in Milwaukee, but the bullet passed through his thick speech in his pocket — Roosevelt insisted on delivering his address before being taken to the hospital.

Wilson received 6 million votes, Roosevelt 4 million, Taft 3 million, and Socialist candidate Eugene V. Debs 1 million. Although there was no majority in the popular vote, Wilson won a majority of the electoral votes and won the Presidency.

1913 [The Melting Pot]

Fairchild, Henry Pratt
IMMIGRATION: A WORLD MOVEMENT AND ITS AMERICAN SIGNIFI-
CANCE.
N.Y.: The Macmillan Company, 1913. 455pp. *First edition.*   (437) 35.00

The migration of over forty million people to the United States between 1820 and
1950 was the greatest movement of population in Western history. Of the 76 million people
in the United States in 1900, 36 million were foreign-born or had a foreign-born parent.

America as the "melting pot" meant a new chance for livelihood and freedom for
millions of Europeans and others. Throughout the 19th century, the country enthusiastically
accepted immigrants, needing their talents and productive abilities. From them developed the
"American," a nationality of hybrid stock that many times put the freedoms of the Constitution to the test, and gave America such diverse great men as Carnegie, Bell, Bok, Audubon,
Agassiz, and Einstein. After 1900, as the frontiers closed, immigration laws gradually began
to regulate and limit the number of immigrants into the country. The number was drastically
lowered during the second decade of the century, but the country has retained its excellent
tradition of allowing immigration from areas of oppression, evidenced notably by the
immigrations from eastern Europe and Vietnam.

1914 [World War I]

DIPLOMATIC CORRESPONDENCE: EUROPEAN WAR, 1914-1916.
Wash., Department of State, 1914-1916. 3 volumes bound in 2. Large folio. Full original
morocco. Comprises (1) *Diplomatic Correspondence with Belligerent Governments Relating*
to Neutral Rights and Commerce, 88pp.; (2) *Diplomatic Correspondence with Belligerent*
Governments Relating to Neutral Rights and Duties, 198pp.; (3) *Diplomatic Correspondence*
with Belligerent Governments Relating to Neutral Rights and Duties, 387pp. Extremely rare
and valuable documents during American neutrality.   (438) 200.00

Wilson, Woodrow
BY THE PRESIDENT OF THE UNITED STATES OF AMERICA, A PROCLAMA-
TION.
Wash., 1914. Three large folio proclamations and one Executive Order, proclaiming American neutrality in World War I and reorganizing the War and Navy Departments to work in
co-operation with the other departments "in connection with the relief, protection, and
transportation" of American citizens and areas under American control.   (439) 60.00

The assassination of the Archduke of Austria in June, 1914, led in a few weeks to
world war, involving England, France, Germany, Austria-Hungary, Belgium, Serbia,
Russia, Japan, and the Ottoman Empire. America felt the effects immediately: travelers and
businessmen abroad were repatriated with difficulty, foreign markets crashed, and international relations were made difficult to the extreme.

Wilson issued neutrality proclamations in August, and began his futile attempt to keep
America out of the war. The diplomatic relations with the warring governments became
strained and quietly the government began preparations for war if it became necessary.

1915   [Small Town Exposed]

Masters, Edgar Lee
SPOON RIVER ANTHOLOGY.
N.Y.: The Macmillan Company, 1915. 248,[6]pp. Fine copy. *First edition, first state,* signed by Masters' friend Harriet Otis Dellenbaugh, 1916, with four contemporary photographs of the Lewiston, Illinois, area around which the book centers. Johnson, High Spots of American Literature, p.56. Robinson #22. Irish 3797.   (440) 175.00

Same, 1924 edition, with new poems added. *Signed by Masters.*   (441) 50.00

Same, 1942. Limited Editions Club issue, with new material. *Signed by Masters and artist Boardman Robinson.* Slipcased.   (442) 90.00

"At last! At last America has discovered a poet!" So exclaimed Ezra Pound upon the appearance of *Spoon River.* In casual free verse form, Masters presented the so-called epitaphs, spoken by the dead themselves, of the citizens of Spoon River, exposing falsities of the typical American small town. "It was as though thousands of restless, defeated, anonymous souls," wrote Horace Gregory, "had suddenly found their voices."

Masters sought to tell what lay under "the false chronicles of the stones" of the the town's graveyard, "the furtive animalisms under the outer austerities, the foul small tyrannies that smothered life, the unexampled falseness of both thought and action."

Critically, the book caused a tempest which has not yet subsided. Masters later said that on one hand "it was called the greatest American book since Whitman, and on the other hand one of the evilest books of all time." "It marks a new approach to poetry and life," wrote Eve Leoff. Ludwig Lewisohn claimed: "I do not in fact know any American book in which there is more fundamental brainwork, more sharp and accurate thinking about life." Stanley Kunitz called it "a milestone in American literature" and *Encyc. Brit.* calls it "one of the most significant American books."

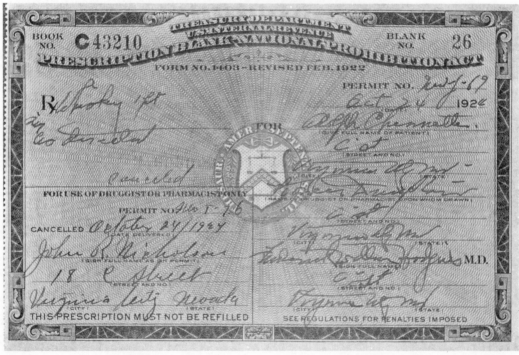

230

Homan, Rev. J. A.
NATIONAL PROHIBITION: ITS SUPREME FOLLY.
Cincinnati, 1916, 78pp. Printed wrappers. *First edition.*   (443) 15.00

OFFICIAL U.S. BULLETIN: NATION-WIDE PROHIBITION.
Wash., January 29, 1919. Full text of the Prohibition Amendment and the official proclamation declaring it a part of the Constitution.   (444) 75.00

*THE NATIONAL PROHIBITION LAW: HEARINGS BEFORE THE SUBCOM-
MITTEE ON THE JUDICIARY.*
Wash., 1926. 2 volumes in 1. 1660pp. Half morocco. Much essential data.   (445) 80.00

McBain, Howard L.
PROHIBITION: LEGAL AND ILLEGAL.
N.Y.: The Macmillan Company, 1928. 171pp. Cloth. *First edition.*   (446) 15.00

Tillitt, Malvern Hill
THE PRICE OF PROHIBITION.
N.Y.: Harcourt, Brace and Company, 1932. 156pp. Cloth. d.g. *First edition, inscribed and
signed by the author* "in memoriam to America's monumental tragedy—Prohibition. . . ."
                (447) 20.00

Original doctor's prescription for whiskey, Oct. 24, 1924, on form headed Treasury Department Prescription Blank, National Prohibition Act, issued by Dr. F. W. Hodgens, Virginia
City, Nevada, to his "patient," Adolph Chennette, for "Whiskey 1 pt."   (448) 12.50

From colonial times there were Americans who wanted to legislate prohibition against
the use of alcohol. From time to time political movements were initiated, such as the Prohibition Party (1869), the Woman's Christian Temperance Union (1874), and the Anti-
Saloon League (1893). By 1916, some twenty-six states had prohibition laws, half of them
totally dry.

An Amendment to the Constitution was proposed in Congress by a movement led by
an otherwise obscure Texas Senator, Morris Shepherd, and the resolution was approved in
December, 1917. On January 29, 1919, it was declared in effect, and the same year the
National Prohibition Act, known as the Volstead Act, was passed over Wilson's veto.

Thus America entered the era of the speakeasy. Illicit traffic in liquor was rampant,
and disrespect for all law brought a great upsurge of crime. Moonshine and rum-running filled
the coffers of organized crime and provided the initial funding of most modern criminal
syndicates. Popular disgust at the state of affairs led in 1932 to the repeal of national prohibition.

By the President of the United States of America

A Proclamation

WHEREAS public interests require that the Congress of the United States should be convened in extra session at twelve o'clock, noon, on the second day of April, 1917, to receive a communication concerning grave matters of national policy which should be taken immediately under consideration;

Now, Therefore, I, WOODROW WILSON, President of the United States of America, do hereby proclaim and declare that an extraordinary occasion requires the Congress of the United States to convene in extra session at the Capitol in the City of Washington on the second day of April, 1917, at twelve o'clock, noon, of which all persons who shall at that time be entitled to act as members thereof are hereby required to take notice.

GIVEN under my hand and the seal of the United States of America the twenty-first day of March in the year of our Lord one [SEAL.] thousand nine hundred and seventeen, and of the Independence of the United States the one hundred and forty-first.

WOODROW WILSON

By the President:
  ROBERT LANSING
    Secretary of State.

[No. 1360.]

1917   [America Enters The War]

BY THE PRESIDENT OF THE UNITED STATES, A PROCLAMATION.

Folio broadside, 1p., Wash., March 21, 1917. Proclamation calling a special emergency session of Congress to meet on April 2.   (449) 75.00

ADDRESS OF THE PRESIDENT OF THE UNITED STATES, DELIVERED AT A JOINT SESSION OF THE TWO HOUSES OF CONGRESS.

Wash., April 2, 1917. 8pp. Printed wrappers. *First printing.* Wilson's message to the emergency session of Congress calling for a declaration of war.   (450) 45.00

BY THE PRESIDENT . . . A PROCLAMATION.

Wash., May 20, 1917, 3pp. Folio. Proclamation drafting all males into the armed services.

(451) 60.00

BY THE PRESIDENT . . . A PROCLAMATION . . .

Wash., July 3, 1917. 2pp. Folio. Proclamation calling up the entire National Guard.

(452) 75.00

TRADING WITH THE ENEMY: ENEMY TRADING LIST.

Wash., War Trade Board, No. 1, Oct. 6, 1917. 28pp. Regulations prohibiting trading with the enemy, including extensive lists in small print of all individuals and firms with whom trade is prohibited, mostly in Latin America.

(453) 45.00

OFFICIAL BULLETIN PUBLISHED DAILY UNDER ORDER OF THE PRESIDENT.

Wash., May 10, 1917-March 31, 1919. Extraordinary set of 573 consecutive issues, each about 8pp., large quarto, in fine condition, wanting only the two issues entered as (444) and (456) in this catalogue. This series of official reports was begun shortly after the declaration of war by President Wilson, "issued as the official news medium of the Government under the direction of the President for the purpose of disseminating official news during the present war crisis." It contains literally a complete record of the United States during World War I, as well as official acts of the Executive Department during those years. In addition, it was used by Wilson to release battle reports and casualty reports, and constitutes one of the major research repositories for these fateful years.

(454) 600.00

A LEAGUE FOR PEACE: ADDRESS OF THE PRESIDENT OF THE UNITED STATES.

Wash., January 22, 1917. 8pp. Printed wrappers. *First printing* of Wilson's proposal leading to the League of Nations.

(455) 65.00

American ships were with some frequency sunk by Germany during 1915 and 1916, in spite of American protests, and when Wilson learned of a German plan by which it might possibly attack the United States through Mexico, he called a special emergency session of Congress. When it convened on April 2, 1917, he asked for a declaration of war, which the Congress passed readily.

A Selective Service Act was passed in May, inaugurating compulsory military service, under which ten million Americans were enrolled and five million drafted. In June troops under Gen. John J. Pershing began sailing to France.

Wilson, looking to the end of the war, proposed a League of Nations, which he called "a great idea which has been growing in the minds of all generous men for several generations, [and] the dream of the friends of humanity through all the ages."

1918 [The Fourteen Points]

Wilson, Woodrow

[ADDRESS AT A JOINT SESSION OF THE HOUSE AND SENATE].
Wash., U.S. Official Bulletin, January 8, 1918. 8pp. Large quarto. In half morocco slipcase.
First printing of The Fourteen Points, the official printing, preceding that described in
Printing and the Mind of Man #409; actually printed before the address was delivered.

(456) 350.00

Firmly confident that the Allies were fighting to win ''the war to end all wars,''
Wilson delivered to Congress on January 8, 1918, a plan to create the basis of a firm and
lasting peace: The Fourteen Points. It was first printed the day he delivered the message,
as the *U.S. Official Bulletin,* and *Printing and the Mind of Man* is in error in stating that
House Doc. 765 is the first printing.

Basically, the Fourteen Points demanded the abolishment of secret diplomacy between
nations at all times, removal of barriers to trade between nations, reduction of armaments,
fair settlement of colonial claims, adjustment of boundary disputes on the principle of self-
determination, and the establishment of an international league of nations.

234

TREATY OF PEACE BETWEEN THE ALLIED AND ASSOCIATED POWERS AND GERMANY . . . SIGNED AT VERSAILLES, JUNE 28TH, 1919.
London, 1919. [453]pp. Folding maps in pocket. Large folio. Text in French and English. *First edition.* Printing and the Progress of Man (Inlerlibrum Vaduz 256) #270: "One of the great monuments of modern politics; magnificent in its aims, disastrous in its consequences. Very rare, as published for official use only." Includes as Part I the first printing of the Covenant of the League of Nations.   (457) 850.00

TREATY OF PEACE WITH GERMANY.
Wash., July 10, 1919. 537pp. Folding maps. Folio. *First American edition.*   (457A) 175.00

CONDITIONS DE PAIX/CONDITIONS OF PEACE/CONDIZIONI DI PACE.
Original top secret working proofs of the preliminaries for the Treaty, Versailles, 1919, approx. 200 galleys, folio, loose in printed heavy wrapper stamped "Epreuves."
                                                                                   (457B) 650.00

The Armistice between the Axis and the Allies was signed in Foch's railroad car in France on November 11, 1918. Wilson attended the Peace Conference at Versailles where he attempted to institute the Fourteen Points and to create the League of Nations as a climax for "this final war for human liberty."

The conference quickly degenerated into a slicing up of Europe among the victorious allies. Germany was stripped of much territory, disarmed, and obligated to prolonged reparations. The covenant of the League of Nations was included in the proposed treaty, but without significant power. On June 28, the Treaty of Versailles was signed. It was ratified by the principals except for the United States. In spite of a valiant effort that in the end killed Wilson, the United States rejected the treaty and refused to ratify it or to enter the ill-fated League of Nations. In 1921 the war with Germany was formally ended by the Treaty of Berlin.

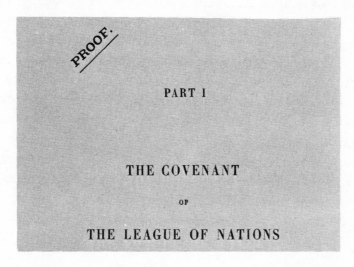

Bok, Edward
THE AMERICANIZATION OF EDWARD BOK: THE AUTOBIOGRAPHY OF A DUTCH BOY FIFTY YEARS AFTER.
N.Y.: Charles Scribner's Sons, 1920. 461pp. *Limited edition,* issued prior to the first trade printing, one of fifty numbered, autographed copies. Slipcased. Downs, Famous American Books #35. Kaplan #556. This copy, inscribed to John William Rogers, the man who succeeded Bok, who had just retired as editor of Scribner's: "My dear Mr. Rogers: As the present occupant of my old Scribner position, may your predecessor hand you this evidence of what you may come to? Only, if you commit a like murder, I hope you will do it better. Yours very sincerely, Edward W. Bok, September 20, 1920." The book won the Pulitzer Prize for that year.   (458) 110.00

Same, *first trade edition.*   (459) 20.00

   Edward Bok's life was a true Horatio Alger story: at 6 a Dutch immigrant to New York; window cleaner, paper boy, stenographer; at 26 a magazine editor; at 29 married to his publisher's daughter; at maturity a wealthy, famous, important and powerful force in his adopted country; at 58, author of a Pulitzer Prize winning classic.

   His genius and influence were felt mainly through his thirty-year editorship of *Ladies Home Journal.* "Under his guidance," states Robert Downs, "it became a national institution to a degree which no other magazine had ever achieved. By the time Bok retired . . . two records had been set: the magazine's circulation had reached 2 million, and each issue carried advertising in excess of a million dollars." Bok's overwhelming influence on American life and history came through his innovations in this single magazine. He introduced departments to advise girls on personal problems, young mothers on child care, and women on their intellectual needs. These have become so much a part of our lives today that it is difficult to comprehend how startling they were at the time.

   Bok crusaded for bringing the American woman out of her Victorian parlor—literally and figuratively. Teddy Roosevelt declared Bok was the only man who ever changed the architecture of an entire nation, with his crusade for eliminating the parlor and improving the American home. Bok introduced the taboo subject of venereal disease and lost 75,000 subscribers overnight, but ultimately brought this and many other problems into the realm of public discussion. He fought patent medicine frauds, which cost Americans hundreds of millions of dollars annually, and refused to allow them to advertise in his journal..

   In his famous autobiography, Bok was equally independent in spirit—he condemned American wastefulness, its emphasis on quantity over quality, its inadequate public school system, and other faults, at the same time acknowledging his and all immigrants' unique debt to America's opportunities and possibilities. While all the Horatio Alger tales have faded and passed, Bok's autobiography has continued to live and to be read, generation after generation.

236

1921 [The Unknown Soldier]

Harding, Warren G.
ADDRESS OF THE PRESIDENT OF THE UNITED STATES AT THE BURIAL OF AN UNKNOWN SOLDIER AT ARLINGTON CEMETERY, NOVEMBER 11, 1921.
Wash., 1921. 6pp. Printed wrappers. First printing of the speech declaring November 11 as Armistice Day and dedicating the Tomb of the Unknown Soldier.　　　　　(460) 25.00

Of the nearly five million Americans who were called into service in World War I, two million went ''over there.'' In all, there were 350,000 American casualties, of which 126,000 died. Nearly 500 were missing in action.

On November 11, 1921, Pres. Warren G. Harding proclaimed a national day of mourning, Armistice Day, and presided at the burial of an Unknown Soldier in Arlington National Cemetery: ''Today's ceremonies proclaim that the hero unknown is not unhonored.'' Harding also stated: ''It was my fortune recently to see a demonstration of modern warfare. It is no longer a conflict in chivalry, no more a test of militant manhood. It is only cruel, deliberate, scientific destruction.''

1922 [Radio for Everyone]

Hausmann, Erich, et al.
RADIO PHONE RECEIVING: A PRACTICAL BOOK FOR EVERYBODY.
N.Y.: D. Van Nostrand Company, 1922. 179pp. *First edition.*　　　　　(461) 25.00

Cameron, James R.
TEXT BOOK ON RADIO.
N.Y.: The Technical Book Company, 1922. 336pp. *First edition.*　　　　　(462) 25.00

The invention of the three-electrobe vacuum tube in 1906 ushered in the era of radio. There followed a decade of experimentation, until World War I perfected the instrument. After the war, radio for public use was demanded by an avid populace.

Stations began to crop up; in 1922 there were 30 radio stations and by the end of the year there were 60,000 sets in operation. Five years later there were 733 stations and 7 million sets. By 1960, there were 4086 AM and FM radio stations in the United States broadcasting to 156 million sets. At the same time there were an estimated 350 million sets in the world, more than the total circulation of all daily newspapers.

Coolidge, Calvin
ANNUAL MESSAGE OF THE PRESIDENT . . . TO A JOINT SESSION OF THE SENATE AND HOUSE . . .
Wash., Dec. 6, 1923. 16pp. Printed wrappers. *First printing.* "Since the close of the last Congress the Nation has lost President Harding. . . . He has left his mark upon history."

(463) 20.00

Harding, Warren G.
SPEECHES AND ADDRESSES OF WARREN G. HARDING . . . JUNE 20 TO AUGUST 2, 1923.
Wash., 1923. 395pp. Cloth. Fine copy, mostly uncut. Compiled by James W. Murphy. *Special limited, numbered edition, this being copy No. 1, presented to J. Bennett Gordon.*

(464) 65.00

Ravage, M. E.
THE STORY OF TEAPOT DOME.
N.Y.: Republic Pub. Co., 1924. [6],198pp. Original pictorial wrappers. *First edition.*

(465) 20.00

On April 7, 1922, Secretary of the Interior Albert B. Fall executed a lease of U.S. Navy-owned oil land at Teapot Dome formation, Wyoming. The lease was made to H. F. Sinclair of Mammoth Oil Company without competitive bidding.

While on a speaking tour in the summer of 1923, President Harding learned that an investigation and probable prosecution of this and other acts by Secretary Fall and high members of his administration was imminent. The message, sent in cipher, disturbed him so much that "for a day or so he was near collapse." On July 28 he became ill and on August 2, 1923, died. "At the time, his sudden end was regarded as tragic," writes Allan Nevins, "but before the lapse of many months it became evident that it was fortunate for him and his party. A series of public investigations of naval oil leases, revealed the extent to which Harding had been victimized by treachery and corruption in many parts of his administration. These exposures showed a looseness and dishonesty which paralleled those of the era just after the Civil War. They resulted in the revocation by the Supreme Court of the oil leases signed by Secretary Fall, and his sentence to a term in federal prison," the resignation in disgrace of the Attorney General and Secretary of Navy, and imprisonment of several other high officials. "The assessable evidence indicates that till the end Harding was ignorant of a large part of the corruption surrounding him, and was stunned and completely perplexed when he discovered its proportions." Nevertheless, his responsibility for those under him led most historians to consider him the worst American President until the events of 1972.

It may be of interest to note that the recent oil crisis prompted the Federal government to lease out part of the notorious Teapot Dome fields, and part of the funds for preparing this catalogue came from a .44% of one-eighth interest in one oil well from that lease.

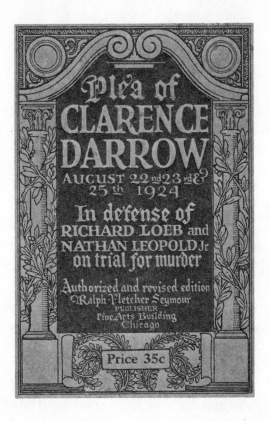

1924 [Darrow for the Defense]

Darrow, Clarence
THE PLEA OF CLARENCE DARROW IN DEFENSE OF RICHARD LOEB AND NATHAN LEOPOLD, ON TRIAL FOR MURDER.
Chicago: Ralph Fletcher Seymour, 1924. 121pp. Original printed wrappers. Also contains a summary of the facts of the case.   (466) 30.00

On May 21, 1924, a 13-year-old boy named Robert Franks was picked up on his way home from school in Chicago by 19-year-old Nathan Leopold and 18-year-old Richard Loeb. He was hit on the head by them with a chisel and killed instantly. Leopold and Loeb were two highly intelligent youngsters from wealthy families in Chicago. They had decided to commit a murder on a stranger simply ''in order to commit the perfect crime'' and ''for the thrill of it.''

It was not long before they were arrested. Their families hired the great Clarence Darrow to defend them. For the only time in his career, he demanded that his clients plead guilty. In one of the most celebrated murder trials of the century, Darrow made a moving plea not so much for the two boys as against the principle of capital punishment. His eloquent defense and summation plea caused the jury to deny the death penalty and sentence the boys to life imprisonment.

1925 [The Jazz Age]

Dreiser, Theodore
AN AMERICAN TRAGEDY.
N.Y.: Boni & Liveright, 1925. Two volumes. *Special edition of the first printing,* limited, numbered, and autographed by Dreiser. Johnson, High Spots of American Literature, p.30. Magill, Masterpieces of World Literature, I-29. Grozier-Gillett, The 100 Best Novels, p.19. Pizer 1925-A1.   (467) 150.00

Fitzgerald, F. Scott
THE GREAT GATSBY.
N.Y.: Charles Scribner's Sons, 1925. [6],218pp. Original cloth. Fine copy. *First edition, first issue,* with the error "sick in tired" on p.205. Hindus, p.35. Brucolli, p.2. Connolly Hundred #48: "One of the landmarks of the American novel."   (468) 135.00

An American Tragedy has been one of the most hotly debated of modern novels. Charles Shapiro called it a masterpiece, "one of the most important novels in all of American literature." J. Donald Adams called it "the most overpraised novel of its period." Irving Howe said "it is a masterpiece, nothing less." H. L. Mencken declared it dull, "the Hindenburg of the novel." Merle Johnson wrote: "I twitter among the lava flows from the Dreiser volcano." Alfred Kazin said that even Hemingway never wrote "a novel that has the objective power of Dreiser's." William Faulkner called Dreiser one of the four or five greatest 20th century writers. Edmund Wilson said that "Dreiser handles words abominably" but his "prose has a compelling rhythm."

Donald Heiney says that *An American Tragedy,* "like *Crime and Punishment,* is a moving literary experience." It is, writes Shapiro, "hailed and cursed, Dreiser's best testament to the America he found so wondrous and so puzzling."

The Great Gatsby is the most striking analysis of the wealthy, extravagant, and irresponsible American society of the Jazz Age, which Fitzgerald named. T. S. Eliot said that "this remarkable book seems to me to be the first step that American fiction has taken since Henry James," and Eric Mottram called it "one of the most gifted novels of the century."

As a social novel, *The Great Gatsby* offers a profound look into the American dilemma of achieved wealthy—what to do with it and leisure once it has been achieved. Russian critic A. Startsev claimed it was "an inseparable part of the basic rejection of the capitalistic world by the 20th century masters of Western culture," but grudgingly admitted that it "is one of the high points of American literature and can rightly be called one of the most brilliant accomplishments of the American social novel."

1926 [Silent Cal]

Coolidge, Calvin
MESSAGE OF THE PRESIDENT OF THE UNITED STATES TRANSMITTING THE BUDGET.
Wash., 1926. 13pp. 4to. Printed wrappers. Signed in ink by Coolidge at the conclusion.
(469) 125.00

THE AUTOBIOGRAPHY OF CALVIN COOLIDGE.
N.Y.: Cosmopolitan Book Corp., 1929. 249pp. Untrimmed. Special edition of the first printing, limited, numbered, and signed by Coolidge. (470) 125.00

Alice Roosevelt Longworth said Calvin Coolidge was weaned on a pickle. He brought to the American Presidency an incredible and deliberate dullness unmatched before or since. He was a conservative's conservative who valued the homely virtues of hard work and common sense. During his administration he was so stingy that the White House chef quit in despair, and he always audited his wife's bills to be sure she wasn't overspending. William Allen White said Coolidge was "an economic fatalist with a God-given inertia. He knew nothing and refused to learn." Coolidge considered taciturnity a great virtue; he said: "If you don't say anything, you won't be called upon to repeat it."

Will Rogers commented that Coolidge felt the best way to be President was to carefully avoid all the big problems. Coolidge did just that as the nation plunged towards the stock market crash that came shortly after he left office. His two most famous statements were his eloquent refusal to run for re-election — "I do not choose to run" — and his tenet: "The business of America is business."

1927 [The Spirit of St. Louis]

Lindberg, Charles
MON AVION ET MOI.
Paris: Ernest Flammarion, 1927. 283pp. Illus. Original pictorial wrappers, spine supplied, text rather browned but not brittle. Introduction by Myron T. Herrick, U.S. Ambassador, dated Paris, June 16, 1927. *First French edition,* issued shortly after his famous flight.
(471) 185.00

"WE": THE FAMOUS FLIER'S OWN STORY OF HIS LIFE AND HIS TRANS-ATLANTIC FLIGHT, TOGETHER WITH HIS VIEWS ON THE FUTURE OF AVIATION.
N.Y.: G. P. Putnam's Sons, 1927. 308pp. 52 plates. *First edition in English, special limited, numbered edition on handmade paper, signed by Lindberg.* Near mint copy, with two leaflets advertising the edition loosely inserted.
(472) 350.00

Same as above, *first trade edition.*
(473) 12.50

Original handwritten document signed by Lindberg, December 15, 1925, purchasing an "0x5 areoplane" from D. E. Scott. Also signed by C. P. Wiens.
(474) 500.00

In 1927 Babe Ruth hit 60 home runs in one season; the first talking picture, Al Jolson in *The Jazz Singer,* opened; the first successful television transmission occurred; Sacco and Vanzetti were executed. But the people of America had their eyes in the skies — Lucky Lindy, the Lone Eagle, flew to Paris.

A little more than 33 hours after taking off in the Spirit of St. Louis from New York, Charles A. Lindberg arrived at Paris. Over a hundred thousand screaming Frenchmen were waiting that evening of May 21, 1927, and he received the most enthusiastic demonstration for a peacetime hero in history.

1928   [Earhart Over the Atlantic]

Earhart, Amelia
20 HRS. 40 MIN.: OUR FLIGHT IN THE FRIENDSHIP.
N.Y.: G. P. Putnam's Sons, 1928. 374pp. Original cloth. *First edition,* limited to 150 signed and numbered copies, containing an original small silk flag carried by the author on the flight. Kaplan #1724.   (475) 450.00

Original *Typewritten Letter Signed* by Amelia Earhart, Washington, National Aeronautic Assn., June 29, 1931, 1p., 4to, to Col. Clarence M. Young of the Aeronautics branch of the Department of Commerce, an interesting letter about a controversy with his department, in which she denies making "for publication any criticism of the Department, individually or collectively."   (476) 125.00

In 1920 Amelia Earhart was taken for an airplane ride in Los Angeles and immediately took lessons to become what was then called an aviatrix. Within a year she had set a woman's altitude record and was on her way to an amazing career. On June 17, 1928, she set out across the Atlantic with two male fliers in the tri-motored Fokker, "Friendship," landing in Wales twenty hours and forty minutes later — the first woman to fly the Atlantic.

Thereafter she devoted herself almost exclusively to aviation, although in 1931 she married her publisher, George P. Putnam. In 1929 she set the woman's speed record and in 1931 set a record for a rotor craft at 18,000 feet. In 1932 she set out alone in a single engine Lockheed Vega and became the first woman to fly the Atlantic alone. Thereafter she set numerous records over pilots of both sexes, but in 1937 she set out on a round-the-world flight and disappeared off the coast of New Guinea.

Wolfe, Thomas
LOOK HOMEWARD, ANGEL: A STORY OF THE BURIED LIFE.
N.Y.: Charles Scribner's Sons, 1929. 626pp. Blue cloth. *First edition, first state.* Preston
#2.   (477) 175.00

Faulkner, William
THE SOUND AND THE FURY.
N.Y.: Jonathan Cape and Harrison Smith, 1929. 401pp. Boards. *First edition, first state.*
Massey 322.   (478) 175.00

Hemingway, Ernest
A FAREWELL TO ARMS.
N.Y.: Charles Scribner's Sons, 1929. 355pp. Black cloth. *First edition, first state.* Hanne-
man A8a. Connolly Hundred #60.   (479) 65.00

In 1929 the literary world experienced an avalanche of great books in America and in
Europe. In addition to those listed above, the year witnessed the publication of Faulkner's
Sartoris, John Graves' *Goodbye to All That,* Henry Green's *Living,* Jean Cocteau's *Les
Enfants Terribles,* Ivy Compton Burnett's *Brothers and Sisters,* and Edith Sitwell's *Gold
Coast Customs.*

Look Homeward, Angel was Wolfe's first novel and with it his overwhelming personality burst on the American scene. The enormous manuscript had been edited as much as
possible by the great editor, Maxwell Perkins. It comprises his thinly-disguised autobiography
of life in an eccentric family in the South in the early years of the 20th century.

The Sound and the Fury was Faulkner's most radical experiment in form and tech-
nique, and one of his most successful works. The first section, seen through the eyes of the
idiot Benjy, is literally "a tale told by an idiot, full of sound and fury," but Faulkner made it
signify much. The book is still considered by most critics to be his finest book.

A Farewell to Arms was Hemingway's first full-length novel and probably his best.
Cyril Connolly said that "its success was so enormous that it may be said to have ended
Hemingway's influence as a writer." Fictional, but based on his own experiences in World
War I, it is a classic of great strength and vitality.

1930   [Talking Pictures]

Miehling, Rudolph
SOUND PROJECTION.
N.Y.: Mancall Pub. Co., 1930. 528pp. Cloth.   (480) 45.00

Talbot, Frederick A.
PRACTICAL CINEMATOGRAPHY, AND ITS APPLICATIONS.
Phila.: J. B. Lippincott Company, 1913. 262pp. Cloth.   (481) 75.00

In 1902 the first motion picture theater was opened, in Los Angeles. The next year Harry Warner opened one in Pennsylvania. These showed short sequences and were popular because they were a novelty and because they were cheap.

In 1913, Lasky, DeMille, and Goldwyn formed a motion picture company and made the first feature-length Hollywood movie, "The Squaw Man," followed in 1915 by D. W. Griffith's classic "The Birth of a Nation." Movies quickly became a favorite pastime, with Charlie Chaplin, Mary Pickford, and others becoming internationally famous "stars." In 1927 Al Jolson introduced sound with "The Jazz Singer."

In 1930 a remarkable production was issued, "All Quiet on the Western Front," a grimly realistic antiwar movie that greatly influenced future film-making. It was banned in France and Germany, but won the Academy Award at home. Also in 1930 the motion picture industry established its first Production Code of self-regulatory censorship, which has plagued the industry ever since.

1931   [Father of American Drama]

O'Neill, Eugene
MOURNING BECOMES ELECTRA, A TRILOGY.
N.Y.: Horace Liveright, 1931. 256,[16]pp. Entirely uncut and unopened. Full vellum, morocco label. *First edition, special edition limited to 550 numbered, autographed copies.*
                                                                (482) 150.00

Same, *first trade edition.* Very fine copy in dustjacket.   (483) 15.00

In 1907 Eugene O'Neill was suspended at Princeton for throwing a beer bottle through the window of the president's house; the president was Woodrow Wilson. He grew up to become, in the words of Harlan Hatcher, "at home and abroad, America's greatest dramatist."

Based on the Oresteia of Aeschylus, *Mourning Becomes Electra* is a Freudian analysis of psychological interplay and sex repression that make it a true tragedy. It is not only the most exciting of O'Neill's plays, but is by most critics considered his greatest contribution. In 1936 O'Neill became the first American playwright to be awarded the Nobel Prize for literature.

August 30th, 1932

TO ALL PEACE OFFICERS IN THE UNITED STATES

Dear Sir:

I hold felony warrant (assault to murder one of my deputies) for Clyde Champion Barrow, Raymond Hamilton and Bonnie Parker alias Bonnie Thornton, alias Bonnie Smith who tried to kill one of my deputies in making their escape in a stolen automobile August 15th, 1932.

These are EXTREMLY DANGEROUS criminals and every precaution should be taken in arresting them.

Barrow is wanted at Dallas, Texas on two cases of robbery by firearms. At Hillsboro, Texas for MURDER and robbery. At Atoka, Okla. for MURDER and assault murder on SHERIFF and DEPUTY, TOGETHER WITH RAYMOND HAMILTON. And at Carlsbad, New Mexico for kidnapping a deputy sheriff and releasing him at San Antonia, Texas. Auto theft at Victoria, Texas.

Hamilton is described as follows: Age 18 years. Height 5'6"-Weight
130. Blue eyes. Light hair. Fair
complexion. Finger print class:
1 — Ua — 15
1 — U — 16
Barrow is described as Dallas #0084. Age 22. Height 5'7". Weight 125.
Blond hair. Hazel eyes. Finger
Print class: 29 — MO — 9
26 — UOO-9

We have no description of the girl other than she was 19 years old and was raised in Dallas, Texas.

Willis, Sheriff J. C.
TO ALL PEACE OFFICERS IN THE UNITED STATES.
Broadsheet, 2pp., 4to, Wharton, Texas, August 30, 1932, original Wanted notice for Clyde Barrow and Bonnie Parker, for attempting ''to kill one of my deputies in making their escape in a stolen automobile August 15th, 1932. They are EXTREMLY [sic] DANGEROUS criminals and every precaution should be taken in arresting them. . . . Their car may show bullet marks on the left side of the body. . . .''   (484) 250.00

Jenkins, John H., and H. Gordon Frost
I'M FRANK HAMER: THE LIFE OF A TEXAS PEACE OFFICER."
Austin: The Pemberton Press, 1968. 405pp. *Special edition of the first printing,* limited to 300 numbered copies, autographed by the authors and by Hamer's widow and son. This copy, one of 20 containing a gold replica of a Texas Ranger badge embedded in a full morocco binding, contains an original travel pass signed by Hamer as Captain of the Texas Rangers, used by him during the tracking down of Barrow and Parker.   (485) 125.00

Clyde Barrow was born in 1909 in Teleco, Texas. At 21 years old he was sentenced to 14 years in jail for a series of robberies, but in 1932 was given a general parole and immediately thereafter met Bonnie Parker. The two went on a bloody rampage throughout the Southwest, committing dozens of murders and kidnappings and innumerable robberies. They were finally killed in a gun battle with officers under Texas Ranger Frank Hamer on May 23, 1934.

Capt. Frank Hamer, viciously mis-portrayed in the most recent of a series of motion pictures on the two desperadoes, was the greatest of all Texas Rangers. He was so famous and effective as a lawman that Tom Mix once came to Texas to take notes on how a real lawman walked and talked. Hamer killed over fifty men in the line of duty, was wounded seventeen times, and left for dead four times. Walter P. Webb classed him as ''one of the most fearless men in Western history'' and J. Edgar Hoover called him ''one of the greatest law officers in American history.'' His fifty-year career began in the days of the Butch Cassidy gang and ended in the 1948 Ballot Box 13 affair that sent Lyndon B. Johnson to the Senate.

1933   [The New Deal]

Roosevelt, Franklin D.
INAUGURAL ADDRESS OF FRANKLIN D. ROOSEVELT.
Wash., March 4, 1933. 4pp. *First printing.* "Let me assert my firm belief that the only thing we have to fear is fear itself. . . ." (486) 45.00

Roosevelt, Franklin D.
GIVING THE PRESIDENT CONTROL OVER BANKS.
Wash., 73d Cong., 1st Sess., H.D. 1, March 9, 1933. 2pp. *First printing.* The Emergency Banking Relief Act. (487) 25.00

Frederick, J. George
A PRIMER OF "NEW DEAL" ECONOMICS.
N.Y.: The Business Bource, 1933. 322pp. Black cloth. *First edition.* (488) 15.00

Roosevelt, Franklin D. Original *Typewritten Letter Signed,* The White House, Nov. 6, 1933. 1p., 4to, concerning textile industry controls: ". . . In order that there may be no possibility of injustice, I have directed General Johnson to conduct an exhaustive study of price increases, which, I understand, is now in progress. When the modifying data is assembled, he will conduct a public hearing in which every conflicting interest will have an opportunity to be heard. . . ." (489) 185.00

In his first inaugural address, President Franklin D. Roosevelt called for a program of measures of relief, recovery, and reform to give the public a New Deal and bring it out of the Depression. "The money changers have fled from their high seats in the temple of our civilization. We may now restore that temple to the ancient truths. The measure of that restoration lies in the extent to which we apply social values more noble than mere monetary profit."

He also asked for "broad Executive power to wage a war against the emergency, as great as the power that would be given to me if we were in fact invaded by a foreign foe." Almost a third of the labor force was out of work, and over a billion dollars had been withdrawn from banks, making hundreds fold. On March 9, Congress passed the Emergency Banking Relief Act, giving Roosevelt broad controls over the banking industry and shortly thereafter a dozen similar emergency actions. On March 12, he began his long series of fireside chats.

Roosevelt, Franklin D.
ON OUR WAY.
N.Y.: The John Day Company, 1934. 300pp. Cloth d.j. *First edition. Inscribed and signed by President Roosevelt, October, 1934.*   (490) 225.00

NATIONAL RECOVERY REVIEW BOARD REPORT TO THE PRESIDENT OF THE UNITED STATES.
N.p., 1934. 3 volumes of mimeographed typescripts, about 160 pages each, tied with ribbons. Signed by Wm. J. Kennitzer on the cover of each.   (491) 125.00

ADDRESS OF THE PRESIDENT BEFORE A JOINT SESSION OF THE TWO HOUSES OF CONGRESS.
Wash., Jan. 4, 1935. 8pp. *First printing.*   (492) 20.00

BANKING ACT OF 1935: HEARINGS BEFORE A SUBCOMMITTEE ON BILLS TO PROVIDE FOR THE SOUND, EFFECTIVE, AND UNINTERRUPTED OPERATION OF THE BANKING SYSTEM.
Wash., 1935. 1022pp. Printed wrappers.   (493) 30.00

As Roosevelt's war on the Depression began to take effect, economic conditions improved although in 1934 there were still eleven million out of work. The stock market began to climb back slowly upward. The National Recovery Review Board, The National Industrial Recovery Act, The National Labor Relations Board, and other similar activities worked gradually to revitalize the nation.

At the same time, Roosevelt began to institute social reforms that he felt would benefit the public, including many liberal and labor-oriented reforms that profoundly influenced the decades following. "The test of our progress is not whether we add more to the abundance of those who have much; it is whether we provide enough for those who have little."

One citizen wrote to Roosevelt: "Dear Mr. President, this is just to tell you that everything is alright now. The man you sent found our house alright, and we went down to the bank with him and the morgage can go on for awhile longer. You remember I wrote you about losing the furniture too, well, your man got it back for us. I never heard of a President like you."

EDUCATIONAL PROGRAM
FOR SHARE OUR WEALTH SOCIETY

Government Assumes the Cost and Burden to Guarantee College, Professional, and Vocational Education to All Students

Under the present policy of government the young man and young woman whose parents are possessed of means can be given a college education or vocational and professional training. There are some exceptions to this rule; that is to say, that in some few cases students can find work by which to pay their expenses through college. As a general rule, however, only those with parents possessing extraordinary means can attend college.

"All men are created equal," says the Declaration of Independence, and to all those born the constitution of our Nation guarantees "life, liberty, and the pursuit of happiness."

These provisions of our immortal national documents are not observed when the right to education rests upon the financial ability of one's parents rather than upon the mental capacity of a student to learn and his energy to apply himself to the proper study necessary for him to learn.

The "share our wealth" program contemplates that from the billions of excess revenue brought into the United States Treasury by limiting fortunes to a few million dollars to any one person, that such large sums will be expended by the Government as will afford college education and professional training to all students based upon their mental capacity and energy rather than upon the wealth of their parents. Such an education contemplates not only the scholarship but such supplies and living costs as a student may have in order to attend college.

This will transfer the youth of our land into making preparation for building a better and greater nation. It will take their surplus labor out of the ranks of employment and afford more room for others; it will mean an immediate expansion of our educational facilities and the bringing back into active service of hundreds of thousands of learned instructors whose intellect and capacities, now idle, may be used for the moral, spiritual, and intellectual uplift of the Nation. Architects, engineers, builders, material men, and craftsmen now idle would find extensive and continued field for employment in providing and maintaining such extended educational facilities in the Nation.

All in all, the program is one of national organization; it means no great or burdensome outlay because there is a surplus of the goods and things needed for the care of all students, and the consuming of the same will immediately aid our problems of overproduction.

HUEY P. LONG,
United States Senator.

1935   [Kingfish]

Long, Huey P.
SHARE OUR WEALTH: EVERY MAN A KING.
Wash., [1935]. 32pp. Printed wrappers. Extensive underlining. With original Typewritten Letter Signed, 1p., 4to, from Long written as Governor of Louisiana.   (494) 75.00

Long, Huey P.

PEOPLE OF AMERICA: — IN EVERY COMMUNITY GET TOGETHER AND ORGANIZE A SHARE OUR WEALTH SOCIETY . . . PRINCIPLES AND PLAT-FORM.

Broadside, 1p., large folio, printed in three columns. N.p., c.1935.   (495) 65.00

Long, Huey P.

EDUCATIONAL PROGRAM FOR SHARE OUR WEALTH SOCIETY.

Broadside, 1p., 4to, n.p., 1935.   (496) 40.00

Garlin, Sender

THE REAL HUEY P. LONG.

New Orleans: Worker's Library, May, 1935. 48pp. Original pictorial wrappers. The first violent anti-Long publication.   (497) 35.00

Huey P. Long hated big business but not big politics. He was born in the piney woods region of Louisiana in a family background that "was culturally meager and was most strongly marked by pious Baptist evangelicalism and by a Populistic, hillbilly animosity toward wealth and sophistication." The family nevertheless managed to send six children to college.

Long was elected governor of Louisiana in 1928 at the age of 34. He made reforms, built bridges and highways, and became very popular with the people, but stole state money, used state police for political vendettas, bribed legislators, and was accused of plotting the assassination of an enemy. In 1929 he was impeached by the House and barely escaped conviction.

In 1930 he was elected to the U.S. Senate but kept the governor's seat as well, finally turning it over to a lackey in 1932. In the Senate, the Kingfish, as he was known, advocated radical redistribution of wealth programs and organized "Share Our Wealth" societies. When his political base back home was threatened, he reorganized "the governmental structure of the state, creating the most complete absolutism that had ever existed in the United States. During 1934-35, eight sessions of the legislature enacted, without debate, a series of laws that abolished local government and gave Long control of the appointment of every police-man, fireman, and school teacher in the state. His complete control of the militia, the judiciary, the election officials, and the tax-assessing bodies left all citizens at his mercy."

In August, 1935, he declared himself a candidate for President in the next year's election, denouncing Roosevelt as "a liar and a faker." On September 8, 1935, a leading New Orleans surgeon shot and killed Long in the state capitol; Long's bodyguards fired 61 bullets into the assassin.

1936   [Frankly, My Dear, I Don't Give A Damn]

Mitchell, Margaret
GONE WITH THE WIND.
N.Y.: The Macmillan Company, 1936. 1037pp. Cloth with dustjacket. *First edition, first issue,* with May copyright.   (498) 110.00

GONE WITH THE WIND.
N.Y.: E. B. Greenstone, 1939. 20pp. Large quarto. Color illus. Original booklet issued at the premiers of the MGM motion picture.   (499) 20.00

Margaret Mitchell wrote only one novel, but its success was so overwhelming that it won a Pulitzer Prize and sold over eight million copies in the first decade it was in print, with translations into thirty languages. Edmund Wilson told the story of how infuriated Ernest Hemingway was when he learned Mitchell's book not only outsold all his put together, but was the best-selling American novel ever up to that time. As a literary work, it never rated high, although critic J. Donald Adams said: "It is not a profound or original book, but it is an exceptionally vivid and consistently interesting one." Roger Rosenblatt said of its heroine: "Scarlott is the muse of ham and cheese, the all-American fatal woman with the soul of a perky car-hop." William Rose Benet said she was the "embodiment of the indomitable spirit of the South."

The book was made into one of the first technicolor motion pictures in 1939, a movie which broke all attendance records and was still being shown 37 years later. It starred Clark Gable and Vivien Leigh and won almost all of the Academy Awards for that year, at the ceremonies of which Margaret Mitchell's name was not mentioned a single time.

1937   [Packing the Supreme Court]

Roosevelt, Franklin D.
RECOMMENDATION TO REORGANIZE JUDICIAL BRANCH: MESSAGE FROM THE PRESIDENT OF THE UNITED STATES.
Wash., HD142, 1937. 11pp. *First printing.*   (500) 35.00

Pearson, Drew, and Robert S. Allen
THE NINE OLD MEN.
N.Y.: Doubleday, Doran & Co., 1937. 325pp. Red cloth. Fine copy. *First edition.*
(501) 15.00

In 1936 Roosevelt was re-elected by the largest majority in over a hundred years, losing only Maine and Vermont. His opponent, Alf Landon, parodied an old political saw by saying, "As Maine goes, so goes Vermont." The Democrats captured strong majorities in Congress.

But the Supreme Court had declared seven of Roosevelt's major New Deal measures unconstitutional. Roosevelt responded by stating that he felt it unnecessary to try for a new constitutional amendment in behalf of his programs, but only for a more cooperative judiciary.

Roosevelt then proposed in 1937 a scheme to raise the number of members of the Supreme Court from 9 to 15, adding one new Justice for each present Justice who was past 70 and refused to retire. The ill-conceived act was never passed, but "the nine old men" shortly thereafter underwent a marked change in their decisions, upholding in the spring of 1937 several important New Deal measures. Moreover, in June an archconservative Justice died and Roosevelt's appointment of liberal Hugo L. Black tipped the majority of the Court towards a liberalism that remained for over thirty years thereafter.

1938   [Patriotic Hymn]

Berlin, Irving
GOD BLESS AMERICA.
N.Y.: Irving Berlin, Inc., 1938-39. "First Performance by Kate Smith, Armistice Day, 1938." *Inscribed and signed by Berlin.* Original sheet music, [6]pp., folio.   (502) 225.00

Irving Berlin wrote many well-known songs in his long career, beginning with *Alexander's Ragtime Band* in 1911. They included *White Christmas, Easter Parade, Oh How I Hate to Get Up in the Morning,* and over 800 more by 1952. He was a major force in shaping 20th century popular music.

God Bless America was written in 1918 but never performed until Armistice Day, 1938, when it was introduced by Kate Smith. All income from the song was donated to the Boy and Girl Scouts; Charles Van Doren says: "For the song, which has come to be considered as almost a second national anthem, Berlin was awarded a special Congressional gold medal in 1955."

254

1939   [Social Protest]

Steinbeck, John
THE GRAPES OF WRATH
The only known and apparently only surviving set of original galley proofs, 324 tall-folio leaves, printed on one side only and numbered in pencil, in plain brown wrappers with two printed and one typewritten slips pasted on the front cover. The top states: "Unrevised proofs. Confidential." The middle is a broadsheet, 5x6 inches, advertising the book as forthcoming in April. Below this is a typed notice stating: "These proofs are strictly confidential. . . . The publishers particularly wish to keep them out of the hands of motion picture companies and other unauthorized persons."   (503) 2500.00

Steinbeck, John
THE GRAPES OF WRATH.
N.Y.: The Viking Press, 1939. [6],619pp. *First edition, first issue.* Hayashi, p.2. Goldstone and Payne A12a.   (504) 35.00

Sometimes called the 20th century *Uncle Tom's Cabin,* this novel summed up the despair of the migrant poor in the 1930's. Beyond doubt Steinbeck's most mature and important novel, it is generally recognized as "the most eloquent novel of social protest written in this country." Moreover, it is a strong affirmation of the solidity of mankind; Edmund Wilson wrote: "The subject of *The Grapes of Wrath,* which is supposed to deal with human society, is the same as the subject of *The Red Pony,* which is supposed to deal with horses: loyalty to life itself."

It won the Pulitzer Prize in 1940 and was the major factor in Steinbeck's winning of the Nobel Prize for literature in 1962. Over 430,000 copies sold in the year of its printing, and a total of nineteen editions had been issued by 1963. In 1940 it was made into a motion picture which, incredibly, was a faithful, realistic, and almost faultless rendering of the novel and its themes.

255

THE GRAPES OF WRATH
JOHN STEINBECK

To those readers who have thought that John Steinbeck was writing a new kind of American prose, which would eventually ring out as an authentically great voice, it is thrilling to announce *The Grapes of Wrath*. His genius, so often foretold by commentators upon his earlier works, has found here a theme upon which it grows to full maturity. The dust-bowl—the countless acres of fertile corn-land destroyed; the tight-strung, laconic men and women watching their lives blown away upon a whining air—watching, and calling upon the resources of their heritage to dare to move again to new lands—it is a theme which only the creator of *In Dubious Battle* and *Of Mice and Men* could realize to its full.

Steinbeck's story, if it can be reduced to a few words, is the saga of the new march to the West. As the trucks and the broken-down sedans extricate themselves from the dust, as the families whose lives were predicated upon a crop no longer to be gathered turn their faces to a new frontier, Steinbeck picks out from the long caravan the faces he would have his readers recognize. Carrying on the story of a latter-day migration, he carries on also the story of a few people whose lives are woven into a family group. In the minds and through the eyes of these few we see a new pioneer movement sweeping across the land, reaffirming the tradition of America on the march.

STEINBECK, JOHN	THE GRAPES OF WRATH	APRIL
NOVEL	832 pages 5¼ x 8	$2.75

256

Faulkner, William
THE HAMLET; THE TOWN; THE MANSION.
N.Y., 1940-1957-1959. 3 volumes. Original cloth. Very fine, near mint copies, comprising *a complete set of the limited, autographed editions* of the first printing, each with separate limitation page certifying 250, 450, and 500 copies respectively. Each volume specially bound. Slipcased. Massey 55,139, and 346.   (505) 1350.00

Same, *first trade editions, in dustjackets.* Fine copies. Massey 56,140, and 347.

(506) 250.00

Malcolm Cowley wrote: ''Faulkner performed a labor of imagination that has not been equalled in our time, and a double labor: first, to invent a Mississippi county complete and living in all its details; second, to make his story of Yoknapatawpha County stand as a parable or legend of all the Deep South.'' The Snopes characters, it has been said, are like men facing backwards as they are driven down a road, and are only able to see the road that has already been travelled. Kenneth Douglas wrote: ''His characters brood on the past. Every line written by Faulkner exudes a fascination akin to that exercised by the snake on the rabbit.''

Faulkner was born Falkner but the printer of his first book misspelled his name and he decided to live with it that way. He worked as a stunt pilot and as a postmaster, quitting the latter job with the comment, ''I won't be at the beck and call of every son-of-a-bitch who happens to have two cents.'' It is perhaps fortunate that he became a novelist rather than a postmaster general.

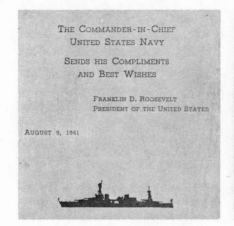

1941 [The Atlantic Charter and Pearl Harbor]

Churchill, Winston S., and Franklin D. Roosevelt
STATEMENT BY THE PRIME MINISTER OF ENGLAND AND THE PRESIDENT OF THE UNITED STATES.
Wash., Aug. 21, 1941. 3pp. *First printing of the Atlantic Charter.*   (507) 75.00

Morton, H. V.
ATLANTIC MEETING: AN ACCOUNT OF MR. CHURCHILL'S VOYAGE IN H.M.S. PRINCE OF WALES, IN AUGUST, 1941, AND THE CONFERENCE WITH PRES. ROOSEVELT WHICH RESULTED IN THE ATLANTIC CHARTER.
London, 1944. 160pp. Cloth. W. G. Nunney's copy, signed. Nunney was a seaman on the H.M.S. Prince of Wales. Accompanied by the card printed on board the ship announcing that Churchill and Roosevelt were meeting, *signed by Churchill,* together with 5 unpublished photographs taken by Nunney on board of Churchill and Roosevelt, the typed menu for their luncheon on Aug. 10, 1941, with signed certification by Churchill's Chief Stewart stating that Nunney cooked the meal. A historic assemblage.   (508) 385.00

WHAT NEXT IN ASIA?
N.Y., The New Republic, Dec. 8, 1941, complete issue with major article on why the U.S. and Japan will not go to war: "There could hardly be a war between Japan and the U.S. because neither could get at the other in order to fight it. In addition . . . there is the deterring influence that neither wants very much to make war on the other. . . . Unless there is some unlikely error in our information about the naval situation, sane strategists would never permit Japan to start such a hopeless war."   (509) 12.50

Churchill, Winston S.

SPEECH ON THE FAR EAST WAR, DECEMBER 8TH, 1941.

N.Y., 1941. 4pp. Stamped received Dec. 23, 1941. Woods A82. *First printing, preceding English publication.* Churchill makes the historic announcement of the Japanese attack on Pearl Harbor. ''Last night [Dec. 7] Japan attacked the United States. . . . [In the Atlantic Charter] I pledged the word of Great Britain that should the United States become involved in a war with Japan, a British declaration would follow within the hour. I therefore spoke to President Roosevelt on the Atlantic telephone last night with a view to arranging the timing of our respective declarations. . . .'' Accompanied by an original 8x10 photograph of Churchill dated Dec. 15, 1941.   (510) 125.00

REPORT OF ARMY PEARL HARBOR BOARD.

N.p., Oct. 20, 1944. 304pp. Folio. Mimeographed and stapled. Top Secret cover notice removed. Advance issue of the first report on what occurred at Pearl Harbor, issued by Generals George Frunert, H. D. Russell, and Walter H. Frank.   (511) 85.00

PEARL HARBOR ATTACK: HEARINGS BEFORE THE JOINT COMMITTEE ON THE INVESTIGATION OF THE PEARL HARBOR ATTACK . . . AND EVENTS AND CIRCUMSTANCES RELATING THERETO.

Wash., 1946. 39 volumes (about 30,000 pages). Hundreds of maps, aerial photographs, and illustrations. *First edition* of the most complete and detailed investigation into the attack and American unpreparedness.   (512) 1350.00

When war broke out in Europe, America once again tried at first to remain uninvolved. Realizing that sooner or later America was bound to be drawn into the conflict, Roosevelt met in the middle of the Atlantic Ocean in a top secret meeting in August, 1941. They drew up an eloquent and dignified statement of mutual aims for peace that became known as the Atlantic Charter. Similar to the Fourteen Points but a bit more practical, it offered guidelines for maintaining peace among nations after the conclusion of the war.

On December 7, 1941, Japan ''suddenly and deliberately attacked'' the American navy base at Pearl Harbor in Hawaii. The attack took the United States by surprise, severely crippled its naval force, and left Japan able to control the Pacific and Southeast Asia. Within 24 hours of the attack, the United States entered World War II.

NOTICE

Headquarters
Western Defense Command
and Fourth Army

Presidio of San Francisco, California
April 1, 1942

Civilian Exclusion Order No. 5

1.   Pursuant to the provisions of Public Proclamations Nos. 1 and 2, this headquarters, dated March 2, 1942, and March 16, 1942, respectively, it is hereby ordered that all persons of Japanese ancestry, including aliens and non-aliens, be excluded from and after 12 o'clock noon, P. W. T., of Tuesday, April 7, 1942, from that portion of Military Area No. 1 in the State of California described as follows:

All that portion of the City and County of San Francisco, State of California, lying generally west of the north-south line established by Junipero Serra Boulevard, Worchester Avenue, and Nineteenth Avenue, and lying generally north of the east-west line established by California Street, to the intersection of Market Street, and thence on Market Street to San Francisco Bay.

2.   A responsible member of each family, and each individual living alone, in the above described affected area will report between the hours of 8:00 a. m. and 5:00 p. m., Thursday, April 2, 1942, or during the same hours on Friday, April 3, 1942, to the Civil Control Station located at:

1701 Van Ness Avenue
San Francisco, California

3.   Any person affected by this order who fails to comply with any of its provisions or with the provisions of published instructions pertaining hereto, or who is found in the above restricted area after 12 o'clock noon, P. W. T., of Tuesday, April 7, 1942, will be subject to the criminal penalties provided by Public Law No. 503, 77th Congress, approved March 21, 1942, entitled "An Act to Provide a Penalty for Violation of Restrictions or Orders with Respect to Persons Entering, Remaining in, Leaving, or Committing Any Act in Military Areas or Zones," and alien Japanese will be subject to immediate apprehension and internment.

J. L. DeWITT
Lieutenant General, U. S. Army
Commanding

1942 [America's Most Shameful Deed]

NOTICE! . . . CIVILIAN EXCLUSION ORDER NO. 5.

Broadside, 10x22 inches, Headquarters Western Defense Command and Fourth Army, Presidio of San Francisco, April 1, 1942, Lt. Gen. J. L. DeWitt, Commanding. Orders "all persons of Japanese ancestry, including aliens and non-aliens" to surrender to the military authorities on the following day.   (513) 350.00

Spicer, E. H.

IMPOUNDED PEOPLE: JAPANESE AMERICANS IN THE RELOCATION CENTERS.

Wash.: Dept. of Interior, 1946. 239pp. Printed wrappers. Official government report and apology for the imprisonment of the Japanese. A detailed analytical report on the hysteria (which led Gen. J. L. DeWitt to demand evacuation of "Japanese and other Subversive Persons" from the West Coast), the evacuation, life in the prison camps, release, and re-entry into society.   (513A) 45.00

In early 1942, President Roosevelt approved the plan which led to the nadir of American history. Orders were issued to move 112,000 Japanese-Americans from their homes in California to concentration camps. Over 75,000 of these were native-born citizens of the United States. Because of the panic over a possible Japanese invasion, the public accepted this dastardly act, and stood by as barbed-wire barricades were erected around the prison camps.

In addition to the degradation and sufferings inflicted by the "exclusion order," much property damage was suffered. The imprisonment lasted until January, 1945.

1943 [America at War]

Roosevelt, Franklin D.

PROGRESS OF THE WAR: A REPORT TO CONGRESS.

Wash., The White House, Sept. 17, 1943. 12pp. Printed wrappers. "Major battles in Europe and Asia are beginning to be joined. In recent months the main tides of conflict have been running our way. . . . The Allied forces are now engaged in a very hard battle south of Naples. Casualties are heavy. . . ."   (514) 25.00

During the first five months of 1943, over seven hundred warships were built in the United States, more than in all of 1942, with war factories working at full tilt. In June the Allies invaded Sicily and then the Italian mainland. In the Far East, the United States pushed the Japanese steadily back on all fronts. Roosevelt and Churchill held several meetings to plan strategy, and appointed Gen. Dwight D. Eisenhower Commander-in-Chief in the European theater of war.

1944 [D Day]

Eisenhower, Dwight D.

SOLDIERS, SAILORS AND AIRMEN OF THE ALLIED EXPEDITIONARY FORCE! YOU ARE ABOUT TO EMBARK . . .

Broadside, 1p., 4to, Supreme Headquarters, [England, June 5 or 6, 1944], directing the D Day invasion troops to be brave and victorious. Issued on the eve of or the morning of the invasion. Very rare.   (515) 200.00

Eisenhower, Dwight D.

PROCLAMATION.

Large broadside, 1p., elephant folio. ''Citoyens Francais: Le jour de la delivrance se leve. Vos freres sont maintenant sur le sol francais. . . .'' N.p., ca. June 6, 1944. Issued by Eisenhower as Supreme Commander, calling on the French to rally behind the D Day Invasion.
(516) 200.00

INVASION EXTRA: INVASION ON! ALLIES HIT NORTHERN FRANCE.

Austin American, June 6, 1944. 8pp. Large folio. Text in one column across entire page. One of many newspaper extras issued when news of the invasion was announced. (517) 20.00

Ryan, Cornelius

THE LONGEST DAY: JUNE 6, 1944.

N.Y.: Simon and Schuster, 1959. 350,[2]pp. d.j. *With an 8-line signed presentation inscription from Ryan to Basil Rathbone.* Of this book, Gen. James Gavin said: ''If you have read all the accounts of D Day or none of them, if you were in the fighting or on the sidelines, you will be spellbound, as I was, by this magnificent telling of a glorious and tragic story.''
(518) 45.00

262

Eisenhower, Dwight D.

REPORT BY THE SUPREME COMMANDER TO THE COMBINED CHIEFS OF STAFF ON THE OPERATIONS IN EUROPE OF THE ALLIED EXPEDITIONARY FORCE, 6 JUNE 1944 TO 8 MAY 1945.

Wash., July 13, 1945. 123pp. Large folio. Original boards. *First edition. With an intimate seven-line signed presentation inscription from Dwight D. Eisenhower to Arthur Page,* ". . . with lasting appreciation of his invaluable war services and with gratitude for his demonstrated affection for the U.S. Army, from his friend and admirer. . . ." Page was Chairman of the Joint Congressional Committee on the Army and Navy and Chief Advisor to the American delegation at the London Naval Conference, and was one of the key figures supporting the military operations under Eisenhower. (519) 450.00

Gunther, John

D DAY.

N.Y.: Harper & Brothers, 1944. 276pp. d.j. *First edition.* (520) 20.00

Patton, George S.

PHOTOGRAPH.

Original 8x10 photograph, March, 1945, of Gen. Patton pissing in the Rhine River.

(521) 25.00

Planning for the invasion of France had begun in March, 1943, with the realization that this would be the turning point in the war, the invasion that would drive through France into Germany and crush the Nazi regime. Utmost secrecy was maintained, and only a handful of officers under Eisenhower knew when or where the attack would be made.

On June 6, 1944, the attack was made. Known as D Day, it was the greatest amphibious invasion in history. Over 5300 ships and landing craft carried the invaders and equipment, in addition to 12,000 paratroopers dropped from airplanes, across the English channel to the Normandy coast. By June 19, over 600,000 American and British troops were ashore and driving into France, amidst stiff opposition. On August 25, the American troops entered Paris, and by the end of September most of France was in Allied hands. By March of the next year, Patton had crossed the Rhine.

ATTENTION AMERICAN SOLDIERS!

I CEASE RESISTANCE

THIS LEAFLET GUARANTEES HUMANE TREATMENT TO ANY JAPANESE DESIRING TO CEASE RESISTANCE. TAKE HIM IMMEDIATELY TO YOUR NEAREST COMMISSIONED OFFICER.

By Direction of the Commander in Chief.

上の英文の内容は「この人は最早や敵でなく國際條約により生命衣食住は勿論醫療等が完全に保證さるべき者なり」と云ふ意味が書かれてゐる。

出来ればこの紙を木の枝にはさみそれを手に持って両手を揚げ我方に接近して来られ我將兵に會へば恐れず安心して手眞似に從へばよい。

25-J-1

Draft

CHARTER OF THE UNITED NATIONS

WE THE PEOPLES OF THE UNITED NATIONS
DETERMINED

> to save succeeding generations from the scourge of war, which twice in our life-time has brought untold sorrow to mankind, and

> to reaffirm faith in fundamental human rights, in the dignity and worth of the human person, in the equal rights of men and women and of nations large and small, and

> to establish conditions under which justice and respect for the obligations arising from treaties and other sources of international law can be maintained, and

> to promote social progress and better standards of life in larger freedom,

AND FOR THESE ENDS

> to practice tolerance and live together in peace with one another as good neighbors, and

> to unite our strength to maintain international peace and security, and

> to ensure, by the acceptance of principles and the institution of methods, that armed force shall not be used, save in the common interest, and

> to employ international machinery for the promotion of the economic and social advancement of all peoples,

HAVE RESOLVED TO COMBINE OUR EFFORTS
TO ACCOMPLISH THESE AIMS.

Accordingly, our respective Governments, through representatives assembled in the city of San Francisco, who have exhibited their full powers found to be in good and due form, have agreed to the present Charter of the United Nations and do hereby establish an international organization to be known as the United Nations.

I CEASE RESISTANCE!

Broadsheet, narrow folio, 2pp., c.1945, in English and Japanese. Original leaflet dropped over battle areas in the Pacific for use by Japanese who wished to surrender. Brightly colored, the sheet if held aloft would prevent American troops from unwittingly firing on those who desired to surrender. It also explained that Japanese would not be tortured or killed by the Americans. This highly effective broadside is cited and pictured in the *Encyclopedia Britannica* article on Propaganda. Exceedingly rare.   (522) 150.00

PROCLAMATION BY THE PRESIDENT: VICTORY IN EUROPE.

Broadside, 1p., 4to, Wash., May 9, 1945, issued by Gen. George C. Marshall, issuing Truman's proclamation declaring V-E Day: "The Allied armies . . . have wrung from Germany a final and unconditional surrender." Issued on the day of Germany's surrender.
(523) 60.00

PORT OF NAGASAKI.

Wash., May, 1945. 38pp. Long folio. Large folding maps and aerial photographs. Top secret document used in preparing for the atomic bomb attack a few weeks later. Very rare, almost surely used by the bombing expedition members while planning the attack.   (524) 150.00

EXTRA! PEACE! JAPAN SURRENDERS. MACARTHUR TO BOSS NIPS.

Austin American, August 14, 1945. 4pp. Large folio. Chipped. "Fighting in the second world war has ended. . . ."   (525) 20.00

Smyth, H. D.

A GENERAL ACCOUNT OF THE DEVELOPMENT OF METHODS OF USING ATOMIC ENERGY FOR MILITARY PURPOSES, UNDER THE AUSPICES OF THE UNITED STATES GOVERNMENT, 1940-1945.

[Wash.], August, 1945. 191pp. Stapled. With rare and possibly unique separate War Department pre-release notice, headed in red ink: "Future Release, Please Note Date," announcing that the top secret report may be released "after 9:00 P.M. EWT, Saturday, August 11, 1945," cautioning that the report must be kept absolutely secret and mentioning the effects of the Manhattan Project New Mexico atomic bomb test three weeks earlier, announcing for the first time the existence of the atomic bomb. This volume is the exceedingly rare press-only preliminary issue of the famous Smyth Report, issued six days after Hiroshima and two days before Japan's surrender. Printing and the Mind of Man #422 note.
(526) 1000.00

Same, the first edition, 182pp. Printing and the Mind of Man #422.   (527) 500.00

THE CONFERENCES AT MALTA AND YALTA.

Uncorrected galley proofs of the Top Secret meetings of Roosevelt, Churchill, and Stalin. Two folio volumes, 834 galleys, February, 1945.   (528) 150.00

FUNERAL SERVICES OF FRANKLIN DELANO ROOSEVELT, LATE PRESIDENT OF THE UNITED STATES.

Wash., The East Room, The White House, April 14, 1945. Black-bordered announcement, together with another for services in St. Paul's Cathedral, New York, 8pp. (529) 45.00

UNITED NATIONS: VERBATIM MINUTES OF THE FIRST PLENARY SESSION.

[San Francisco,] Opera House, April 26, 1945. 20pp. Stapled. First meeting by representatives of fifty countries calling for a United Nations charter. Extremely rare.   (530) 175.00

GUIDE TO AMENDMENTS, COMMENTS, AND PROPOSALS CONCERNING THE DUMBARTON OAKS PROPOSALS FOR A GENERAL INTERNATIONAL ORGANIZATION.

San Francisco, May 14, 1945. 72pp. Stapled. "For the Use of Delegates." Extremely rare.
(531) 150.00

TEXT OF THE PROPOSED CHARTER OF THE UNITED NATIONS . . .

San Francisco, June 25, 1945. 30pp. Stapled. Each page headed "Draft." Issued on the last day of the conference, it was ratified by all the delegates and became effective October 24. *First printing of a historic document; of the utmost rarity.*   (532) 350.00

CHARTER OF THE UNITED NATIONS: REPORT TO THE PRESIDENT ON THE RESULTS OF THE SAN FRANCISCO CONFERENCE.

Wash., June 26, 1945. 266pp. Printed wrappers. *First printing for the public.* (533) 125.00

In May, 1945, the Nazis collapsed and surrendered and victory in Europe was achieved. Roosevelt had died in April, a few weeks after being inaugurated for his unprecedented fourth term. When the Japanese refused to give up, and showed signs of fighting to the bitter end, Truman felt more lives would be saved than lost by using the atomic bomb.

The bomb had been developed secretly in New Mexico under the code name of the Manhattan Project. In August, Truman ordered the bombing of Hiroshima and Nagasaki, causing over 100,000 civilian deaths. Japan surrendered unconditionally.

At Yalta and Malta conferences were held that ordained the post-war balance of power, particularly dooming the world to a cold war with Russia. But brighter news took place in San Francisco, where representatives of fifty nations met and drew up the charter for the United Nations.

Chapter 10

$$L = c \frac{dm}{dt} \sin \alpha,$$

where $\frac{dm}{dt}$ is the mass ejection rate of the main rocket and α is the angle between the trajectory and the vehicle axis. Eliminating α, we have

$$\frac{c\frac{dm}{dt}}{T} = \frac{\frac{dm}{dt}}{\left(\frac{dm}{dt}\right)_0} = \sqrt{1 + \left(\frac{L}{T}\right)^2},$$

where $\left(\frac{dm}{dt}\right)_0$ is the rocket fuel consumption required to produce the thrust if the guidance force were not present.

For the second case, when a small auxiliary rocket is used,

$$T = c \frac{dm}{dt}_1,$$

$$L = c \frac{dm}{dt}_2,$$

and

$$\frac{\frac{dm}{dt}}{\left(\frac{dm}{dt}\right)_0} = 1 + \frac{L}{T}$$

where $\frac{dm}{dt}_1$, $\frac{dm}{dt}_2$ and $\frac{dm}{dt}$ are the consumptions of the main rocket, the auxiliary rocket and the total.

In the adjoining figure, the ratio of the consumptions with and without guidance force have been plotted against the ratio of guidance force to thrust. It is at once apparent that case 1 is markedly superior to case 2. In fact with case 1, substantial guidance forces may be obtained without appreciable penalty in thrust. Case 1 will be the method of guidance considered in what follows.

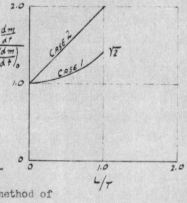

268

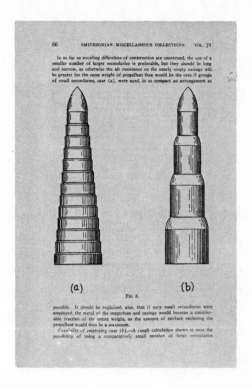

1946   [Plans for the Space Age]

Goddard, Robert H.
*ROCKETS: COMPRISING A METHOD OF REACHING EXTREME ALTITUDES
AND LIQUID-PROPELLANT ROCKET DEVELOPMENT.*
N.Y.: American Rocket Society, 1946. [12],69,[14],10,[18]pp. Cloth d.j. *First complete
edition and first trade edition, with new matter added.*   (534) 85.00

*PRELIMINARY DESIGN OF AN EXPERIMENTAL WORLD-CIRCLING SPACE-
SHIP.*
Santa Monica: Douglas Aircraft Company, May 2, 1946. c.320pp. Folding charts. Illus.
First report of a practical design for a spaceship, prepared for the U.S. government. Exceed-
ingly rare.   (535) 400.00

Dr. Robert H. Goddard built and launched the first liquid-propellant rocket in America
in 1926. It burned for 2.6 seconds and achieved a speed of 60 M.P.H. In 1932 Goddard
launched a rocket to 2000 feet at 500 M.P.H. More experiments were made in the 1930's
but these were interrupted by the war.

As soon as the war was over, the government began studying and experimenting in
rocketry, with the added help of German scientists who had developed the V2 military
rockets. In 1946 Douglas Aircraft in California was commissioned by the government to
design a spaceship, and after intensive study it completed the report and plans on May 2,
1946, marking the beginning of the space age.

Fink, Donald G.
PRINCIPLES OF TELEVISION ENGINEERING.
N.Y.: McGraw-Hill Book Company, Inc., 1940, revised 1947. 541pp. Cloth. First revised (best) edition.   (536) 20.00

Campbell Swinton, A. A.
"DISTANT ELECTRIC VISION"
Nature, June 18, 1908, complete issue, and another issue for June 4, 1908, with article by Shelford Bidwell, ''Telegraphic Photography and Electric Vision.''   (537) 125.00

NETWORK BROADCASTING: REPORT OF THE COMMITTEE ON INTER-STATE AND FOREIGN COMMERCE.
Wash., 1958. 737pp. Extensive, detailed report on the television industry, its past, future, and impact.   (538) 45.00

"In June, 1908," writes R. W. Hubbell, ''Shelford Bidwell . . . stressed that the only feasible way to extend vision electrically over long distances was suggested by the structure of the eye. . . . In answer to Bidwell, A. A. Campbell Swinton, wrote to the magazine *Nature,* setting down *an idea of classic brilliance.* This scientist wrote that while mechanical methods were impracticable, electrical seeing could be accomplished by the use of two cathode ray tubes, in the transmitter and in the receiver.'' From this beginning, the gradual invention of television grew.

By the 1920's, sets were actually in operation, and by the 1930's movements were under way for general public broadcasting. The war slowed the public development but created new techniques. At the end of the war there were stations in five cities and about 7,000 sets in operation.

By 1947, enough of the bugs were worked out of the system to offer sets economically. In that year over 15,000 sets per month were produced and gobbled up by a hungry American public. In that same year Howdy Doody, Gorgeous George, Roller Derby, Meet the Press, and Douglas Edwards and the CBS News hit the screens for the first time, as well as the first televised world series. Within three years a hundred stations were beaming into four million homes — and the boob tube had become an integral part of American civilization.

1948   [Communism in America]

INVITATION TO JOIN THE COMMUNIST PARTY.
N.Y., Workers Library Publishers, 1948. 16pp. Pictorial wrappers.   (539) 15.00

THE 1948 ELECTION PLATFORM OF THE COMMUNIST PARTY.
N.Y., The Communist Party, 1948. 16pp. Printed wrappers.   (540) 15.00

23 QUESTIONS ABOUT THE COMMUNIST PARTY ANSWERED BY WILLIAM Z. FOSTER.
N.Y., New Century Publishers, 1948. 31pp. Printed wrappers.   (541) 15.00

Collection of over 700 different pamphlets, broadsides, manifestos, leaflets, etc., relating to the Communist Party in America, ca.1920-1950. Details on request.   (542) 1250.00

Socialist and liberal movements in America, because of their identification with unionism and labor, led them in the public mind to be lumped with the followers of international Communism as represented by Soviet Russia. From time to time after the Russian Revolution hysteria would lead to fears that plans were afoot to overthrow the government in America. While it is probable that there were Communist efforts to that end, they never presented a serious threat, although during the troubles of the Depression many Americans joined socialist and labor movements, and a few joined the Communist Party.

The Communist Party of America was a legal political party which ran candidates for office such as Earl Browder and William Z. Foster. In 1940 the Smith Act made it unlawful for anyone to preach the overthrow of the government by force of violence. But after the war a mounting fear of Communist influence began to pervade American society and strong pressures were brought to destroy the Communist movement altogether. In 1949 eleven leaders of the party were tried and convicted of advocating the violent overthrow of the government, and the party began to wane almost to the point of non-existence.

Truman, Harry S
[INAUGURAL ADDRESS].
Wash., Jan. 19, 1949, 5pp. Folio. Mimeo typescript issued to a few people the evening before delivery of the address, marked *"Confidential, Hold for Release . . . must be held in strict confidence and no portion, synopsis or intimation may be given out or published until delivery has begun."*   (543) 75.00

In the 1948 election Harry S Truman was elected in a close race with Thomas E. Dewey, so close that Dewey would probably have won it if he had not worn a moustache. Alice Roosevelt Longworth said, "How can you vote for a man who looks like the bridegroom on a wedding cake?" It was also so close that the Chicago *Daily Tribune* announced Dewey the victor.

On January 20, 1949, Truman made a memorable inaugural address proposing a group of programs which had an immense influence on the future history of the country. Truman demanded a strong stand in the Cold War, accusing the Communists of preventing the accomplishment of "world recovery and lasting peace" and of working to take control of Europe and other parts of the world.

He called for a program of four points of action, including the use of the Marshall Plan to help rebuild Europe and the establishment of an Atlantic defense pact, which became NATO. His greatest stress, however, was on providing technical and scientific assistance to underdeveloped nations. This fourth proposal became known as the Point Four Program, from which developed the foreign aid programs of the next three decades.

Winston Churchill, attesting to Truman's farsighted and generous plan, said to him: "I must confess, sir, that I loathed your taking the place of Franklin Roosevelt. I misjudged you badly. Since that time you, more than any other man, have saved Western Civilization."

1950   [McCarthyism]

McCarthy, Sen. Joseph
MAJOR SPEECHES AND DEBATES OF SENATOR JOE MCCARTHY, DELIVERED IN THE UNITED STATES SENATE.
Wash.: Not Printed at Government Expense, 1951. [4],354pp. Blue cloth, gilt. (544) 35.00

INTERNAL SECURITY ACT OF 1950.
Wash., HR3112, Sept. 19, 1950. 68pp. Signed in type by Pat McCarran for the Senate and Richard M. Nixon for the House, managers for final amendments. This is what came to be known as the McCarran Act.   (545) 35.00

Truman, Harry S
INTERNAL SECURITY ACT OF 1950: MESSAGE FROM THE PRESIDENT . . . RETURNING WITHOUT APPROVAL THE BILL . . .
Wash., HD708, Sept. 22, 1950. 44pp. Truman's veto of the McCarran Act.   (546) 35.00

In 1952 the McCarran Act was passed over Truman's veto and became the nation's basic immigration law. While erasing some race and sex barriers for immigrants, it provided for unduly harsh screening of aliens and extended anti-Jewish and anti-Catholic prohibitions.

Senator Joseph McCarthy began to feed on the public's fear of Communist plots in America. He charged that there were 205, changed the next day to 57, ''card-carrying members of the Communist Party in the State Department.'' His accusations caused a sensation and for two years led Congress on a witch hunt that has seldom been matched for vitriol. He was ultimately repudiated by his fellow Congressmen, who formally censured him in 1954 for ''conduct that tends to bring the Senate into dishonor and disrepute.''

McCarthy attacked Truman and Roosevelt for ''twenty years of treason'' and Truman responded by saying McCarthy was ''a pain in the neck.'' The McCarthy days also produced Richard Nixon, who said: ''Truman, Dean Acheson and other Administration officials for political purposes covered up this Communist conspiracy and attempted to halt its exposure.''

Nixon, Richard M.
THE HISS CASE: A LESSON FOR THE AMERICAN PEOPLE.
Wash., Not Printed at Government Expense, 1950. 16pp. Printed wrappers. Interesting history of the Alger Hiss case from Nixon's viewpoint, charging Truman with being soft on Communism. (546A) 45.00

1951 [Old Soldiers Never Die]
TRUMAN RELIEVES M'ARTHUR!
El Paso Times, April 11, 1951. Original newspaper with double-column illustrated headline story subtitled: ''General Accused of Insubordination; Ridgway Succeeds.'' (547) 20.00

ADDRESS OF GENERAL OF THE ARMY DOUGLAS MACARTHUR AT A JOINT MEETING OF THE TWO HOUSES IN THE HALL OF REPRESENTATIVES.
Wash., April 19, 1951. 6pp. *First printing of MacArthur's famous farewell address.*
(548) 45.00

In 1950 North Korea launched the invasion that became the Korean War, and Douglas MacArthur, hero of the Philippines, was placed in command of United Nations forces. In September, 1950, he made the counterattack that drove the enemy back to the Yalu River, the border of China. In late November over a million Chinese poured over the border and drove the U.N. forces back to the 38th parallel, the border between North and South Korea.

MacArthur became convinced that it was an absolute necessity to invade China, an act tantamount to starting World War III. He was so insistent that on April 11, 1951, Truman relieved him of his command. MacArthur returned to a hero's welcome and was invited to address a Congress that was generally hostile to Truman's act. MacArthur recounted his career, ending with the comment that ''old soldiers never die; they just fade away. And like the old soldier of that ballad, I now close my military career and just fade away. . . .''

Truman wrote: ''I fired MacArthur because he wouldn't respect the authority of the President. I didn't fire him because he was a dumb son of a bitch, although he was, but that's not against the law for generals. If it was, half to three-quarters of them would be in jail.''

1952 [Eisenhower–Stevenson Election]

Adams, Sherman

Original *Typewritten Manuscript Signed,* 1p., March 8, 1952, as Chairman of the Eisenhower for President Committee. The manuscript lists detrimental statements made by Adlai Stevenson and offers these as reasons why Eisenhower should be supported. Accompanied by a T.L.S. transmitting the manuscript in hopes that it "can be of some assistance to the cause of the candidate whom we both favor." (549) 50.00

Stevenson, Adlai E.

MAJOR CAMPAIGN SPEECHES OF ADLAI E. STEVENSON, 1952.

N.Y.: Random House, 1953. 320pp. *Limited, numbered edition, signed by Stevenson.* Loosely inserted is an interesting T.L.S., 1p., 4to, Feb. 12, 1956, from Stevenson about his 1956 Presidential campaign: ". . . As you know, I have been campaigning on the West Coast for the last several weeks. The trip has been an exciting one and I am much encouraged. . . . I particularly want to thank you for circulating my nominating petition. . . . I eagerly look forward to working with you in the weeks ahead! . . ." (550) 125.00

Eisenhower, Dwight D.

FIRST INAUGURAL ADDRESS, JANUARY 20, 1953.

N.p., n.d. 10pp. Cloth, *Autographed by Eisenhower.* (551) 110.00

Since the end of World War II, both parties had tried to get Dwight Eisenhower to run for President. The general at first refused, saying "soldiers should stick to soldiering." Nevertheless, at the urging of Henry Cabot Lodge and other influential Republicans, he allowed his name to be put before the 1952 Republican Convention, although he remained at his NATO post in Europe. The party nominated him easily over Sen. Robert A. Taft.

The Democrats nominated a reluctant Adlai Stevenson, Truman's personal choice, and he was defeated overwhelmingly by Eisenhower. The most interesting, and portentous, affair of the campaign centered around Vice Presidential candidate Richard Nixon, who delivered in September his Checkers speech and was allowed to remain on the ticket in spite of campaign fund irregularities.

1953 [Architect of the Future]

Wright, Frank Lloyd

THE FUTURE OF ARCHITECTURE.

N.Y.: Horizon Press, 1953. 325pp. Illus. d.j. *First edition, autographed by Wright.*
(552) 125.00

Wright, Frank Lloyd

AN AUTOBIOGRAPHY.

London, New York, Toronto: Longmans, Green, and Company, 1932. 372pp. plus illus. Fine copy. *First edition, autographed by Wright.* Downs, Famous American Books #39: "The best single source for Wright's ideas. . . . Included in it are virtually all his major statements on the nature of organic architecture, of materials, of the site, and of structure."
(553) 200.00

Frank Lloyd Wright left as his monument some seven hundred completed architectural structures and plans for three hundred more. He achieved a world-wide fame greater than any American artist, and did much to make Americans aware of the meaning of art and architecture.

Edward Durrell Stone writes: "Great ideas in architecture are rare. Throughout history . . . there have been scarcely half a dozen structural innovations. The Greeks perfected the use of the lintel. The Romans added the arch, the vault, and the dome, and Byzantine culture added the square surmounted by the dome. The great Gothic contribution was the flying buttress, designed to counter the thrust of huge vaults. From the Gothic period to Mr. Wright's time no new principle was added to our architectural vocabulary." In our time reinforced concrete, the steel frame, and the elevator brought revolutionary building changes, pioneered by men like Wright's teacher, Louis Sullivan, but "it remained for Frank Lloyd Wright to become the creative inspiration and the prophet who established the still-unexploited principles of 20th century architecture."

It is ironic that with his fame and reputation, his impact on architecture and civilization, ne was never once called upon by his government to plan a building or structure of any kind. Perhaps this was due to his arising from an era in which American habitations were, in the words of Lewis Mumford, "uniquely hideous" and in an atmosphere that celebrated itself with Greco-Roman monstrosities and could not tolerate the quiet suitableness of Wright's structures to their surrounding terrain.

1954   [The Segregation Decision]

BROWN V. BOARD OF EDUCATION (FIRST CASE).
Typewritten Manuscript Signed by Chief Justice Earl Warren, 8 leaves, double-spaced, 1954.
(554) 125.00

BROWN V. BOARD OF EDUCATION (SECOND CASE).
Typewritten Manuscript Signed by Chief Justice Earl Warren, 3 leaves, double-spaced, 1955.
(555) 125.00

The era of integration began on May 17, 1954, when Chief Justice Earl Warren read the unanimous Supreme Court ruling in Brown v. Board of Education, holding that racial segregation in the public schools was unconstitutional. Warren wrote for the Court that education "is the very foundation of good citizenship. . . . We come then to the question presented: Does segregation of children in public schools solely on the basis of race . . . deprive the children of the minority group of equal educational opportunities? We believe that it does. . . . Separate educational facilities are inherently unequal." The court in 1955 ordered integration in the schools to begin "with all deliberate speed" and throughout the next decade continued to knock down segregation laws as civil rights cases made their way up through the courts.

Dr. Jonas E. Salk in His Laboratory
Researcher "never walked when he could run."

Basil O'Connor
Architect of the fight on polio.

1955 [Salk Polio Vaccine]

Collection of original letters and telegrams from the papers of Basil O'Connor, trustee of the Salk Foundation and Franklin Roosevelt's law partner, relating to Dr. Jonas Salk's discovery of the polio vaccine, consisting of the following:

(1) Typed Letter Signed from Eleanor Roosevelt to Basil O'Connor, April 6, 1955, stating: "I am most anxious to know the results of Dr. Salk's work. Can you tell me what has been determined to date?"

(2) Same to same, April 20, 1955, stating it is "gratifying to know Dr. Salk's efforts were so successful and I look forward to a day in the near future when the fear of polio may be completely expelled."

(3) Same to same, April 22, 1955, sending a check for $2500 "to help Dr. Salk either have a holiday or use for research."

(4) Same to same, May 31, 1955, on the same subject.

(5) Retained draft of a letter from Jonas Salk to Mrs. Roosevelt, July 6, 1955, stating that "the events since 12 April have confronted me with an entirely new world," including a 3-line note in ink in his hand, signed with initials.

(6) Five-page telegram of remarks by President Eisenhower on the Salk vaccine, May 11, 1955.

(7) Autograph Letter Signed from Jonas Salk to Basil O'Connor remarking on "what you have contributed to my life. You have provided opportunities as could have been done by no other. To this must be added the devotion and affection that we have for each other. . . . We have been able to do together what has not before been done."

276

(8) Autograph Letter Signed from Jonas Salk to Basil O'Connor, stating: "I find myself expressing, 'Thank God for Basil O'Connor! What would I have done without you? The expression embodies the meaning you have not for me alone, but for society — for mankind." A long letter giving him credit for the opportunity to develop the Salk vaccine.

(9) Typed Letter Signed from Averill Harriman, Jan. 7, 1957, to O'Connor, paying tribute "for the inspiring leadership you have provided in the fight against polio . . . and research and field trials to develop and prove the efficacy of Salk vaccine. All Americans are in your debt for that."

(10) Telegram from Jonas Salk, Jan. 8, 1954, to O'Connor on his birthday remarking on "your many contributions to the future of man."

(11) Signed photograph of Salk.

(12) Miscellaneous ephemera.

(556) 850.00

Salk, Jonas

VACCINATION AGAINST PARALYTIC POLIOMYELITIS: PERFORMANCE AND PROSPECTS.

Mimeo typescript, 39 leaves, University of Michigan, April 12, 1955, announcing the successful vaccine against polio, *signed in ink by Salk.* Spiral bound in wrappers, with charts and graphs. A milestone in medical history. (556A) 225.00

Cohn, Victor

FOUR BILLION DIMES.

Minneapolis, 1955. 134pp. Illus. History of the March of Dimes and polio research, with three Chapters on Basil O'Connor and four on Jonas Salk. (557) 15.00

The polio suffered by Franklin Roosevelt led his law partner, Basil O'Connor, to set up the Warm Springs Foundation and the March of Dimes. Research began in an intensive effort to find a cure for the disease. On April 12, 1955, Dr. Jonas Salk announced that a polio vaccine had been discovered and tested on over two million children — and proved effective. A nationwide effort to innoculate the populace began, virtually wiping out one of the most dreaded of all diseases.

Kennedy, John F.

PROFILES IN COURAGE.

N.Y.: Harper & Brothers, 1956. 266pp. Cloth. d.j. *First edition,* so stated on copyright page. Very scarce thus.   (558) 85.00

In 1952 young John Fitzgerald Kennedy entered the U.S. Senate and in 1956 narrowly lost the Vice Presidential nomination. In that same year his book, *Profiles in Courage,* was published. He had written it in 1954 and 1955, while convalescing from two major spinal operations. The book won the Pulitzer Prize for the year and was a major factor in his winning the Democratic nomination for President four years later. In it Kennedy expressed his political philosophy: ''A man does what he must — in spite of personal consequences, in spite of obstacles and dangers and pressures — and that is the basis of all human morality.''

1957   [Beatniks]

Kerouac, Jack

ON THE ROAD.

N.Y.: The Viking Press, 1957. 310pp. Black cloth. *First edition, first state.* Chartes A2a. Enoch Pratt Future Classics.   (599) 45.00

Jack Kerouac initiated the term, the beat generation. Peacetime American youth in an era of materialism and confidence came increasingly to rebel against what they considered to be the shankles of an outmoded society. Kerouac and his motorcycle friends epitomized their rebellion against society, and *On the Road* became their bible.

Written in three weeks on a roll of teletype paper ''100 miles long,'' it was, said Kerouac, ''directed toward a woman. That's why women like it. It's sexy because it's addressed to a woman but it's not too dirty — it changed the whole country.''

Kerouac states in the book: ''But then they danced down the street like dingledodies, and I shambled after as I've been doing all my life after people who interest me, because the only people for me are the mad ones, the ones who are mad to live, mad to talk, mad to be saved, desirous of everything at the same time, the ones who never yawn or say a commonplace thing, but burn, burn, burn like fabulous yellow roman candles exploding like spiders across the stars and in the middle you see the blue centerlight pop and everybody goes 'Awww!' ''

1958   [The Age of Opulence]

Galbraith, John Kenneth
THE AFFLUENT SOCIETY.
Boston: Houghton Mifflin, 1958. 368pp. Cloth. *First edition.*   (560) 20.00

Galbraith, John Kenneth
THE DEPENDENCE EFFECT.
Typed Manuscript Signed, with initials, 8pp., 4to. A recent typescript of the summation
chapter from *The Affluent Society.*   (561) 45.00

Galbraith studied the economic attitudes of his contemporaries and found that they
were aimed at the increased production of goods without any use for them — that America
had in fact reached the point of having to manufacture wants for the goods produced.

This affluent society, as he called it, should have economic goals that were more
meaningful and rewarding, a rational use of goods. He maintained that a new class of people
had come into being in the new age of opulence, those who wanted more out of their work
than money for goods and material objects — that these people wanted meaningful, interesting work as well.

One reviewer of this provacative work wrote in 1959: "The tone of this book is so
temperate, the argument so sedate — although not without charm — that many readers will
fail to realize the radical nature of Galbraith's proposal. To reconstruct our lives and also our
society in order to do something else with our time than send production quotas soaring
would change the entire conventional face of America. This is a new look worth considering."

1959   [John Birch Society]

Welch, Robert
THE BLUE BOOK OF THE JOHN BIRCH SOCIETY.
N.p., 1959. 182,[4]pp. Spiral binder, blue stiff wrappers.   (562) 40.00

The John Birch Society was founded by Robert H. W. Welch, Jr., a retired Massachusetts businessman, named by him after John Birch, a fundamentalist missionary from
Georgia who was killed by Communists shortly after the end of the war. "The declared aim of
the Society," states T. C. Cochran, "is to fight communism on a so-called 'intellectual basis'
apparently by adopting some of communism's own most vicious and ruthless tactics."
Semi-secret cells were formed to ferret out communist sympathizers and expose them, to "get
the U.S. out of the U.N.," to influence political affairs in the direction of arch-conservatism,
and to fight big government, integration, and socialism. The Society became a potent force for
awhile, culminating in the National Republican Convention of 1964, where it exerted a
decided influence.

280 -->

280

1960   [Trouble with Cuba]

DENUNCIA! EXTRA!
Havana, Revolucion, May 11, 1960. "A Todos los Pueblos del Mundo!" Extreme official denunciation of the United States by the Castro government.   (563) 225.00

Cuban Tourist Commission broadsheet, 2pp., 8vo, c.1960 welcoming American tourists to Cuba, *signed by Fidel Castro in ink.*   (564) 185.00

VENCEREMOS!
Broadside, Havana, 1960, issued by Castro, calling for victory of the Revolution over its enemies.   (565) 125.00

INRA LA HABANA: NUMERO ESPECIAL CON MOTIVO DEL 26 DE JULIO.
Havana, August, 1960. 130pp. Color cover portrait of Castro. Report on the meeting of over a million Cubans, at which Castro tore up the Cuban peace treaty with the United States.
          (566) 45.00

Kennedy, Robert F.
THIRTEEN DAYS: A MEMOIR OF THE CUBAN MISSILE CRISIS.
N.Y.: W. W. Norton & Company, 1969. 224pp. Cloth. Illus. *First edition.*   (567) 15.00

On New Year's Day, 1959, dictator Fulgencio Batista fled Cuba and Fidel Castro and his guerrilla forces entered Havana. A month later, Castro became Premier and began instituting a series of drastic socialist reforms. He showed a marked hostility for the United States from the very beginning, and in 1960 this erupted into an exchange that led in July to a U.S. ban on Cuban sugar, in August to tearing up of the peace treaty with the U.S., and in September to an outright denunciation of the U.S. by Castro in New York before the United Nations.

By 1961 Castro had nationalized all foreign firms in Cuba and made close treaties with Russia. "I am a Marxist-Leninist," exclaimed Castro, "and will be one until the day I die."

In April, 1961, President Kennedy attempted an invasion (by CIA agents and Cuban exiles) of Cuba which was a miserable failure. All the invaders were captured and Castro traded them back to the United States for 1000 tractors. In 1962 the Cuban Missile Crisis arose when it was learned that missile sites capable of striking the American mainland were in place in Cuba. In his greatest success as President, Kennedy ordered Castro and Khrushchev to remove them and for a few breathless days world war was imminent, until the Russians and Cubans acquiesced.

1961   [Kennedy Inaugural]

Kennedy, John F.

INAUGURAL ADDRESS OF JOHN FITZGERALD KENNEDY, PRESIDENT OF THE UNITED STATES.

Wash., Jan. 20, 1961. 3pp. *First printing.*   (568) 30.00

Yarborough, Ralph W. [comp.]

THE JOINT APPEARANCES OF SENATOR JOHN F. KENNEDY AND VICE PRESIDENT RICHARD M. NIXON: PRESIDENTIAL CAMPAIGN OF 1960.

Wash., 1961. 699pp. Verbatim text of the network appearances of the candidates and their famous televised debates, Sept. 26-Oct. 21, 1960. *First edition.*   (569) 35.00

JOHN FITZGERALD KENNEDY: A COMPENDIUM OF SPEECHES, STATE-MENTS, AND REMARKS, 1947-1960.

Wash., 1964. 1143pp. *First printing.*   (570) 35.00

    The 1960 Presidential Campaign was one of the most interesting of the century, marked by a series of televised face-to-face debates between the two candidates, Richard M. Nixon and John F. Kennedy. The election was the closest since 1884, with Kennedy winning by two-tenths of one percent.

    On January 20, 1961, Kennedy was inaugurated and delivered the most eloquent address since Lincoln's of a hundred years before: "Let every nation know," he said, "whether it wishes us well or ill, that we shall pay any price, bear any burden, meet any hardship, support any friend, oppose any foe to assure the survival and the success of liberty. . . . And so, my fellow Americans—ask not what your country can do for you — ask what you can do for your country."

Kennedy, Jacqueline

Original Letter Signed, 1 page, octavo, Dec. 2, 1960, to the noted musician and conductor Meyer Davis: "So glad you are going to play for our Inaugural . . ." (note the "our"), signed in ink by Jackie, accompanied by another L.S. (secretarial), White House, Feb. 21, 1961, to Davis sending thanks for recordings of the ceremonies: "It was sweet of you to record for posterity . . ."   (570A) 225.00

We had a waiting period of ten or twelve days between our
final test and the word on whether or not we had made it. I
went back to my desk at Bu Aer in Washington, and I was
there when I got a phone call from Mr. Charles Donlan at
NASA asking me if I was still interested. I said, "Yes, I am,
very much," and Mr. Donlan said I had made it. I was very
proud – I could not help that – but I also felt a certain humility.
I could not help that, either – not when I saw all of the scientific
talent which was being poured into the program and when I
realized how important it was to the nation that we succeed.
That night Annie and I had a dual celebration. It was also our
wedding anniversary. We went out for dinner and took in a
play.

John Glenn

1962   [First American in Orbit]

Glenn, John
A PAST TO DRAW ON.
Typed Manuscript Signed, 18pp., 4to. Firsthand account of the flight of the Friendship 7,
when Glenn became the first American to orbit the earth.   (571) 85.00

Glenn, John, et al.
WE SEVEN, BY THE ASTRONAUTS THEMSELVES.
N.Y.: Simon and Schuster, 1962. 352pp. d.j. *First edition.*   (572) 20.00

Binder, Otto O.
VICTORY IN SPACE: BEYOND COLONEL GLENN'S TRIUMPHANT FLIGHT.
N.Y.: Walker & Company, 1962. 211pp. d.j. *First edition.*   (573) 15.00

On February 20, 1962, Astronaut John H. Glenn entered the spaceship *Friendship* 7
and became the first American to break the bounds of gravity and orbit the earth. Launched
from Cape Canaveral in Florida, Glenn's Mercury-Redstone rocket completed three orbits in
4 hours 56 minutes and splashed down successfully in the Atlantic Ocean. Several other
American astronauts and Russian cosmonauts were placed in orbit before the end of the year.
The exploration of space began in earnest.

Glenn wrote, in *A Past to Draw On:* ''Project Mercury was a careful test of two big
propositions. First, that we were on the right track as we tried to put together a system that
could take man into space and bring him home safely. Second, that man himself not only
could undertake such a flight but that he was a necessary component of the system. The flight
of Friendship 7 proved both these points.''

	531-15-2	On Main probably just past Lamar.
	1-531	Just crossing Market Street.
	4-125	Talking about the traffic at Love Field.
	1-531	Nearing Triple Underpass.
12:30 pm		Station break.
	1	Go to the hospital, officers, Parkland Hospital, have them stand by. Got men on top of the under-pass, see what happened up there, go up to the overpass. Have Parkland stand by.
	Dallas-1	I'm sure it's going to take some time to get your men in there. Put every one of my men there.
	531-1	Repeat One. I didn't quite understand all of it.
	1-531	Notify station five to move all men available out of my department back into the railroad yards and try to determine what happened and hold everything secure until Homicide and other investigators can get in there.
	531-1	10-4.
12:31 pm	531-1	Any information whatsoever.
	1-531	It looks like the President has been hit, have Parkland stand by.
	531-1	Parkland has been notified.
12:32 pm	4-531	We have K-9 units in that vicinity, don't we?
	1	Straight to Parkland.
	5-1	What disposition do you want me to make with these men I have with me.
	1-5	Just go on to Parkland Hospital with me.
	1	Get out of the way, something about trucks, hold everything, get on the way (record not too clear).
	531-15-2	There is a motorcycle officer on Stemmons with his mike stuck open on Channel 1, could you send somebody up there and tell him to shut it off.
12:34 pm	190-531	You want me to still hold traffic on Stemmons until we find out something?
	1	Keep everything out of the Emergency entrance.
	136-531	A passerby states the shots came from the Texas School Book Depository Building.
	1	Get everything out of the way.
	531-136	Get all the information.

284

December 4, 1963

Mr. J. D. Curry
Chief of Police

                              Subject: Arrest of Lee Harvey
                                       Oswald, w/m/24

Sir:

On November 22, 1963 Officer K.E. Lyon and myself were in the
300 block of East Jefferson assisting in the search for the person who
shot and killed Officer J. D. Tippit.

We heard the police radio report that a suspect had entered the
Texas Theatre. We went to this location Code 3. When we entered
the theatre, we were told by a white female that the suspect was
in the balcony.

We went to the balcony and searched it. While in the balcony, I
heard someone shout that he was on the lower floor. We started down.
Lyon slipped and sprained his ankle; I continued on down. When I
arrived at the lower floor, Lee Harvey Oswald was resisting vigorously.
Sgt. Jerry Hill, Officer M. N. McDonald, C. T. Walker, and Ray Hawkins
and myself converged on Oswald. At this time I observed a pistol with
the muzzle pointed in my direction. I grabbed the pistol and stuck it
in my belt and then continued to assist in the subduing of Oswald. After
Oswald was handcuffed we were instructed by Captain W.R. Westbrook to take
him directly to the City Hall.

We removed Oswald from the theatre. When we were removing Oswald
from the theatre, he was hollering that he had not resisted arrest and that
he wanted to complain of police brutality. There was a crowd in front of
the theatre yelling, "Kill the dirty 'Sob'." We put Oswald into police
equipment #226 and drove directly to the City Hall. While enroute to the

81

AFFIDAVIT IN ANY FACT

THE STATE OF TEXAS

COUNTY OF DALLAS

BEFORE ME, _____ FRANCES BOCK _____

a Notary Public in and for said County, State of Texas, on this day personally appeared J. L. Popplewell
_____

Who, after being by me duly sworn, on oath deposes and says: My name is J. L. Popplewell. I entered the Dallas Police Department January 11, 1957. I have been in the Service Division seven and one-half years. I have worked the fifth floor jail most of this time. I was on duty the 22nd and 23rd day of November, 1963, working 2:30 p.m. till 10:30 p.m. The 23rd day of November, 1963, at 3:00 p.m., I was assigned to guard the area in front of Lee Harvey Oswald's cell, watching all of his movements to see that he didn't hurt himself. About 4:00 p.m. Lt. Lord called on the jail phone and instructed me to put Oswald on the phone. Oswald asked the operator for two telephone numbers - then asked me for a pencil and paper while in the telephone booth. I tore a small piece of plain paper, about two by three inches from the telephone record sheet that hung outside the telephone booth; then handed this piece of paper and my pencil to him. Oswald wrote a number on this paper and returned my pencil. Then he asked if he could call later. Oswald did not get his call through at this time. I called Lt. Lord and informed him Oswald didn't get his party and wanted to call again later. About 8:00 p.m. Lt. Lord came up to the jail and told me to let Oswald use the phone. I was instructed to step back away from the phone booth so the phone call could be private. From this location I watched the prisoner talking to someone. He used the phone about thirty minutes. I asked Oswald if he got his call through and he answered, yes. I then returned him to his cell.

About four months ago on a Monday, I received a call from an F.B.I. agent who wanted to know about a slip of paper with a phone number on it. This was supposed to be in Oswald's pocket when he died. The agent asked if we allowed prisoners to keep phone numbers on their person. I said that if a call wasn't completed the first time, we could let them write the number down and keep it for a later call. The agent asked me the size of the paper I might have given Oswald to write on. I told him it probably was one torn off of a telephone record sheet hanging outside the telephone booth; that the paper was plain, unmarked, about two by

Page 1 of 2 pages.

J. L. Popplewell
_____

_____

SUBSCRIBED AND SWORN TO BEFORE ME THIS 20th DAY OF August _____ A.D. 196 4

Frances Bock
_____
Notary Public, Dallas County, Texas

CPS-GF-413

286

PRESIDENT DEAD, CONNALLY SHOT!

Dallas Times-Herald Extra, Nov. 22, 1963. The first printed announcement of the assassination, issued shortly after noon, even before the arrest of Oswald.   (574) 50.00

An extraordinary file of original reports on the assassination of Kennedy, being one of a few sets of the investigation reports of the Dallas Police made at the time, consisting of 21 separate files including hundreds of investigation reports, interviews, depositions, photographs, etc., into every phase of the event, thousands of pages in all. Entirely unpublished and almost certainly the only set in private hands, includes all of the investigation from the moment of the assassination through the arrest and murder of Oswald and afterwards. It would be difficult to exaggerate the research importance of this file, which was never released and contains much material not in the Warren Commission report.   (575) 2500.00

Warren, Earl, et al.

REPORT OF THE PRESIDENT'S COMMISSION ON THE ASSASSINATION OF PRESIDENT JOHN F. KENNEDY.

Wash., 1964. 888pp. Advance proofs of the Warren Report, with printed warning pasted on front: "For Release at 6:30 P.M. E.D.T. Sunday, Sept. 27, 1964." Warns against violation of the edict of secrecy until that time, nor may "any of its contents be paraphrased, alluded to, or hinted at." Thompson #26. Baird #224.   (576) 125.00

Jenkins, John H.

NEITHER THE FANATICS NOR THE FAINT-HEARTED: THE TOUR LEADING TO THE PRESIDENT'S DEATH AND THE TWO SPEECHES HE COULD NOT GIVE.

Austin: The Pemberton Press, 1963. Cloth. *First edition.* An ugly little book, but it is the first book published on the assassination, has the first printing of the two speeches, and is an eyewitness account of the events, written the evening of the assassination. Thompson #55F. Baird #211.   (577) 10.00

The Dallas *Times-Herald* for the evening of November 21, 1963, contained a large map on the front page showing the route of the Presidential motorcade to be taken the next morning by President Kennedy, Vice President Johnson, and Gov. John Connally. The next morning an article of the front page was headed "Secret Service Sure All Secure." At noon, Kennedy lay dead at Parkland Hospital.

My wife and I watched as Mrs. Kennedy, splattered with blood, entered the hearse with the body of the dead President. I looked at the program for the evening's events; it read: "*Texas Welcome:* On this 22nd day of November, 1963, the welcoming committee greets the two leaders of our nation . . . this is a day long to be remembered in Texas."

King, Martin Luther
WHY WE CAN'T WAIT.
N.Y.: Harper & Row, 1964. 178pp. Cloth. *First edition.* Porter #352. With a Typed Letter Signed, 1 page, 4to, from his wife Coretta King about ''the unfinished work of my late husband'' and the coming ''dawn of a new day . . . when all men will be free.''   (578) 50.00

MARTIN LUTHER KING JR., 1924-1968: AN EBONY PICTURE BIOGRAPHY.
Chicago, 1968. 76pp. Illus. Pictorial wrappers. Much on the assassination and funeral of Dr. King.   (579) 10.00

Ray, James Earl
[ORIGINAL LETTERS].
Group of seven unpublished Typewritten Letters Signed, three by James Earl Ray and four by his brother Jerry Ray, to a British journalist on attempts to get Ray a new trial in the Martin Luther King assassination case. James Earl Ray writes from prison about his hopes for a new trial and he and his brother hint at conspiracy possibilities; both want money before granting an interview.   (580) 285.00

Martin Luther King, Jr., led the movement for peaceful integration in the segregated areas of the South and in Northern cities. His Grandhian strategy of nonviolent confrontation made him one of the most effective leaders in achieving rights for blacks. He was frequently jailed, stoned, and beaten; his home was bombed. In 1963 he led 200,000 civil rights marchers on a peaceful march to Washington where he made his notable address, ''I Have a Dream.'' In 1964 he was awarded the Nobel Prize for Peace.

On April 4, 1968, he was shot to death by James Earl Ray in Memphis, Tennessee, leaving an irreplaceable void in the ranks of the nonviolent black protestor.

1965   [The Consumer Advocate]

Nader, Ralph
UNSAFE AT ANY SPEED: THE DESIGNED-IN DANGERS OF THE AMERICAN AUTOMOBILE.
N.Y.: Grossman, 1965. 365pp. Original cloth. *First edition.* Downs, Famous American Books #49.   (581) 25.00

A brilliant young muckraker, Ralph Nader created a whole new segment of the political spectrum — the consumer advocate. Beginning a one-man crusade against governmental agencies and industrial giants, he prepared a devastating indictment of the automobile industry, related engineering groups, government control agencies, and safety organizations.

Nader demanded that the automotive industry stop manufacturing "death-traps" for the public. He did not ask for new technological discoveries to improve safety, but only for the deliberate application of what was already feasible. He quoted engineer J. Douglas Brown: "If engineers can design space ships to go to the moon, why can't they design a safer automobile?" Nader's answer was that government and business interests never moved without an economic reason, and that organized public pressure must be brought against them to achieve the goal.

In so doing, he led the way for what became numerous organized consumer groups operating outside government channels to lobby and pressure for consumer goals. On Sept. 9, 1966, Congress passed the Traffic Safety Act which was called "an almost direct result of Ralph Nader's book *Unsafe at Any Speed,* setting automobile production safety standards."

1966   [The Black Muslims]

Muhammad, Elijah
MUHAMMAD SPEAKS: UNITY! POWER!
Chicago, September 9, 1966. 28pp. Large folio. Wrappers.   (582) 25.00

Meredith, James
THREE YEARS IN MISSISSIPPI.
Bloomington, Ill.: Indiana University Press, 1966. 328pp. Illus. Mint copy in dustjacket. *First edition.* Issued just prior to his being shot.   (583) 15.00

James Meredith was the first black to integrate the University of Mississippi, graduating in 1963 with a degree in political science. In 1966, during a break from his law school classes in Columbia University, he made a peace walk through Mississippi to dramatize that Southern blacks had nothing to fear and should register to vote. He was ambushed and shot on June 6 near Jackson.

The event was a catalyst in the integration cause; it brought widespread sympathetic attention to the plight of the black man in the South, but also further split the black movement into two factions, one in favor of non-violence under Martin Luther King, the other under more radical black power leaders.

One of the main black power groups was that of Elijah Mohammad, who had helped form a black religious sect in Chicago, known as the Black Muslims, that taught that blacks would some day rule the world. As the rednecks of the South brutalized more and more integration marchers and black citizens, the Black Muslims grew in strength and numbers. The most famous convert was boxer Cassius Clay, who changed his name to Mohammad Ali.

HEARINGS BEFORE THE NATIONAL COMMISSION ON URBAN PROBLEMS.
Wash., 1967. 5 volumes (ca. 1800pp.). Paul H. Douglas, Chairman. Wrp. x-1. Volume I: Baltimore, New Haven, Boston, Pittsburgh; II: Los Angeles, San Francisco; III: Denver, Atlanta, Houston, Dallas, Miami; IV: New York City, Philadelphia; V: Detroit, Washington, St. Louis. (584) 45.00

Johnson, Lyndon B.
ECONOMIC REPORT OF THE PRESIDENT, TOGETHER WITH THE ANNUAL REPORT OF THE COUNCIL OF ECONOMIC ADVISERS.
Wash., 1967. 314pp. Printed wrappers. (585) 20.00

In 1967 race riots on an unprecedented scale and intensity swept over one hundred cities, including Boston, Tampa, Cincinnati, New York, Philadelphia, Chicago, Minneapolis, Hartford, Washington, and Pittsburgh. The worst hit were Detroit and Newark, where 72 people were killed in eleven days of rioting, burning, and looting. Thousands of people were arrested and an estimated $200 million in damage was inflicted.

These riots, while largely in black areas, seemed to arise not so much from segregation as from troubles within the cities themselves. Large cities had gradually developed ghettos where conditions were intolerable and from which the poor and ignorant were unable to escape. Studies were initiated to try to find some way to improve conditions and to train people in the ghettos for jobs in more favorable locales, but the attempts were hampered but distrust, prejudice, and apathy.

1968 [The Radical Movement]

Rubin, Jerry, and Abbie Hoffman
THE YIPPIES ARE GOING TO CHICAGO.
N.Y., The Realist, September, 1968. 24pp. Wrp. (586) 25.00

WHAT NEXT? BLACK POLITICAL POWER, ORGANIZED SELF-DEFENCE, ARE KEYS.
N.Y., The Militant: Published in the Interest of the Working People, April 15, 1968. 8pp. Large folio. (587) 25.00

MARCH OF THE POOR WILL PASS THROUGH MEMPHIS.
N.Y., The Worker, April 16, 1968. 8pp. Large folio. (588) 25.00

*REPORT OF THE NATIONAL ADVISORY COMMISSION ON CIVIL DIS-
ORDERS.*
N.Y., 1968. 609pp. plus 49pp. of charts. Original cloth. The Kerner Commission Report.
(589) 25.00

In March, 1968, President Johnson announced he would not run for another term, and in June the leading candidate, Robert F. Kennedy, was assassinated. The country seemed to be falling apart, with hatreds and bitterness over the war in Vietnam and integration dwarfing every other event and issue. From these emotional times arose a wide variety radical movements.

At the Democratic Convention in Chicago a group called Yippies of rather indefinable goals and antiwar protesters met with overreaction from local police and a bloody riot ensued, witnessed by the nation on television. Hubert Humphrey, the Democratic nominee, failed to disassociate himself from the Vietnam war in time to turn the electorate in his favor, lost narrowly to Richard M. Nixon.

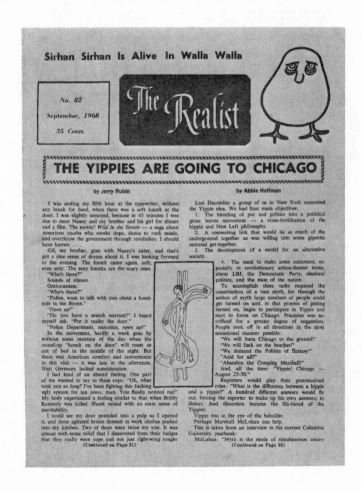

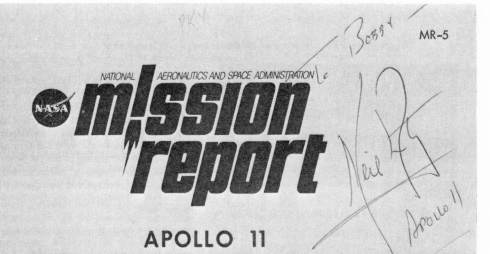

NATIONAL AERONAUTICS AND SPACE ADMINISTRATION

mission report

APOLLO 11

"Old Glory" flies on the lunar surface. Astronaut Edwin Aldrin at right.

1   14 August 1969

APOLLO II MISSION COMMENTARY . . . 295/2.

Houston, July 20, 1969. 27 leaves, stapled. *The first printed announcement of the landing on the moon,* issued by Mission Control at NASA about ten minutes after touchdown on the moon. It comprises a verbatim tract of the words passed between the Eagle and Control. ''Houston, tranquility base here. The Eagle has landed. . . .'' Only a few were issued and most were thrown away by reporters soon afterwards. Slipcased.   (590) 65.00

APOLLO II MISSION COMMENTARY . . . 330/2.

Houston, July 20, 1969. 26 leaves, stapled. *The first printed announcement of man's first steps on the moon,* issued about ten minutes later. Similar to the above. ''I'm going to step off the LM now . . . that's one small step for man. One giant leap for mankind. . . .'' Slipcased.   (591) 65.00

MISSION REPORT: APOLLO II.

Houston, NASA, August 14, 1969. 8pp. *Signed by Neil Armstrong,* first man on the moon.
(592) 185.00

Extensive space and moon landing archive; thousands of items, printed and manuscript. Details on request.   (593) 15,000.00

On July 16, 1969, a six-million-pound Saturn-Apollo rocket took off for the moon with three astronauts aboard. As the rocket was travelling at 24,000 miles per hour through space on its history-setting mission, Senator Edward Kennedy was driving his car off a bridge at Chappaquiddick Island, altering American political history.

On Sunday, July 20, the Lunar Module landed safely on the moon and shortly thereafter space commander Neil Armstrong made the first footprint on the lunar surface. It culminated an effort planned since the Douglas Aircraft Report of 1946 and initiated in 1961, involving over 300,000 people in industry and science. A flag and plaque were placed on the surface, the latter reading: ''Here Men from Planet Earth First Set Foot Upon the Moon. July 1969 A.D. We Came in Peace For All Mankind.''

```
APOLLO 11 MISSION COMMENTARY, 7/20/69, GET 109:20, CDT 21:52   339/2
        ARMSTRONG          I'm going to step off the LM now.
        ARMSTRONG          That's one small step for man.
One giant leap for mankind.
        ARMSTRONG          As the - The surface is fine
and powdery.  I can - I can pick it up loosely with my toe.
It does adhere in fine layers like powdered charcoal to the
sole and sides of my boots.  I only go in a small fraction
of an inch.  Maybe an eighth of an inch, but I can see the
footprints of my boots and the treads in the fine sandy
particles.
        CAPCOM             Neil, this is Houston.  We're
copying.

END OF TAPE
```

1970   [Nuclear Power and Pollution]

Lyerly, Ray L., and Walter Mitchell
NUCLEAR POWER PLANTS.
Wash., U.S. Atomic Energy Commission, 1970. 54pp. Illus. Printed wrappers.   (594) 10.00

Carson, Rachel
THE SEA AROUND US.
N.Y.: Oxford University Press, 1951. 230pp. Fine copy in dustjacket. *First edition.*
(595) 45.00

Carson, Rachel
SILENT SPRING.
N.Y., 1962. Fine copy in dustjacket. *First edition.*   (596) 30.00

When Rachel Carson published *The Sea Around Us,* it became a national bestseller and was eventually translated into 30 languages. Eleven years later she published another bestseller, *Silent Spring,* which created a national controversy. She decried the imminent dangers to the ecological balances of nature from man-made pollutants. From this beginning arose hundreds of environmentalist groups throughout the country who worked to clean up the environment and stop destructive practices.

At the same time, developments in nuclear reactors made nuclear power available for peaceful uses, and plants were started in various areas around the country. Advocates of the nuclear plants and environmentalists were frequently at odds.

1971   [The Vietnam War]

WHEN A MAN IS SUFFERING, CAN OUR BOMBS MAKE HIM FREE? HOW MUCH BLOOD MUST WE SPILL IN VIETNAM BEFORE WE ADMIT A MISTAKE?
Broadside, 1p., 4to. Nashville, Committee for Alternatives to War in Vietnam, [1971].
(597) 25.00

WHAT MUST WE DO NOW? AN ARGUMENT FOR SABOTAGE AS THE NEXT LOGICAL STEP TOWARD OBSTRUCTION AND DISRUPTION OF THE U.S. WAR MACHINE.
Toronto?, c.1971. 12pp. Mimeographed. Illus. The last four pages contain instructions and illustrations for making Incendiary Time Bombs, Molotov Cocktails, etc. At bottom of p.[8]: "This pamphlet was prepared in Toronto, Canada. It has been distributed to 327 anti-Vietnam war groups across the United States."   (598) 100.00

Acheson, Dean. Original Typewritten Letter Signed, 1p., 4to, Oct. 4, 1976, about the war: ". . . I can only go so far as to say that it is necessary for the United States to withdraw completely from the scene of battle in Vietnam. . . ." (599) 45.00

Walt, Gen. L. W. Original Typewritten Letter Signed, 1p., 4to, about his services as Commander of the Marines in Vietnam, to newsman George Fielding Eliot. (600) 35.00

THE PENTAGON PAPERS.

N.Y.: Quadrangle Books, 1971. 810pp. d.j. *First edition.* (601) 17.50

Protest against the horrific war in Vietnam reached a peak in 1971. Antiwar protests became increasingly violent as American casualties increased in Vietnam, and as the government and military told compound lies to the public. In June, Daniel Ellsberg leaked what became known as the Pentagon Papers to the press, revealed the extent to which lies had been told about the war.

Unknown to the public at the time, President Nixon established a "Plumber's Unit," which burglarized the office of Ellsberg's psychiatrist in an effort to find defamatory material to use to discredit him.

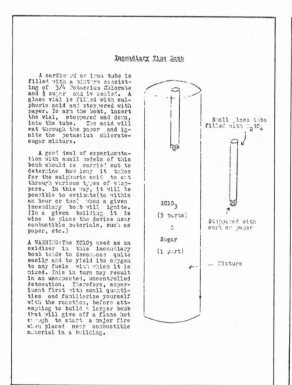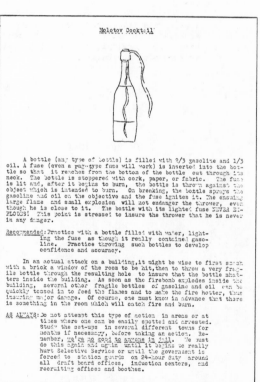

4. The Watergate operation was not a CIA operation. The Cubans may have been misled by others into believing that it was a CIA operation. I know for a fact that it was not.

5. Some statements were unfortunately made by witnesses which left the Court with the impression that they stating untruths, or withholding facts of their knowledge, when in fact only honest errors of memory were involved.

6. My motivations were different than those of the others involved, but were not limited to, or simply those offered in my defense during the trial. This is no fault of my attorneys, but of the circumstances under which we had to prepare my defense.

Following sentence, I would appreciate the opportunity to talk with you privately in chambers. Since I cannot feel confident in talking with an FBI agent, in testifying before a Grand Jury whose U.S. Attorneys work for the Department of Justice, or in talking with other government representatives, such a discussion with you would be of assistance to me.

I have not discussed the above with my attorneys as a matter of protection for them.

I give this statement freely and voluntarily, fully realizing that I may be prosecuted for giving a false statement to a Judicial Official, if the statements herein are knowingly untrue. The statements are true and correct to the best of my knowledge and belief.

James W. McCord, Jr.
James W. McCord, Jr.

296

1972 [Watergate: The Seventh Crisis]

Nixon, Richard M.
SIX CRISES.
N.Y.: Doubleday & Company, Inc., 1962. 460pp. d.j. *First edition, autographed by Nixon.*
                                                                            (602) 125.00

An extensive file on the Watergate Scandal, including original letters from Howard Hunt, John Mitchell, Dwight Chapin, Donald Segretti, John Sirica, Maurice Stans, and Pat Gray, as well as official reports and documents relating to Watergate and its cover-up. Details upon request.   (603) 850.00

On June 17, 1972, five men were arrested while burglarizing Democratic headquarters in the Watergate building in Washington. President Nixon denied involvement and the perpetrators were convicted. Nixon was overwhelmingly reelected in November, but further investigations about the Watergate case began to lead inexorably towards the White House. The President seemed unaware that the issue presented his seventh and final crisis.

1973 [Agnew Resigns]

Agnew, Spiro T.
ADDRESS BY THE VICE PRESIDENT OF THE UNITED STATES TO THE NATIONAL ASSOCIATION OF ATTORNEYS GENERAL: TRANSCRIPT.
St. Louis, June 11, 1973. 8pp. Mimeo typescript issued to the press just prior to delivery. *Inscribed and signed by Agnew.* First printing of his attack on the Senate Watergate Committee.   (604) 200.00

On June 11, 1973, Vice President Spiro T. Agnew addressed the National Association of Attorneys General in St. Louis, where he made an intense and bitter attack on the Senate Watergate Committee, then probing into White House connections with the case. He also attacked the press coverage of the whole Watergate affair.

Five weeks later, as the Senate hearings drew to a close, Alexander Butterfield inadvertently mentioned that Nixon had a secret recording system that taped all his conversations. On October 10, Vice President Agnew pleaded no contest to a verdict of guilty on a charge of evading income tax, part of a deal to avoid prosecution for accepting bribes and graft. He resigned and two days later Gerald Ford was nominated by Nixon to replace him.

On October 10, in the "Saturday Night Massacre," Nixon fired special prosecutor Archibald Cox and a number of high officials resigned in protest.

ARTICLE I.

That Richard M. Nixon, President of the United States, in violation of the Constitution and laws of the United States, did participate in acts, individually and in concert with others, to obstruct the investigation and prosecution of criminal acts committed against the people of the United States;

In that Richard M. Nixon, in concert with others, caused funds to be raised and disbursed for the purpose of inducing certain persons to conceal information relating to a breaking and entering of the headquarters of the Democratic National Committee in Washington, D. C., on June 17, 1972;

In that Richard M. Nixon did on March 21, 1973, authorize the payment of money to E. Howard Hunt, a defendant charged with having participated in said breaking and entering of the headquarters of the Democratic National Committee in Washington, D. C., the purpose of said payment being to induce said defendant Hunt to refuse to cooperate with law enforcement agencies and prosecutors;

In that Richard M. Nixon did on March 21, 1973, authorize the payment of money to E. Howard Hunt, the purpose of said payment being to induce E. Howard Hunt to refrain from disclosing knowledge of the commission of criminal acts, including the breaking and entering of the office of Dr. Lewis Fielding in Beverly Hills, California, on September 3, 1971;

In that Richard M. Nixon did, individually and in concert with others, destroy or fail to produce evidence relating to the investigation of the

Extensive collection of original letters, documents, typed and printed documents and reports on the Watergate case, Senate and House hearings, and Nixon resignation, including some private impeachment records from the House Judiciary Committee. An important archive. Details on request.   (605) 1500.00

THE WHITE HOUSE TRANSCRIPTS: SUBMISSION OF RECORDED PRESI-DENTIAL CONVERSATIONS TO THE COMMITTEE ON THE JUDICIARY BY PRESIDENT RICHARD NIXON.
N.Y., 1974. 877pp. Cloth.   (606) 15.00

COMPARISON OF WHITE HOUSE AND JUDICIARY COMMITTEE TRANS-CRIPTS OF EIGHT RECORDED PRESIDENTIAL CONVERSATIONS.
Wash., June, 1974. 63pp. Printed wrappers.   (607) 15.00

PROCEDURE AND GUIDELINES FOR IMPEACHMENT TRIALS IN THE UNITED STATES SENATE.
Wash., 1974. 85pp. Printed wrappers.   (608) 15.00

St. Clair, James D., and Charles Alan Wright
SUMMARY: AN ANALYSIS OF THE CONSTITUTIONAL STANDARD FOR PRESIDENTIAL IMPEACHMENT.
Wash., 1974. 6pp. Mimeographed.   (609) 25.00

Woodward, Bob, and Carl Bernstein
THE FINAL DAYS.
N.Y.: Simon and Schuster, 1976. 476pp. Cloth. Account of the last days of the Nixon Presidency.   (610) 12.00

On April 30, 1974, President Nixon released an edited version of the White House tape recordings concerning Watergate.

On May 9, 1974, the House Judiciary began formal hearings on the impeachment of President Nixon, and on July 27, after listening to some of the tapes, voted 27 to 11 to recommend impeachment. On August 5 Nixon released a tape that revealed he had approved the cover-up only six days after the Watergate break-in.

On August 5, 1974, Richard Nixon became the first President of the United States to resign from office. On September 8, President Ford granted him ''full, free and absolute pardon'' for any crimes he may have committed.

Class 1375 (Continued)

FIRING DEVICE KIT

AC delay, thumb screw activated; 1 per metal can; c/o:

      1 ea. firing device body
      1 ea. delay ampule, 3 hr delay, red
      1 ea. delay ampule, 7 hr delay, orange
      1 ea. delay ampule, 15 hr delay, yellow
      1 ea. delay ampule, 20 hr delay, green
      1 ea. delay ampule, 100 hr delay, violet
      1 ea. delay ampule, 30 day delay, black
      1 ea. delay ampule, 50 day delay, clear
      1 ea. delay ampule, 60 day delay, gold
      1 ea. wrench
      1 tube, waterproofing compound
      1 ea. temperature correction table

H00-1932   with 1 ea model M-34 detonator

1375-H00-1932

H00-0017   w/o detonator.

FUSE, BLASTING, TIME
H00-6287   40 sec per ft at 5000 ft altitude; Dupont "Black Monarch".

028-5151   very wet work condition; 0.205 in. od, 50 ft lg o/a; 120 sec ±10% per yd burning speed; ICC marking required is SAFETY FUSE; Spec JAN-F-360; 2 coils per package.

BLACK POWDER CORE
FIBER WRAPPING
OUTER COVER
WATERPROOFING

1375-028-5151

028-5152   very wet work condition; 0.205 in. od, packed as required; 120 sec ±10% per yd burning speed; ICC marking required is SAFETY FUSE; Spec JAN-F-360.

H02-1935   weatherproof white wax finish for use in wet work; 100 ft per roll.

1375-H02-1935

028-5246   underwater work condition; 0.195 in. od, 50 ft lg o/a; 120 sec ±10% per yd burning speed; ICC marking required is SAFETY FUSE; Mil Spec MIL-F-45144; model M700; 2 coils per paper wrapper.

H00-6398   50 ft per roll; not for high level use; packed 2 rolls per package; commercial model M700.

H02-1182   inert; 0.2 in. dia, 50 ft lg coil; for training purposes; packed as required.

HAVERSACK, FLOTATION
H00-1021   with 1 flotation bladder.

HEAD, STEEL
H00-6086   dished; 6.0 in. od x 0.25 in. thk, with 6.0 in. radius of dish; f/u/w platter charges.

HIGH EXPLOSIVE
H00-0005   Composition; RDX pigmentized (80%), wheat flour (20%); powder form; 15 lb per paper bag.

1375-H00-0005

H00-2837   trinitrotoluene (TNT); crystalline type; light yellow; grade III is used in priming composition or special composition that requires either high purity or fine crystalline form.

H00-1944   trinitrotoluene (TNT); flaked type; packed as required.

IGNITACORD
H00-9805   thermalite, type B; 100 ft spool packed 10 spools per fiberboard carton.

45

1975   [Rockefeller Commission]

Rockefeller, Nelson A.
REPORT TO THE PRESIDENT BY THE COMMISSION ON CIA ACTIVITIES WITHIN THE UNITED STATES.
Wash., June, 1975. 299pp. Blue printed wrappers. First printing.   (611) 10.00

CIA SPECIAL WEAPON SUPPLY CATALOG.
N.p., n.d. 60pp. Red printed wrappers. Illus. Remarkable catalog, with numerous illustrations of pistols, rifles, submachine guns, demolition kit, exploding devices, secret weapons, etc.
(612) 10.00

On December 19, 1974, President Ford nominated Nelson A. Rockefeller to be his Vice President, and he was confirmed. On January 5, 1975, Ford appointed Rockefeller to head an eight-member commission to investigate charges that the Central Intelligence Agency was involved in domestic spy activities or other acts contrary to its charter and to the law.

On June 6, 1975, the Rockefeller Commission submitted its report, charging the CIA with a number of illegal acts and recommending Congressional action.

1976   [The Jimmy Carter Phenomenon]

ACCEPTANCE SPEECH BY GOVERNOR JIMMY CARTER, DEMOCRATIC NATIONAL CONVENTION.
N.Y., July 15, 1976. 11pp. Stapled. *First printing,* issued to the press a few minutes before delivery, with: "Embargo: For Release Upon Delivery" on front.   (613) 20.00

Collection of material from the 1976 Democratic Convention, including broadsides, leaflets, invitations, pamphlets, speeches, instructions, buttons, and a peanut. Includes a vote-count sheet recording the votes by state in pencil during the vote for Carter's nomination. A very full archive on all of the activities of the convention.   (614) 200.00

The nomination of Jimmy Carter for President in what looks like, during July, 1976, a Democratic year, culminated an astonishing campaign performance. Virtually unknown a year earlier, the Georgia governor swept the primaries and overwhelmed the Democratic Convention.

In his acceptance speech, Carter attempted to bring the country out of its malaise and look to the future. "There is a new mood in America . . . an America on the move again, united, a diverse and vital and tolerant nation, entering our third century with pride and confidence. . . . This is the America we want. This is the America we will have."

ACCEPTANCE SPEECH
BY
GOVERNOR JIMMY CARTER

DEMOCRATIC NATIONAL CONVENTION
NEW YORK CITY
THURSDAY, JULY 15, 1976

I accept your nomination.

I accept it in the words of John F. Kennedy: "With a full and grateful heart -- and with only one obligation -- to devote every effort of body, mind and spirit to lead our party back to victory and our nation back to greatness."

1976 will not be a year of politics as usual. It is a year of concern, and of quiet and sober reassessment of our nation's character and purpose -- a year when voters have already confounded the political experts.

It can be a year of inspiration and hope.

And I guarantee you, it will be the year when we give the

THE
BICENTENNIAL

Today, a special Bicentennial edition

The Philadelphia Inquirer

Historic Philadelphia's Oldest Daily—The Bicentennial Newspaper

Vol. 20, No. 4   ©℗Ⓓ   © 1976, The Philadelphia Inquirer   Sunday, July 4, 1976   NEW JERSEY EDITION   35 CENTS

America's Bicentennial Begins

Israelis liberate hostages

Raiders strike at Uganda airport

Associated Press

TEL AVIV, Israel — Airborne Israeli commandos raided the airport at Entebbe, Uganda, early today and freed all the hostages held by the pro-Palestinian hijackers of an Air France jetliner, an Israeli army spokesman said.

An Air France spokesman in Nairobi, Kenya, where the three Israeli military planes stopped over on their way back to Israel, said the commando unit "apparently has eliminated" the hijackers.

He said surgical operations were performed on some wounded persons on the runway of the Nairobi airport. It was not immediately clear how many casualties there were.

The raid took place about 12 hours before the deadline for Israel and four other nations to meet the hijackers' demands of freedom for 53 militants jailed in those nations.

According to the Air France spokesman in Nairobi, fighting was reported around an old terminal building at Entebbe where the hostages were being held captive.

He reported that the Israeli planes flew directly to Uganda from Israel — 2,500 miles — and landed in Nairobi on their return yesterday afternoon.

Kenyan soldiers surrounded the Israeli planes and prevented any personnel from going near it, the Air France spokesman said, "but one of the Israelis said, 'The operation at Entebbe is over.'" From that we gather that the Palestinians have been eliminated."

He reported that the Israeli raiders he saw - Nairobi were wearing civilian clothes.

An Air France plane that had been prepared to take the hostages out of the country was still standing by in Nairobi.

Tonight Israel defense forces extracted and freed the hostages, including the Air France crew from the airport at Entebbe," an Israeli army communique issued in Tel Aviv said. A military command spokesman told reporters, "As far as we know they were all freed. We do not know if they are all OK."

Most of the hostages, held for a week, were Israelis or Jews of other nationalities, the hijackers had freed 141 other passengers — Wednesday and Thursday.

The military command did not say whether the commandos encountered resistance from Ugandan soldiers at the airport.

The French jetliner was commandeered by four hijackers over Greece last Sunday during a flight from Tel Aviv to Paris. After a refueling stop in Benghazi, Libya, the pilot was forced to fly to Uganda, where the hijackers reportedly were joined by three or four others.

Israel said Thursday that it was willing to negotiate with the hijackers. Form of the prisoners the hijackers wanted released were being held in Israeli jails.

After that, there were meetings of a ministerial group headed by Prime Minister Yitzhak Rabin, and Israelis secret the efforts it was making.

Deborah De Medio, holding a toy gun and wearing a sash proclaiming herself a 'Minute Woman,' watches parade of wagons

Crowds expected at Mall

By John F. Clancy and Bernard S. Shapiro
Inquirer Staff Writers

The nation's 200th birthday celebration began in earnest here yesterday as thousands of people greeted wagon trains in Valley Forge, viewed a mammoth birthday cake in Fairmount Park, watched an air show in Willow Grove and visited historic sites in the Independence Hall area.

President Ford will commence today's celebration, which is expected to draw more than a million people to the city's historic area. After the President's first appearance, a speech at 8:20 a.m. at Valley Forge, he will deliver a Bicentennial address at 10 a.m. at Independence Hall.

Also speaking at Independence Hall, where the Declaration of Independence was signed, will be Gov. Milton J. Shapp and Mayor Frank L. Rizzo. The declaration will be read by opera singer Marian Anderson.

Nearly another threatened to dampen the big day. However, showers late yesterday cut short the U.S. Navy's Bicentennial air show, which drew a crowd of 125,000 to Willow Grove Naval Air Station. By 8:45, a heavy rain was pounding in Philadelphia, but officials went ahead with a 9:30 p.m. fireworks display at Penn's Landing, on the Delaware River after the rain subsided an hour later.

The National Weather Service, which earlier yesterday had predicted sunny skies for the day, amended its forecast last night to include a 40 percent chance of rain.

The weather notwithstanding, city officials were making final preparations for a multitude of Bicentennial events today. A first-hour parade is scheduled to begin at 12:30 p.m. at Fourth and Market Streets, move through center city and proceed up to

(See FOURTH on 6-A)

Finally, the wagons are here

By Richard L. Papiernik, Tom Masland and Marc Schogol
Inquirer Staff Writers

The Bicentennial wagon trains finally rolled into Valley Forge yesterday afternoon, and about 15,000 to 20,000 people, who first created and then finally their way through miles of traffic jams, were on hand to greet them.

Sitting on chairs set out for the occasion, or sprawling on the grassy hillsides of the natural amphitheater in the park where the official reception stand was placed, the onlookers cheered as the first of the approximately 200 wagons rolled into view shortly after 1 p.m.

And they continued to cheer for hours, especially for those main contingents, as the procession rolled by.

Not even the overwhelming of one wagon just as it was about to pass the receiving stand, and a brief but intense altercation on the party's perimeter about whether an "independent" wagon train could enter, marred the day.

The two occupants of the overturned wagon were not injured, and the independent's — seven wagons and a buggy from Texas on a cross-country trek — finally allowed to take their place in the line of march.

There in the grand-scene of events, after getting caught in bumper-to-bumper traffic on the way to Valley Forge, had packed their cars where they could and walked to get their wagon train could enter, enjoying themselves.

Phil Keisling, a college student from Portland, Ore., who has been visiting the Philadelphia area, said of the wagon trains, "I think it's probably the most meaningful thing anyone could do for the Bicentennial. I can't think of anything that would capture the spirit better."

"You can fight the crowds in Philadelphia and try to create the tavern feeling for a day, but these people represent it."

Out on Route 363 near the park, (See WAGONS on 6-A)

Unions reject city's proposal

By Ray Holton
Inquirer Labor Writer

Unions representing the city's 24,400 uncontracted employes have rejected the Rizzo administration's offer of a two-year contract.

The proposal, which did not call for a pay raise until the second year, was turned down as too low, sources said yesterday.

The offer came late Friday in a message to the executive board of District Councils 33 and 47 of the American Federation of State, County and Municipal Employes (AFSCME) from City Managing Director Hillel Levinson.

The executive board then met late into the night, but "never came to an agreement," said a high union source.

"It wasn't sweet enough in the second year," the source added. "By the second year, without a pay raise now, we would be 17 percent behind in the cost of living and taxes alone."

Earl Stout, president of District Council 33, had said he could recommend that his members accept the offer if there were sizable wage increases and a clause giving cost-of-living raises in the second year. Stout was unavailable for comment yesterday.

Meanwhile, a union work slowdown entered its third day, with sanitation workers refusing to accept overtime on the July 4th weekend.

Officials at the Philadelphia Museum of Art decided late yesterday to keep the museum closed tomorrow, when most of the guards refused to work overtime for the holiday.

Other effects of the job action could not be immediately determined, but there were reports of large piles of garbage outside the

(See UNIONS on 8-A)

The work slowdown was the factor in the decision to close the Bicentennial antique show Page 7-A.

AERIAL GYMNASTICS thrilled crowds at the Navy Bicentennial air show in Willow Grove. Story on Page 6-A.

Ford's text: 'Still so much to be done'

Associated Press

President Ford, saluting the nation's 200th birthday, says he welcomes questioning, examination and criticism of society because "the American adventure is a continuing process."

In a Bicentennial text prepared for delivery today at Independence Hall, Ford said:

"As one milestone is passed, another is sighted.

"As we achieve one goal — a longer life span, a literate population, a leadership in world affairs — we raise our sights.

"As we begin our third century, there is still so much to be done."

The President went on to talk about increasing independence and opportunity for all Americans, insurance of the right to privacy, the creation of a more beautiful and safer America and the promotion of a saner international order.

"Each generation of Americans, indeed of all humanity, must strive to

(See FORD on 4-A)

The Bicentennial Inquirer

Washington in Albany

An American Journey

Once it was to construct a nation it was a job. Washington slept here. But progress had crept over the land since Washington slept, and one only determination preserves the presence of the general. This is clear in An American Journey, Section B.

The latest news 200 Years Ago

If in the morning of July 4, 1776, Congress is expected to approve a declaration of independence. But the major story of the morning is the landing of 10,000 redcoats in New York. The laughter of today reports the news of 200 Years Ago. Section D.

Business: City's fortunes

The economy of Philadelphia has

changes. Gone are the manufacturing jobs. Here too are many more service jobs. The change has not been all for the good. But in Business, there's optimism. Page 7-H.

Review and Opinion: America's future

And as this is the Bicentennial, it is time to recall our history. It is also time to consider the nation's future. In Review and Opinion, some of America's do just that. Section F.

Today magazine: Our abiding faith

Americanism might be called a religion. There are shrines. There are creeds. Most of all, there is a deep, abiding faith. A special issue of Today magazine.

Elfreth's Alley

Living: The American family

The American family, after 200 years, has come to be almost anything you want it to be. That's Living, Section G.

Real Estate: The Alley

Famous Elfreth's Alley once was the farmers' Grater covered all. But a group of urban renewers have made it the pride of Philadelphia. A story of Real Estate. Section I.

Arts & Leisure: What to do today

The city is alive today with the Bicentennial. In Arts & Leisure, you'll find maps and listings to help you join the celebration. Section K.

Food: Our tastes

The all-American meal could include a number of courses. But careful research produces this menu: Hamburger, baked potato, corn on the cob and chocolate cake for dessert. That's American Food. Section L.

The weather

Variable cloudiness with a chance of a shower or thundershower. Highs today in the 80s, lows in the 60s. Full weather report, Page 1C-E.

Other features

Action Line   1-C   Obituaries   16-E
Books   12-K   Puzzles   7-G
Bridge   18-K   Sermon   14-K
Crosswords   6-F   Comic Section
Editorials   6-F   TV Week
Metropolitan news, Page 9-A.

304

AMERICA'S BICENTENNIAL BEGINS.

Philadelphia Inquirer, July 4, 1976, complete issue, with much news of the bicentennial celebration activities. (615) 10.00

President Ford, at Independence Hall, on July 4, 1976, said:

"As one milestone is passed, another is sighted.

"As we achieve one goal — a longer life span, a literate population, a leadership in world affairs — we raise our sights.

"As we begin our third century, there is still so much to be done."

Jenkins, John H.

AMERICAN CELEBRATION: THE CREATION AND EVOLUTION OF THE UNITED STATES AS REFLECTED IN THE PRINTED AND WRITTEN WORD, 1776-1976.

Austin, 1976. 312pp. Illus. Printed wrappers. (40% discount to dealers). (616) 9.50

Same as above, special edition bound in boards, limited to 125 numbered, signed copies, each containing a leaf from the first edition, Columbus, 1860, of the Lincoln-Douglas Debates. (20% discount to dealers). (617) 37.50

PARTIAL INDEX

Carson, Kit: 105
Carson, Rachel: 294
Carter, Jimmy: 301
Cartography: 17, 18, 30, 33, 38, 42, 50, 55, 56, 64, 67, 81, 92, 93, 96, 104, 112, 124, 131, 141, 152, 154, 162, 163, 184, 188, 193, 205, 206, 207
Carver, George W.: 212
Carver, Jonathan: 18
Cass, Lewis: 67
Castro, Fidel: 281
Cattle: 188, 189, 218, 219
Central Pacific: 157
Chapin, Dwight: 297
Chase, Samuel: 49
Chastellux, Francois de: 22
Cherokee Indians: 221
Chicago: 161, 189, 218, 219
Chickasaw Indians: 221
Child, E. B.: 73
Childs, Francis: 22
China: 171
Christian Science: 166
Churchill, Winston S.: 258, 259
Civil War: 136-161, 203
Clark, Champ: 227
Clark, William: 51
Clay, Henry: 60, 63, 71, 89, 120
Claypoole, David: 24
Clemens, Samuel L.: 187
Cleveland, Grover: 202
Clinton, DeWitt: 69
Cobbett, William: 64
Cohn, Victor: 277
Coleman, William: 47
Colorado: 55, 167, 290
Communism: 271, 272, 279, 281
Confederacy: 139-151
Connecticut: 24
Connolly, John: 287
Constitution, U.S.: 24, 27, 84
Coolidge, Calvin: 238
Corbett, Boston: 149
Courtauld, George: 61
Crane, Stephen: 203
Crawford, William: 71
Credit Mobilier: 164
Creek Indians: 221
Crittenden, T. T.: 183
Crook, George: 191
Cuba: 206, 281
Custer, Elizabeth: 193
Custer, George A.: 193

D

Dakotas: 198
Dana, Richard Henry, Jr.: 101
Darrow, Clarence: 239
Davis, Jefferson: 139, 140, 141, 149
Declaration of Independence: 10, 20, 26
Delavan, James: 117
Dent, F. T.: 164
Dewey, George: 207
DeWitt, J. L.: 261
Dickerson, E. N.: 181
Dickerson, Mahlon: 92
Dimsdale, Thomas J.: 152
Doane, Gustavus C.: 163
Dole, Sanford B.: 200, 201
Dorr Rebellion: 103
Dorr, T. W.: 103
Douglas, Paul H.: 290
Douglas, Stephen A.: 136
Downes, John: 92
Dreiser, Theodore: 240
DuBois, W. E.: 116
Dunbar, William: 45
Dunlap, John: 10, 24

E

Earhart, Amelia: 243
Eastman, Seth: 67
Eckfeldt, J. R.: 116
Economics: 36, 41, 54, 56, 64, 106, 107, 116, 117, 144, 150, 175, 188, 189, 204, 205, 210, 218, 222, 223, 226, 228, 231, 237, 238, 248, 249, 251, 270, 279, 288, 290
Eddy, Mary Baker: 166
Edison, Thomas A.: 177
Eisenhower, Dwight D.: 262, 274
Emancipation Proclamation: 144, 145
Emerson, Ralph Waldo: 102
Emmett, Daniel D.: 134
Erie Canal: 69
Evarts, W. H.: 155
Everett, Edward: 145

F

Fairchild, H. P.: 228
Faulkner, William: 244, 257
Fearon, Henry B.: 64
Federalist: 29
Field, Cyrus: 131
Field, Henry M.: 131